MODERN METALLURGY
FOR ENGINEERS

MODERN METALLURGY
FOR ENGINEERS

by

FRANK T. SISCO

*Metallurgist and Editor, Alloys of Iron Research, The Engineering
Foundation; Formerly Chief of Metallurgical Laboratory,
U. S. Army Air Corps, Wright Field.*

PITMAN PUBLISHING CORPORATION

NEW YORK   CHICAGO

ASSOCIATED COMPANIES

SIR ISAAC PITMAN & SONS, LTD.

Bath · London · Melbourne · Johannesburg · Singapore

SIR ISAAC PITMAN & SONS (CANADA), LTD.

381-383 Church Street Toronto

PREFACE

The author had three objectives in mind in writing this book. The first was to give to the undergraduate or graduate student in engineering a broad but concise outline of the art and science of metallurgy, with the hope that this outline will afford a sound understanding of the important characteristics of the metals he will use. The second and equally important objective was to summarize the present status of metallurgy for older engineers who, in the years they have been practicing their profession, have lost touch with advances in metallurgical thought and who may not be familiar, therefore, with all of the recent developments in metal products. The third objective, which is probably as important as the other two, was to survey the whole field of ferrous and non-ferrous metallurgy, with especial attention to structure and properties, for the benefit of those in the metal industries who either have not had the advantage of a broad fundamental training or have been working in such a narrow orbit that they too have lost touch with developments in metallurgical fields other than their own.

Keeping up with metallurgical developments in all branches of the art, as reported in the technical literature of the world, is practically impossible for those actively engaged in the manufacture, processing, or the industrial use of engineering metals and alloys; it can be done effectively only by those who have the time, in other words, by those who are fortunate enough to spend their days in the "cloistered halls of learning," in research institutes that do not need to worry about profit and loss, or in editorial sanctuaries where papers describing "recent developments" pass over their desks. For the thousands of individuals, therefore, who work with or who use metallic materials and who cannot possibly find time to read everything, summaries have a well-defined place in the scheme of things.

The method of attack used in summarizing ferrous and non-ferrous metallurgy in 400 pages and the relative space given to the various subjects evolved from the author's experience—and the experience of his coworkers, Samuel Daniels, R. R. Moore, D. M. Warner, and Lt. (now Col.) A. J. Lyon—at Wright Field, in teaching metallurgy and metal testing to officers of the U. S. Army Air Corps (most of whom were graduate engineers), with the addition of valuable advice from friends who have been, or are, teaching metallurgy or engineering in colleges and universities. Because this book is written primarily for engineers, much of the available space is devoted to the art of metallurgy; there is little on the science because it is believed that the reader at whom this book is aimed is not likely to be more than casually interested in the mental gymnastics of physical metallurgy. Pole figures and Laue

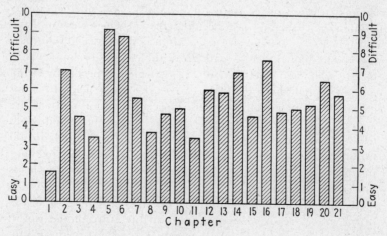

diffraction patterns make pretty pictures, and long differential equations of free energy give such an air of dignity to the printed page that the temptation to use them is strong, but they butter no parsnips nor do they improve the design of a bridge or increase the performance of a dive bomber.

A conscientious effort has been made to keep the text of this book as accurate as possible. In attempting, however, to outline ferrous and non-ferrous metallurgy in 100,000 words, shortcomings are inevitable, and the author will appreciate it if his attention is called to any, either explicit or implied, which may be apparent to the reader. A conscientious effort was also made to keep the text as elementary as possible. The accompanying graph gives an idea of the relative ease with which an engineering student, or a graduate engineer who has forgotten most of his college metallurgy—if he ever had any—can absorb the subject matter. It is unfortunate that the various phases of ferrous and non-ferrous metallurgy do not lend themselves readily to more equitable treatment. It might be added, however, that the most difficult chapters of this book are relatively easy when compared with some of the subjects taught to second- and third-year college students.

It is a privilege to acknowledge here the splendid assistance given by a number of the author's friends in reviewing and commenting frankly upon the various drafts of the manuscript. The whole text, including the questions and the bibliography, was read and criticized by Dr. Francis M. Walters, Jr., Chief Metallurgist, Naval Research Laboratory, and by John S. Marsh, Physical Metallurgist, Alloys of Iron Research. Dr. R. H. Aborn, Research Metallurgist, U. S. Steel Corporation, and Dr. G. B. Waterhouse, Professor of Metallurgy, Massachusetts Institute of Technology, reviewed most of the chapters on ferrous metallurgy, and Dr. Cyril Stanley Smith, Research Metallurgist, American Brass Company, and E. H. Dix, Jr., Chief Metallurgist of the Aluminum Company of America, reviewed the chapters on non-ferrous metallurgy. The chapters on precipitation hardening and on light alloys were also read by Drs. W. L. Fink, L. K. Jetter, D. W. Smith, and J. J. Bowman, research metallurgists of the Aluminum Company of America. The chapter on cast and malleable iron was reviewed and criticized by Dr. James T. MacKenzie, Chief Metallurgist, American Cast Iron Pipe Co., and the chapter on effect of temperature was reviewed by Dr. H. W. Gillett, Technical Advisor, and H. C. Cross, Metallurgist, of Battelle Memorial Institute.

Sincere thanks are also due to the numerous individuals, companies, and publishers of technical journals and books who supplied or permitted the use of data or illustrations. Acknowledgment of the original source of the material so used is made in the text or in the captions of the illustrations. All photomicrographs not otherwise credited were made by John Hester and Clifford McMahon in the author's laboratory at Wright Field.

FRANK T. SISCO

New York

CONTENTS

CHAPTER 1

METALLURGY AND ENGINEERING

THE first use of metal by man was an important step forward on his long road to a higher civilization. Before that time he led a precarious existence, living in caves or other equally rude habitations and defending himself and his family from marauding enemies, both four- and two-footed, with wooden clubs or spears tipped with bone or shell. His food was obtained by wooden or stone weapons or by grinding grain between slabs of stone.

The date of man's first use of metal is uncertain; in some parts of the world it was at least 10,000 years ago, in other parts less than a thousand. There is little doubt that his first useful metal was native copper; gold and copper are the only native metals which are widely distributed, but gold is too soft for use as either a weapon or a tool. Copper, however, is readily hardened by hammering cold and even if copper alloys or iron are unknown, copper can be made to serve, both for weapons and tools, much more effectively than stone.

From the use of native metal to the deliberate reduction of an ore by carbon is a long step, and it is probably the most important advance that *homo sapiens* made after he began to use fire. The date of this forward step varies widely in different parts of the world: on or near the eastern shores of the Mediterranean it probably occurred between 4000 and 5000 B.C.; on the North American continent, however, native copper was the only metal known to the Indians until the Europeans arrived about 400 years ago.

One of the major unsolved problems of archeology is how man discovered the method of reducing a metallic oxide or other compound with carbon to produce the metal. The best guess is that the first reduction was accidental: stones consisting chiefly of copper oxide or carbonate were used in the construction of a primitive hearth or campfire; the heat of the fire and the carbon in the charred wood reduced the ore to metal, which was discovered and identified as the same as the native metal with which man had long been familiar. Even if this explanation is correct, it was still a long step before man could perceive that a relation existed between cause and effect—between a particular kind of stone, the charred logs and the fire—and could produce metal intentionally. The first man to recognize this relation was the first metallurgist, and he was one of the most important individuals in the long history of mankind.

1. **The Field of Metallurgy**—Metallurgy is an art and a science. It is the art of extracting metals from their ores, refining them, and alloying them with one another and with certain non-metals to produce thereby a variety of metallic materials which, owing to their wide range of useful properties, are, for many purposes, more valuable to man than the individual metals themselves. It is also the art of shaping, or otherwise treating, metals and alloys to form objects and structures [1] useful to a complex industrial society. It is the science of the constitution and internal structure [2] of metals and alloys, and of the relation of composition and structure to properties, and of the laws, theories, and hypotheses which purport to explain this relation.

Metallurgy is commonly divided into two branches according to the science with which its various fields are most closely allied: chemical or process metallurgy, including the numerous extractive and refining processes such as reduction of ores, refining and purification of metals, manufacture of alloys, and the operations involved in mechanical and thermal treatment; and physical metallurgy or metallography, which includes constitution and structure of pure metals and of alloys, and all the factors which

[1] Readers who have an engineering training should be careful not to confuse the engineering and the metallurgical meaning of the words structure and structural. Structure as an engineering term means "that which is constructed; a combination or aggregation of related parts as in a building or machine." Structure as a metallurgical term means "the arrangement or union of the component parts in a metal or an alloy." Generally, in speaking of the structure of a metal or an alloy, it is implied that a section has been specially prepared and treated so that the structural units making up the metal or alloy can be studied. When the words structure or structural are used in this volume the meaning should be clear from the context.

[2] See footnote 1.

affect the structure and constitution and thus control the physical and mechanical properties.

Metallurgy, therefore, is closely allied to chemistry and physics. It is also closely related to engineering through the mechanical and other properties of metallic materials which fit them for engineering use. Metallurgy is, in fact, so closely related to chemistry, physics, and engineering that until recently it had, in some large universities, no department of its own; courses in various branches of metallurgy were given as part of the curricula in the departments of mining, physics, chemistry, and mechanical engineering.

Engineers are interested primarily in having readily available materials with properties that permit the design of structures and machines of satisfactory safety, utility, and durability. It is the job of the metallurgist to provide metallic materials which will meet the engineers' requirements economically. If this were the only liaison between metallurgist and engineer, it could hardly be claimed that the relation is close. Far more important, however, is the job of the metallurgist to point out and even to emphasize the factors which may affect the properties of a metal or an alloy and which may make a metallic material especially suitable or entirely unsuitable for a particular structure or machine. These factors may be differences in the process by which the metal or alloy is made, worked, or treated, or they may be inherent in the structure and constitution. The importance of these factors makes metallurgy as closely akin to modern engineering as it is to physics and chemistry.

2. **Metallurgy as an Art**—The art of extracting metals from their ores and working them into useful objects is a venerable one. Our forefathers, as indicated on a previous page, produced their first metal—undoubtedly copper—by reducing the ore with charcoal or other carbonaceous material at least 6000 years ago. The art of shaping metals by mechanical work is as old or even older. It is more than likely that early man knew that metals were malleable long before he knew enough so that he could deliberately reduce a metallic oxide. When the pyramids were built in ancient Egypt man was doubling the strength and hardness of his copper tools by hammering them cold, and almost as soon as he was working his copper he was annealing it to restore the ductility so that it could be forged into smaller sections.

It did not take man long—as time is measured in ancient history—to discover that by adding one part of a certain stone (tin ore) to 10 or 15 parts of another stone (copper ore) and by heating the mixture with some form of carbon, he could produce a metal which was as strong or stronger and as hard or harder than his hammered copper, and that by hammering his new metal he could make a tool or weapon at least twice as valuable as anything he had possessed before—or anything his neighbor possessed, which was more important. History tells us nothing about the beginnings of thermal treatment of metals and alloys other than annealing, but it is reasonable to assume that very soon after man learned he could soften cold-worked material by slow cooling from a high temperature he would have wanted to see what happened if the metal was cooled quickly. Little would happen, of course, until early man began to use iron containing carbon. The date of this has been hotly disputed, some authorities maintaining vigorously that the pyramids could not have been built without hardened high-carbon steel; others claiming with equal vehemence that iron was not used until about 1200 B.C., and that heat-treated carbon steel came much later.

Establishing approximate dates for the beginning of the arts of metallurgy, including alloying, mechanical treatment, and heat treatment, and marshaling arguments in support of one's choice, are an interesting pastime but are certainly not worth extended discussion in a treatise on modern metallurgy for the engineering profession. The important fact is that knowledge of these primary operations is very old and that, as a consequence, it may be taken for granted that the art is well developed.

3. **Metallurgy as a Science**—Metallurgy as an art is a sage old man who impresses everyone with his wisdom; metallurgy as a science is an infant still in his swaddling clothes and with a world full of trials and tribulations yet to be faced. Because man is a practical animal concerned first of all with improving his own lot and establishing a steadily increasing superiority over animate and inanimate nature, he has accumulated much utilitarian knowledge about metals and alloys in the last 3000 or 4000 years —how to produce them economically and how to secure the most useful properties. In other words, he knows a great deal about the effects of the various chemical and physical reactions entering into metallurgical processes, but he has paid very little attention

to the *causes,* the underlying fundamentals which are, in the last analysis, the controlling factors in understanding the nature of metallic materials. He is an expert in the art but a tyro in the science.

It is, of course, unjustified to be too critical because the science of metallurgy got such a late start. Until about 75 years ago it had neither the methods for exact chemical analysis, nor the metallurgical microscope, nor the X-ray with which to work. Until tools were available for the study of the internal structure of metals, little could be done. The science of metallurgy really began when Sorby, a British scientist, reported in 1864 the results of his investigations on the use of the microscope to study the structure of meteoric iron. This was followed by studies in the same general field by Martens in Germany, reported in 1878. The work of these two scientists, however, aroused little interest at the time, and nothing further was accomplished until Sorby showed to the British Iron and Steel Institute in 1886 some photomicrographs of iron and steel. This aroused much interest in the internal structure of metals, and from 1890 to 1920 many distinguished metallurgists devoted themselves to developing a science of physical metallurgy.

The paramount early problem of metallurgy, which fairly cried for solution, was that of the hardening of steel—why steel containing considerable carbon was soft when cooled slowly from a red heat but hard when cooled rapidly from the same temperature. This problem occupied most of the workers in the science of metals for more than two decades. Despite the efforts of many brilliant minds, which resulted in a volume of published literature that amazes present-day metallurgists, little that was wholly decisive was accomplished until confirmatory X-ray crystallographic methods came into use about 30 years ago. Although some cynics say that the X-ray has created more problems than it has solved, X-ray crystallography has been a useful tool in the study of the structure of metals and the constitution of alloys.

In the past two decades the science of physical metallurgy has changed remarkably. Always closely related to chemistry and physics, it has been greatly affected by the revolution that has occurred in these two sciences since 1920. The gap between chemistry and physics has been largely eliminated, and, as these sciences came together, the science of metallurgy changed from simple speculations on the structure of metals and alloys, as affected by composition or mechanical or thermal treatment and as observed by the microscope, to speculations which involve such complex abstractions as spinning electrons, statistical mechanics, electromagnetic theory, quantum theory, wave mechanics, and thermodynamics.

Present-day physical metallurgists are inclined to smile condescendingly at the battles over beta iron, cement carbon, and amorphous metal which filled the transactions of the metallurgical societies 20 or 30 years ago. It is not at all certain that even broader smiles will not be in order 20 years from now over the discussions of free energy, entropy, and mosaic structure which are filling our journals at the present time. Especially apropos in this connection are the words of a venerable man of science, Sir Ambrose Fleming, who presented a paper to the first meeting of the Physical Society of London in 1874 and who, in a recent address to the same body of scientists on "Physics and Physicists of the Eighteen Seventies," [3] summarized his 70 years of experience by saying:

When we come to look back then on the world of physicists during the eighteen seventies, what we find is that their inventions, discoveries of fact, and ascertained principles remain with us today of permanent value, forming part of our useful knowledge. But their theories and speculations as to underlying causes and nature have nearly all passed away. Perhaps it will also be the same with our present-day work. If some sixty years hence a fellow of the Physical Society gives a talk on the physics of the nineteen thirties, he will have to record the great additions then made to knowledge of physical facts. But he may also have to say that our explanations and theories concerning them have all vanished, or at least been replaced by others also destined in turn to pass away.

Life, never a bed of roses for the metallurgist who tries to keep abreast of important developments in his field, would be far simpler if research workers would spend more time seeking out a few of the thousands of facts still needed to fill the gaps of metallurgical knowledge, and less time in spinning webs of ephemeral theory upon the pages of our technical journals.

[3] *Nature,* v. 143, 1939, pp. 99-102.

4. Metallurgy and Engineering—Until 25 years ago there was little need for the engineer to know anything about metallurgy since untreated carbon steel, hot rolled or cold drawn, was used for at least 95 per cent of steel structures and machines. The engineer was interested primarily in four properties—tensile strength, yield point, elongation, and reduction of area—and in having available an ample supply of cheap steel which, in addition to meeting specifications for tensile properties, would machine easily and fabricate readily. It was considered sound engineering practice to build machines and structures that would carry a much higher load than was anticipated; weight was synonymous with quality, and the heavier the structure the better the design. High factors of safety were used; consequently slight variations in quality, such as structural inhomogeneity, surface irregularities, and numerous others, made little or no difference in designing.

This is no longer true. In the past 20 or 30 years weight and the strength-weight ratio (tensile strength divided by specific gravity) have become very important. Under the leadership of the automotive and aircraft industries engineers have come to realize that excess weight not only indicates poor design, but is an inexcusable economic loss. The experience of the automotive and the aeronautical engineer in designing light-weight structures and machines stimulated similar efforts in other fields of engineering. This is shown by the recent developments in machine tools, in light-weight railway rolling stock, and even in bridge and building structures.

It is, of course, self-evident that the present-day emphasis on light weight in engineering design as exemplified by the automobile, airplane, and the streamlined train is directly related to the development of new types of steels and light non-ferrous alloys and to new treatments for these materials. It is a moot question whether the metallurgist or the engineer was responsible for most of this development. Enthusiastic metallurgists insist that engineering progress has been the direct result of metallurgical progress; that engineers only improved their tools, machines, and structures because metallurgical art and science had produced new metallic materials for the engineer to use. There is no doubt that many engineers are too conservative and that engineering progress has at times lagged behind progress in metallurgy. On the other hand, examples could be cited where the metallurgist did not improve his product until insistent engineering demand forced it upon him. A discussion whether this advance was pioneered by the metallurgist or the engineer is as futile as arguing whether the egg or the chicken came first; the essential fact is that important changes have taken place and that the engineer should know something of the metallurgical progress that has accompanied his changes in design.

It is, therefore, the object of this book to outline the recent developments in metallurgical art and in metallurgical science. This does not mean that there are long descriptions of melting and refining, or of mechanical and heat treatment, or of thermodynamics and wave mechanics; it does mean, however, that sufficient details of the present state of metallurgical art and science are given so that engineers should recognize the importance of the variables, inherent in the manufacture and treatment of metals and alloys, which affect the engineering properties and the suitability of these materials for engineering applications. Thus, mosaic structure is properly left unmentioned, but precipitation hardening is discussed in some detail; thus, the mechanism of the deoxidation of steel by aluminum is, happily, passed over, but the effect of grain size on the structure and the properties of steel receives considerable attention.

5. Metallic Materials Used in Engineering—Metals and alloys are used by man because (1) they fulfill his requirements in certain applications more economically than any other material or because (2) they give to man an esthetic or some other special satisfaction which makes their cost of minor importance. In general, the cost of a metal has no fixed relation to its utilitarian or esthetic value. Platinum is used in industry for certain specific purposes because no substitute is known; in jewelry, however, it may compete with white gold and silver. Its use for ornament, therefore, depends wholly upon the personal satisfaction the individual receives from owning it.

When relatively large tonnages of a metallic material are required, the cost is important only when two or more competing materials fulfill the requirements equally well. If one metallic material costs more than another, its use is justified if its properties for a specific application are so much superior to the properties of the other that its net cost is lower than the cost of the competing material. In judging the relative merits of competing materials the nature of the specific application is the most important variable, as a given material may be economical under some conditions and very costly under other conditions. This, however, is well known to most engineers and need not be enlarged upon.

Of the 92 chemical elements, more than half are classified as metals, and of these about 40 are of industrial importance. The pure metals have a wide range of properties, but with a few exceptions none of them is so valuable to an industrial civilization as the alloys. The thousands of known industrial alloys may be divided into three groups: (1) the iron-rich alloys containing more than 50 per cent iron, and including the unalloyed carbon steels and cast irons and all the alloy steels and alloy cast irons; (2) the heavy non-ferrous alloys containing copper, zinc, nickel, lead, or tin as the principal metal; and (3) the light non-ferrous alloys, based upon the light metals, aluminum and magnesium.

The iron-rich alloys are, as everyone knows, the foundation of our machine civilization. Steel and cast iron possess such a favorable combination of properties and low cost that they have been the preeminent engineering material for nearly a century and probably will remain in this role indefinitely. This is shown by Table 1 [4] which gives world production of pig iron and all of the non-ferrous metals combined. Pig iron is the basic raw material for the manufacture of steel which, on an average, is melted from a charge containing 60 to 70 per cent pig and 30 to 40 per cent scrap steel.

Non-ferrous metals are not close industrial competitors of steel and cast iron, but their use is increasing. Between 1900 and 1915 the production of pig iron was about 20 times that of all the non-ferrous metals combined. This has decreased steadily (Table 1), until at present the ratio is only 15 to 1. The leaders of the non-ferrous metals are copper, lead, and zinc; the use of aluminum, however, is increasing, and it seems likely that before long it may be the first of the non-ferrous metals in industrial importance.

[4] Based upon a chart by Zay Jeffries, *Metal Progress*, Jan. 1935, p. 20.

TABLE I.   WORLD PRODUCTION OF PIG IRON AND NON-FERROUS METALS

Period	Production, millions of metric tons		Ratio, lb. of pig iron for 1 lb. of non-ferrous metals
	Pig iron	Non-ferrous metals	
1900 to 1904	218	10.9	20.0
1905 to 1909	284	13.3	21.4
1910 to 1914	344	16.1	21.4
1915 to 1919	326	17.8	18.4
1920 to 1924	293	15.9	18.5
1925 to 1929	425	25.1	17.0
1930 to 1934	280	20.0	14.0
1935 to 1939	445	29.6	15.0

6. **Recent Trends in the Metal Industries**—Since the manufacture of metallic materials is classed as a capital-goods industry, it is more affected by economic conditions than are the utilities, textiles, foods, and other consumption-goods industries.   For many years the manufacture of the metals—especially iron and steel—has been known as a prince-or-pauper industry: it is either riding a high crest of prosperity or is plunged deep into the trough of depression.   This is evident from a comparison of steel ingot production in the United States for two years: 61.5 million tons in 1929, and only 15 million tons in 1932.

The curves for the year to year production of steel and other metal products may show an erratic course, but, if these statistics are analyzed mathematically over a period of years, certain definite trends are evident.   Until about 20 years ago the trend for the production of metallic materials in the United States was steadily upward; the production or, more accurately, the consumption of metals per capita increased greatly each decade. This is no longer true; the trend curve has flattened out, and in the case of steel it has turned slightly but distinctly downward. There are several reasons for this.   In the first place, building a machine civilization in the United States is practically complete.   Moreover, the age of the population has increased to the point where a large part of the country's income, formerly spent in building new things for the young, must be spent in supporting the old.   In the second place, marked advances in metallurgical art have increased the life expectancy of the metallic materials used by industry, and the structures and machines made from them, at least 50 per cent.

There is nothing in sight which warrants the assumption that the trend line will turn upward in the future.[5] It is unlikely that any new industries will increase the total metal consumption in this country. Despite many statements to the contrary, the automotive industry has had no effect on metal consumption. In fact the total amount of metal going into all forms of transportation has actually decreased in the past 20 years. Types of steels have changed and large tonnages have been transferred from railroad construction to automobiles, and from railroads to pipe lines, but the total amount has declined.

7. Effect of Changes in the Metal Industries on Metallurgical Art and Science—The leveling off of the trend line of metal production and consumption has been accompanied by very great changes in metallurgical art and science and is evidenced by a marked improvement in the quality of metallic materials. Consumers are demanding and the steel industry is supplying "tailor-made steels" of higher quality, for the same price paid for the old "hit-or-miss-take-it-or-leave-it" product of a decade or two ago. To old requirements for chemical composition and mechanical properties have been added new requirements for grain size, internal cleanness, better surface, and homogeneity, to which the steel mills (after a hard struggle in some cases) are conforming. More than $350,000,000 has been invested in the past ten years in rolling equipment for sheet and strip so that these products would be higher in quality and lower in cost.

[5] Despite the large increase in steel production in the past three months, this statement is still true. While this book was on the press, considerable space in newspapers and popular magazines has been devoted to prophesies of an impending shortage of steel-making capacity, based upon estimates by Government economists, and made on the assumption that steel consumption increases directly with national income. Aside from the fact that these estimates contain enough errors to throw doubt on the data obtained, they are the result of statistical gymnastics which are of questionable validity, to say the least. If from present production are deducted the tonnages being used for national defense, for export to Great Britain, and those being bought by other consumers who are hysterical over the possibility of a shortage—all of which are temporary stimuli—domestic civilian consumption per capita is probably no greater now and probably will be no greater in 1942 than it was in 1938 or 1939. This has been discussed recently by T. W. Lippert (*The Iron Age*, Jan. 23, 1941, p. 21).

Low- and high-alloy steels have been developed which bid fair to revolutionize railway equipment by saving 30 to 50 per cent in dead weight. Machine tools have been reduced in weight and increased in efficiency, and by means of the hard carbides recently developed it has become possible economically to machine materials that had to be ground a few years ago. Machine parts built up from sheet and strip by welding are replacing forgings with marked savings in cost. On the other hand, new cast ferrous alloys of low damping capacity are replacing more expensive forgings for crankshafts and camshafts. The perfection of welding processes in the aircraft and automotive industries has led to the use of this method of fabrication in building construction and shipbuilding with savings in weight and cost.

Metallurgical research in corrosion and its prevention has been a large factor in increasing the life expectancy of metals, especially steel. Similar research in the mechanism of quenching has resulted in new standards of quality and performance in heat-treated steels and may in the near future have an important effect on the quality of steel for which the only treatment is cooling after rolling.

Although the development in ferrous metallurgy has been outstanding, developments of great importance have occurred in the non-ferrous field. One of these is the clarification of the mechanism of precipitation hardening and the application of this method of treatment—long used for aluminum alloys—to other alloys which are finding important, if limited, industrial application. In the light-alloy field, forgings considered impossible a few years ago are now produced in large quantities. High-strength aluminum alloys are used increasingly in construction; streamlined trains of these materials are competitors of the much publicized stainless steel streamliners. In aircraft the use of high-strength aluminum alloys, always important, doubled between 1937 and 1939. The problem of intercrystalline corrosion has been practically solved by Alclad and other methods of protection. Aluminum alloys are becoming active competitors of bronze and stainless steel for architectural trim.

In the field of pure metals, development has been no less noteworthy. Copper of an average purity of 99.96 per cent is a common industrial product and of 99.99 per cent is readily available. The purity of commercial zinc and lead has been stepped up to

99.999 and 99.995 per cent respectively. Commercially pure iron commonly contains 99.93 to 99.95 per cent iron.

In many other fields, as for example die casting and powder metallurgy, advancement has been equally outstanding. It would take a dozen pages even to list the more important developments in metallurgical art and science in the past 10 or 15 years. It is sufficient, however, to list the foregoing developments briefly as examples of what has occurred, and to note that these and the others not mentioned here are discussed in more detail in the other chapters of this volume.

8. Trade Names, Nomenclature, and Specifications in the Metal Industries—One of the evils or virtues, depending upon one's viewpoint, of an economy based on profit is the wide use of trade names and the constant, and usually obnoxious, effort to fix these trade names in the purchaser's mind by advertising. There is undoubtedly a plethora of trade names in the metal industries, far too many in the opinion of many metallurgists and engineers, but certainly in this respect the metal industries are no worse and probably not so bad as some of the other large fields of business. In advertising, the metal industries have, in the past, been exceptionally modest; in the trade papers and in catalogues and handbooks the data presented as a part of advertising are nearly always so accurate that technical writers frequently cite them as authoritative. In the popular press metal advertising is still in its infancy and, in comparison with such products as automobiles, radios, household appliances, and especially foodstuffs and cosmetics, advertisements for metals are models of propriety and truthfulness.

Those products of the metal industries that are manufactured in large tonnages and at relatively low cost are seldom sold under trade names. These common and well-standardized products are made and purchased under specifications with definite requirements for chemical composition, properties, and—in some cases—structure. After careful consideration by manufacturers and users, these specifications are drawn up by technical societies such as the American Society for Testing Materials, the Society of Automotive Engineers, the American Society of Mechanical Engineers, the American Standards Association, and others, and by large consumers such as the U. S. Army, U. S. Navy, automotive and aircraft manufacturers, bridge and shipbuilders, the railroads, and many others.

Metal products which have been introduced recently, or which are used in a few special applications, or which are manufactured in small quantities, usually under rigid control of all manufacturing processes, are often made and marketed with distinctive identifying names. Included in this class are some of the recently introduced low-alloy structural steels and some copper-rich, nickel-rich, and aluminum-rich alloys, stainless and other special-purpose high-alloy steels, tool and other special unalloyed steels, and a few others.

There are many manufacturers of metal products who for 25 years or more have tried conscientiously to produce a uniform high-quality material which is sold at a fair price, and who have, therefore, succeeded in making a trade name stand for a reliable high-quality product. This practice has been widespread in the manufacture of tool steels. As discussed in Chapter 15, it is very difficult to evaluate accurately a tool for a specific machining operation by any acceptance test; drawing up rigid specifications for the purchase of tool steel is impracticable, if not impossible. As the result, large quantities of tool steel are purchased by brand name alone and are used with perfect satisfaction.

The chief, and probably the only, advantage of purchasing a steel or a non-ferrous alloy by its trade name is that there is reasonable assurance that the lot purchased today will be of the same quality as that purchased a year or ten years ago, and that if a certain branded material gives satisfaction for a certain purpose today, it probably will give equal satisfaction tomorrow. Most metallurgists do not object to trade names so long as they are not confusing or misleading. Unfortunately, however, many of them have been used in the past, and are being used at present, which are both. These are a nuisance to metallurgist as well as engineer. It is certainly confusing, for example, to call a cast iron "semisteel" because some steel scrap was used in the cupola when the cast iron was melted, and it is equally misleading to call a copper-zinc alloy a "bronze" because its color is approximately the same as the color of some copper-tin alloys. In this connection, Mathewson [6] has said with much justification:

[6] C. H. Mathewson in *Modern Uses of Non-ferrous Metals*, American Institute of Mining and Metallurgical Engineers, New York, 1935, Chapter VII, p. 118.

Except for commercial preferences reaching all the way from the proprietory right of a manufacturer to supply his customer with his own carefully branded, often commonplace product, which may be just like that of his competitor produced under another name, to the general sense of thrift that brings competitors on the common ground of calling a brass alloy by the more patrician name of bronze, provided it possesses a sufficient nobility of color to permit the dissimulation, the whole industry might well standardize on a very few mixtures.

This confused nomenclature is regrettable, but unfortunately little can be done about it, as some of the names used are firmly fixed by years of usage. When engineers encounter an unfamiliar branded metallic material for which certain claims are made, it is well, however, to be skeptical of these claims until more information about the alloy, including the composition, is made available. Frequently the manufacturer willingly supplies this information; if not, data on the material can usually be found by looking for the alloy by name in a handbook [7] or by having it analyzed and tested.

[7] For example, N. E. Woldman and A. J. Dornblatt, *Engineering Alloys*, American Society for Metals, Cleveland, 1936.

CHAPTER 2

THE FUNDAMENTAL STRUCTURE OF METALS AND ALLOYS

IF a polished bar of a metal or an alloy and a rod of glass are examined with the unaided eye, the surface of each appears to be perfectly homogeneous and continuous, differing only in the way in which they reflect the light. If, however, these smooth surfaces of metal and glass are etched lightly with a suitable chemical reagent and are examined with a microscope, a great difference is at once apparent: the surface of the glass, which is amorphous, is still homogeneous and continuous despite its roughness after etching; the surface of the metal or alloy, on the contrary, is no longer continuous but is broken up into an aggregation of irregularly shaped grains (see for example Fig. 3). These grains may be uniform and homogeneous in size and structure or they may vary widely in size and may be heterogeneous in structure. This is important, as the properties of a metal or an alloy are closely related to the size, shape, and constitution of its grains.

Physical metallurgists have two methods for studying the internal structure of metals and alloys: the microscope and X-ray diffraction apparatus. The microscope gives detailed information on the size and external appearance of the grains and usually considerable information on their composition and homogeneity or heterogeneity. The X-ray gives precise data on the arrangement of the atoms and the distances between them. Both are valuable tools, and their use has made possible much of our present knowledge of the constitution and structure of metallic materials and of how they affect the properties. Unfortunately, however, many changes in internal structure (and properties) are caused by reactions which cannot be followed readily because the particle size of the participants is below the resolving power of the microscope's lenses but much above the size of the atoms.

There is, therefore, a large unknown land in physical metallurgy, between the spacing of the atoms and the arrangement and characteristics of the crystalline grains, which must be left unexplored until suitable equipment for its study is available. As metallurgists are well aware, there are numerous alloys of apparently identical chemical composition and structure which are different in properties. For the present, when such phenomena are encountered, the best that can be done is to guess the cause intelligently or, better yet, to admit ignorance gracefully and frankly.

Metals and alloys owe their importance as engineering materials primarily to the fact that in general they combine a high degree of plasticity with high strength. Such a combination of properties, found in no other class of materials, permits them to be shaped cheaply into a wide variety of products which can be used safely where high strength plus ability to deform under varying stress without rupturing are necessary. The fundamental basis of the strength and plasticity is found in the crystal structure. It is desirable, therefore, to examine with some degree of thoroughness what is known positively about this structure.

9. **Pure Metals**—In the English language the word metal is used in two ways. In the narrow and more precise meaning—which is used only in this chapter—a metal is a chemical element having metallic properties; in the broader, more colloquial usage, it signifies any material, either element or alloy, which has metallic properties. In the narrow sense the word metal has been defined as "an element which is hard, heavy, lustrous, malleable, ductile, tenacious, and usually a good conductor of heat and electricity." This is probably as satisfactory a definition as can be formulated concisely. It certainly is not precise, because an element can be soft, light, relatively dull, brittle, or weak and still be a metal. The qualities used to define metal are, therefore, those that are more or less characteristic of the group of some 50 elements which are classed as metals. It is a matter of fact that some of these elements, which possess all or most of these qualities or in which they are very pronounced, are more metallic than others which possess only a few of them or in which they are relatively feeble. It is also a fact that some elements possess so few metallic qualities that it is uncertain whether they should be called metals or non-metals. Carbon and silicon are such elements. They are, for example, fairly good con-

ductors of heat and electricity and thus resemble the metals; they have, however, no appreciable strength nor ductility, and in this respect they resemble the non-metals. Such elements, on the borderline between the metals and the non-metals, which cannot be classified readily as one or the other, are usually called metalloids.

In the past 15 or 20 years the physicists have tried very hard to discover the basic cause or causes of the properties which are more or less common to the metallic elements, but with only partial success. Hardness, strength, and plasticity have been correlated with considerable certainty with the atomic architecture—with the way the atoms are held together and with the nature and strength of the bonds. An attempt has been made to correlate thermal, magnetic, and electric phenomena in metals and alloys with the presence of free or "valence" electrons, but the result has not been wholly satisfactory, except possibly to the physicists themselves.

The status of recent opinion on the more speculative aspects of the physics of metals, while interesting from a scientific point of view, is hardly important to the engineer who uses metals and alloys for tools, machines, and structures. It is important, however, that he be familiar with what is known definitely about crystal structure and grain structure, and about their relation to mechanical properties. Such knowledge will help him to understand why steel hardens when it is quenched, why a specific alloy steel is more ductile than an unalloyed steel of otherwise comparable structure, why duralumin gets stronger when it is quenched and aged, why high-chromium steel is rust resisting, why some alloys are brittle and others of almost similar composition are tough; it will, in brief, enable him to understand more thoroughly the peculiarities and the advantages and disadvantages of the various metallic materials he has available.

One of the important facts which led to the assumption that metallic properties are associated with a specific form of atomic bonding is the marked difference in the properties of a metal and its oxide, sulphate, or other compound. Iron oxide (Fe_2O_3), for example, contains about 70 per cent iron atoms, but this substance has none of the properties that characterize iron. The only feasible deduction, therefore, is that the electrons of iron atoms and oxygen atoms interact (form "bonds") in a manner altogether different from that in the pure metal. This argument applies equally well to similar compounds of other metals.

10. **Crystallization of Metals**—If a pure metal is heated uniformly, a temperature is finally reached where melting begins. If heating is continued, there is no rise in temperature until the mass of metal is completely molten. This constant temperature is the melting point and is clearly evident if a curve of temperature versus time is plotted. Upon cooling, the reverse change takes place: at the freezing point the temperature remains constant (see Fig. 5A) despite the fact that heat is being extracted from the metal at a constant rate, until the whole mass is solid. Under ideal conditions of heating and cooling the melting and freezing points of a pure metal occur at the same temperature.

When a metal is molten the atoms are arranged haphazardly; when the metal solidifies it crystallizes, in other words, the atoms arrange themselves in a regular geometric pattern characterized by more or less perfectly formed faces intersecting at precise angles. As crystallization starts at a large number of centers at the same time, the growth of the crystals in the regular geometric pattern is finally halted by collision with neighboring growths. The process of crystallization is shown schematically in two dimensions in Fig. 1,[1] and the appearance of more or less perfectly formed crystals of iron is shown in Fig. 2.[2] The collision of the growing crystals with each other and with the mold wall usually prevents perfection of form. The result is a mass of irregular polygonal grains, shown for nearly pure iron in Fig. 3. Each one of these grains is made up of hundreds of thousands of very small crystals in which the atoms are arranged in definite patterns.

The essence of the crystalline state is not only that the atoms are arranged in regular, repeating geometric patterns, but also that the crystal faces and edges are arranged symmetrically; in other words, that the principal planes of the crystal are oriented in definite directions (Fig. 1). The orientation of the crystal units is the same throughout each of the grains, but it naturally changes at the grain boundaries as shown in Fig 1.

In all crystals, whether of metals, alloys, or crystalline non-

[1] W. Rosenhain, *An Introduction to the Study of Physical Metallurgy*, Constable, London, 1935, 368 pp.

[2] H. M. Howe, *Metallography of Steel and Cast Iron*, McGraw-Hill Book Company, Inc., New York, 1916, 641 pp.

metals, there are planes of weakness, which have low resistance to shear. The presence of such cleavage planes is shown by the fact that failure under stress usually occurs through the crystalline grains (intercrystalline) rather than by following the grain

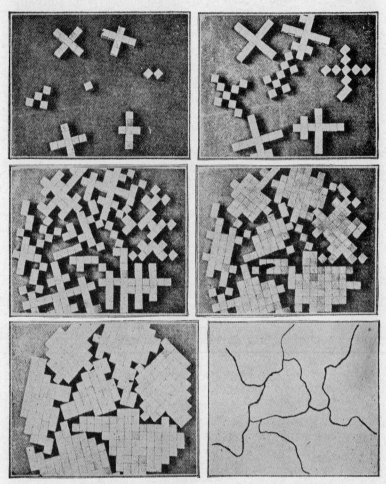

Fig. 1—Schematic representation of crystallization (Rosenhain).

boundaries (intracrystalline). If the cleavage planes of all the hundreds or thousands of grains in a metal section were similarly oriented, the metal would be relatively weak. Fortunately, however, the grains are not all oriented alike; hence, although a single grain may not resist deformation very well, the whole section will show very strong resistance.

The essentials of the crystalline state are therefore (1) that the atoms or molecules are grouped in minute geometric units like marching soldiers; (2) that the individual units are arranged symmetrically, in other words, are similarly oriented in the crys-

Fig. 2—Iron crystals (Howe).

tals like companies of soldiers in a regiment on dress parade; (3) that there are planes of weakness in each crystal; and (4) that the direction of symmetry or orientation, also of cleavage planes, changes in different grains. These four essentials should be remembered as they are fundamental in explaining how the strength, hardness, ductility, malleability, toughness, and other important properties of metals and alloys are affected by alloying or by mechanical or thermal treatment. Practically the entire science of metallurgy is based upon these four principles of crystallization; explanations of changes in structure and properties have as a basis a change in the form or orientation of the crystal unit, or a change in the form or size of the crystalline grains.

11. Internal Structure of Crystals—The geometric pattern which the atoms tend to form when a metal or alloy solidifies

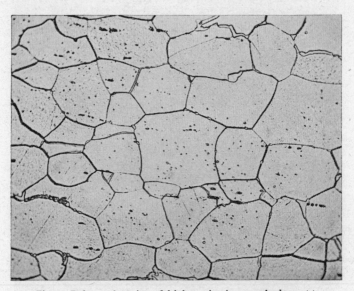

Fig. 3—Polygonal grains of high-purity iron, etched, 500×.

is known as a space lattice. Several types of lattice are recognized, three of which are the most important in the structure of metals and alloys. These are the cubic, the tetragonal, and the hexagonal, which differ in the length of the axes and in the angles the axes make with each other. Most of the metals are cubic, a few—zinc, magnesium, and cadmium are the common ones—are hexagonal, and only two—manganese and tin—have a tetragonal lattice.

The cubic type of lattice is characterized by three axes of equal length at right angles to each other. Three varieties of this type are common: the simple cubic lattice, which contains one atom at each of the eight corners of the cube; the body-centered cubic, which contains one atom at each corner and one in the center; and the face-centered cubic, which contains one atom at each corner and one atom at the center of each of the six faces of the cube. The simple cubic lattice is not important in metals, the other two are. The diagrammatic representations of the body-centered and face-centered cubic lattices are shown in Fig. 4. The black circles are the assumed locations of the atom centers, the atoms themselves are presumably packed closely together.

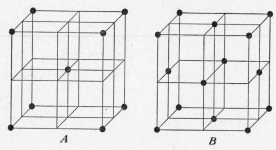

Fig. 4—Schematic representation of (A) body-centered and (B) face-centered cubic lattice.

In an actual crystal of a metal or alloy thousands of these unit blocks are joined together. In the body-centered lattice each of the corner atoms is shared by seven other cubes. There are, therefore, a total of eight cubes to each atom. Hence the body-centered lattice contains the equivalent of one whole corner atom and one whole body atom, or a total of two. In the face-centered lattice each of the six atoms in the faces is shared by one other cube. This lattice has the equivalent of one corner atom and three face atoms, or a total of four.

The properties of a metal depend to a considerable degree upon the type of lattice, upon the distance between the atoms and upon the way in which the various planes which intersect the edges of the lattice are populated by atoms. As a general rule, the metals with a face-centered crystal structure are more ductile than those that are body-centered.

Our knowledge of the internal structure of metals, how the atoms are spaced in the lattice, of the distances between them, and how these are affected by alloying and by mechanical and thermal treatment is due to the discovery by von Laue in 1912 that the collections of atoms in the planes of the crystal act as a diffraction grating for X-rays of certain wave lengths. In the past 25 years extensive use has been made of X-ray diffraction as a means of attack on the problems of physical metallurgy.

12. Allotropy—In chemical terminology allotropy—or polymorphism—is the occurrence of an element in two or more modifications differing markedly in properties. Carbon is the most familiar example of such an element. It occurs in nature as the hard crystalline diamond and as soft, flaky, crystalline graphite. The third form is amorphous (non-crystalline). In this state it occurs in coal, coke, charcoal, and lampblack. In metals, allotropy signifies the existence of a metallic element in two or more crystal forms, differing markedly in properties. Tin is an example of an allotropic metal: in its usual form it is silvery white; at a low temperature it changes gradually into a gray powder.

The most important example of allotropic metals is iron, which can exist in the solid state in three crystal forms. At normal temperatures the arrangement of atoms in the fundamental crystal unit is body-centered. If iron is heated, no change takes place in the crystal structure until a temperature of about 1670° F. (910° C.) is reached when an allotropic transformation occurs and the body-centered cubic lattice shifts to the face-centered cubic lattice. The body-centered type is known as *alpha iron;* the face-centered allotropic form is known as *gamma iron.* If heating is now continued, the fundamental crystal structure remains unchanged until a temperature of 2550° F. (1400° C.) is reached. At this point there is another change, from the face-centered gamma back to a body-centered lattice, similar to alpha iron but called *delta iron.* Delta iron exists only in the temperature range 2550 to 2800° F. (1400 to 1535° C.). It is never present in commercial carbon and low-alloy steels at temperatures at which they are useful, for which reason it is not discussed further in this book. In cooling, the reverse changes take place: at the freezing point iron crystallizes as body-centered delta; at 2550° F. (1400° C.) this undergoes an allotropic change to face-centered gamma which cools unchanged to 1670° F. (910° C.), at which temperature another allotropic change to body-centered alpha occurs. There is no further change as the iron cools to atmospheric temperature.

There are various outward manifestations of the changes in

the crystal structure of iron. Some of the most important of these, in addition to changes in the spacing of the atoms, which can be determined by X-ray, are absorption of heat in heating and evolution of heat in cooling, marked changes in dimensions,

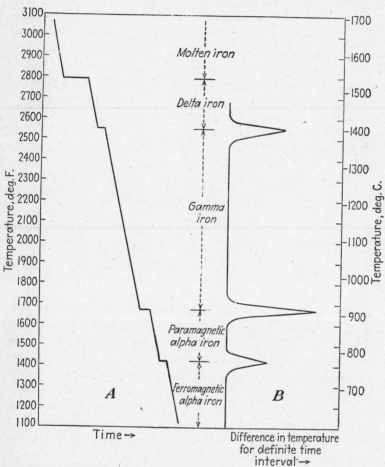

Fig. 5—Idealized cooling curves of pure iron resulting from plotting temperature (A) against time and (B) against the difference in temperature between the specimen and a neutral body for a definite time interval.

in electric resistivity, and in microstructure. For more than 40 years the metallurgist has been studying the allotropy of iron. By adopting more and more specialized technique and by using more and more sensitive apparatus he has been able to follow more and more closely the changes taking place at the transformation temperatures and to determine these temperatures with considerable accuracy. As an example of one method, a cooling curve of a specimen of pure iron is given in Fig. 5, in which temperature is plotted against time (A) or against the difference in temperature (as determined by a sensitive galvanometer) between the specimen of pure iron and a similar specimen of a neutral material which has no allotropic transformation (B).

It will be noted that there is a jog in the curve at a temperature of approximately 1420° F. (770° C.). This is the temperature where iron loses magnetism (becomes paramagnetic) when heated and regains it (becomes ferromagnetic) upon cooling. Despite the fact that this change is manifested by a distinct break in the heating and cooling curve, there is no change in crystal structure such as occurs at 1670° F. (910° C.) and at 2550° F. (1400° C.).

13. Importance of the Allotropy of Iron—At this point the engineer is probably wondering why the metallurgist has spent so much time studying the allotropy of iron, and why so much space in this chapter has been devoted to describing it. In fact he may with complete justification inquire in what way this change in atomic arrangement affects him, why he should be interested in how the atoms of a crystal of iron are spaced. It probably would be of little interest except for one vital fact: carbon dissolves in gamma iron but is practically insoluble in alpha iron. Since practically all the ferrous materials the engineer uses are alloys of iron and carbon, there is much in this to interest the engineer; in fact this phenomenon is one of the most important in the whole material universe and is the keystone of our machine civilization. It is just as important and probably more important than electricity or steam.

To justify such a broad statement, it is only necessary to attempt to picture what civilization would be like if iron did not possess the property of changing its crystal structure or its dissolving power for carbon. We would have a metal inferior in most of its properties to common brass and bronze. There would be no modern tools and nothing that modern tools have built: no skyscrapers, no automobiles, no railroads, no airplanes, no ocean liners, no steam, gas or oil engines, no turbines for motive power and for generating electricity (except some woefully inefficient curiosities), no battleships nor submarines to throttle a country's trade and starve its women and children, and no big guns or airplanes to kill non-combatants miles behind a battle front. Wood, stone, and brick would be left and such soft metals as copper, brass, bronze, aluminum, and carbonless iron, all of which would have to be cast or worked into shape by hand hammering. Concrete might be left, but it is doubtful if cement could be ground without hard steel grinding mills. If steel would disappear from the world and could not be replaced, the engineering professions would be decimated or worse, and some of them would become practically extinct.

If iron were a metal with no allotropic transformations and there were no cheap and equally efficient material to take the place of steel—and it is unlikely that there would be any unless precipitation-hardening alloys were developed very much farther than it is considered possible now—mankind would still be living in a civilization now called medieval. It is the job of the sociologist and of the philosopher to tell us, if they can, what we would have missed.

14. Metallic Compounds and Alloys—As the metals, like non-metallic elements, possess valence, they combine with other elements to form definite chemical compounds. Compounds of metals and non-metals, such as sodium chloride (salt), $NaCl$, and iron oxide (rust), Fe_2O_3, are very common and are familiar to everyone. Less common and less familiar are compounds of metals and metalloids, for example iron carbide, Fe_3C, and tungsten carbide, WC. Still less common, and relatively unfamiliar to all but chemists and metallurgists, are compounds of metals with metals—intermetallic compounds—such as copper aluminide, $CuAl_2$, which plays an important role in the strong alloys of aluminum and copper.

There are approximately 300 intermetallic compounds, some of which are very important in the constitution of those metallic materials that are widely used in industry. Intermetallic compounds and compounds of metals with metalloids differ from such common compounds as sodium chloride and iron oxide in that, in general, they do not obey the ordinary rules of valence. Compared with pure metals, they are usually hard and brittle and have low electric conductivity. Structurally they are crystalline, and they usually have a much more complex crystal structure than the metals. The importance of the intermetallic and the metal-metalloid compounds (which are generally worthless by themselves) lies in the fact that when they are present in small quantities in a metallic material their size and state of dispersion can frequently be closely controlled, so that effective use can be made of them in increasing the strength and hardness of the material. It is discussed in detail later that the heat treatment of steel and the hardening of duralumin are due to control of the particle size of the metallic compounds present in the alloys.

In addition to the ability of combining chemically with other elements, the metals also possess the valuable property of dissolving in each other or mixing intimately with each other or with certain metalloids or non-metals in both the liquid and the solid state to form an alloy. With very few exceptions, all metals are mutually soluble in each other, like alcohol and water, when they are molten. Moreover, when this molten solution of a metal (or in some cases of a metalloid or non-metal) in a metal solidifies the solid material has properties that are usually very different from the properties of the components making up the alloy.

Since alloys are rarely used in the molten state, the properties of such materials are of little or no interest to the engineer. He is, however, vitally interested in the properties of alloys when they are solid, mostly when they are at normal temperatures (50 to 100° F.), but also when they are at temperatures higher or lower than normal. It is important, therefore, that considerable attention be paid in subsequent chapters of this book to the structural changes in the industrially important alloys when they are heated or cooled between their solidification point and normal or subnormal temperatures.

15. Types of Alloys—In the molten state there are two types of alloys: (1) those in which the components are wholly soluble in each other, and (2) those in which the components are practically insoluble in each other. The second type is of little interest either theoretically or practically and, except for a few free-machining materials containing lead in suspension, will not be considered further.

If an alloy of the first type, in which the components are mutually soluble when molten, is cooled to the solidification point a variety of changes may take place during freezing. The possibilities are as follows:

1. The components may remain in solution in the solid state.[3]
2. The components may be insoluble in the solid state.
3. The components may be partially soluble in each other.
4. The components may, in part, form intermetallic compounds which may in turn be soluble, partially soluble, or insoluble in either or both of the excess components.
5. There may be a reaction (called a peritectic reaction) in the solid state which results in the formation of a solid solution, one or more intermetallic compounds, or both.
6. If an element such as iron is present which can exist in two or more crystal forms, this element may undergo allotropic change.
7. Any one of these six possibilities may be further complicated by one or more of the others.

It is evident from this that the constitution of metallic alloys is not a simple science. It is not easy to determine the structural changes and the amounts and character of the constituents present in a binary alloy system in which only two components are present; in a ternary system in which three components participate, such determination becomes a Herculean job; and when more than three components are present it is almost impossible.

The constitution of metallic alloys is studied by preparing a series of high-purity alloys ranging in composition from 100 per cent of one constituent to 100 per cent of the other constituent. Suitable specimens of these alloys are subjected to treatments which produce a state of equilibrium. This is followed by studying the changes in length, electric resistivity, microscopic and atomic structure, absorption and liberation of heat, and others, which occur when the alloy is heated and cooled from normal temperature or below to the melting point or above. The temperatures at which the changes occur are plotted against the composition; the result is an equilibrium diagram (also called constitutional or phase diagram) of the series. Examples of such dia-

---

[3] The concept of one solid dissolving in another solid (solid solution) is not always easy to grasp. A solution of a solid in a liquid, as salt in water, or a liquid in a liquid, as alcohol in water, presents no difficulty. A solution of molten gold in molten silver is wholly analogous to alcohol in water, except for a large difference in temperature. When this metallic solution solidifies the gold remains in solution in the silver; the atoms of the one metal are uniformly dispersed in the other metal, and the gold cannot be detected by any method short of chemical analysis. Solid solutions have all the characteristics of liquid solutions except possibly mobility.

grams with a brief explanation of their meaning are given in later chapters for iron-carbon and a few of the more important industrial non-ferrous alloys.

In the past 20 years most binary alloy systems including the important iron-carbon, aluminum-copper, copper-tin, and copper-zinc systems have been studied in considerable detail. Of the thousands of possible ternary alloys only a few—the alloys which are important industrially—have been investigated, and most of these incompletely. The field of quaternary alloys is practically untouched.

An equilibrium diagram of a series of alloys is of value in that, if the changes in structure with changes in temperature are known for a few representative alloys, similar changes are also known for all the alloys in the series. Because many of the properties are dependent upon the structure, the properties of all the alloys can be anticipated from the known properties of a few. The diagram also enables thermal treatments to be worked out which will produce a desired structure in any alloy of the series. The greatest objection to the equilibrium diagram is that it represents only equilibrium conditions and tells nothing if equilibrium is not attained. This is enlarged upon in detail in connection with the discussion of the iron-carbon diagram in a later chapter.

16. Crystal Structure and Plastic Flow—If a crystal of a pure metal is subjected to a stress of even low magnitude, the space lattice is distorted and the metal changes dimensions slightly. So long as the applied stress is less than the force that holds the atoms together, removal of the stress causes the groups of atoms to return to their original position and eliminates the distortion. If, however, the applied stress is greater than the force holding the atoms together—in other words, if the elastic limit is exceeded —the groups of atoms are displaced along what might be called the cleavage planes, and permanent deformation (plastic flow) occurs. The important point about this deformation is that it can occur without actually breaking the atomic bonds, that is, considerable movement of the atom groups can take place without rupture of the crystal or of the crystalline aggregate.

The ability of a crystal to deform or flow under stress without rupture is one of the most important properties of metals and alloys. In general, it varies with the temperature. It is made use of in all the metallurgical operations known under the generic term mechanical treatment or mechanical working, including rolling, forging, drawing, extruding, stamping, spinning, bending, riveting, and others. Among the chief reasons why metals and alloys are so widely used industrially are that they can be worked economically into useful shapes and that they withstand without failure the abuse of deformation.

The plastic flow of metals and alloys is accompanied by changes in properties, which are especially marked when the material is cold worked. Tensile strength,[4] yield strength, and hardness increase; ductility, on the other hand, decreases. Electric and magnetic properties are also affected.

The amount of deformation that a metal or alloy withstands, at any specific temperature, is related to the structure of the individual crystal unit and to the structure of the crystalline aggregate. Plastic flow and its effect on the properties are discussed later. What should be emphasized here is that plasticity is an outstanding characteristic of the metals as a class and that it is responsible for much of their economic importance.

[4] This and other properties are discussed later in this book.

CHAPTER 3

THE MANUFACTURE OF IRON AND STEEL

M AN has been using iron for at least 5000 years. For almost
half of this time he used it as a precious metal which came from
heaven—as meteorites—and which was seized when found and
laboriously worked into jewelry, charms, and amulets. These
he wore for personal adornment or to ward off the evil spirits
that harassed him daily. For the last 2500 years, he has had ter-
restrial iron, reduced from its ores, and it is characteristic that
the first use he made of it was to fashion weapons so that he could
extend his control over the other species of the animal kingdom
and demonstrate his superiority over those of his own species
who did not yet possess this useful metal. His next use of iron
was to fashion tools, so that he could make life easier for himself.
Despite the fact that the development of large-scale manufacture
about 80 years ago made iron and steel the cheapest metallic
materials on earth, man never did become civilized enough to
realize that the tool was more important than the sword. Events
of the past 25 years have amply demonstrated that man values
iron and steel primarily as a means of subduing his fellow human
beings, and only secondarily as a means of making the world a
better place in which to live.

Since the beginning of large-scale manufacture about 1870,
steel production has increased greatly each decade; by 1930 the
world was using over 130 million tons a year. Of this the steel
industry of the United States has been producing since 1920
between 20 and 65 million tons annually. About 97 per cent of
this output is poured into ingots that are hot or cold worked into
sections for use in engineering structures, machines, and tools.
The remainder is poured into castings that are used in the form
which they assumed in the mold, except for necessary machining.
In addition to this large steel output, there are produced annually
in the United States between 20 and 40 million tons of pig iron,

80 to 85 per cent of which is used as an intermediate product in steel manufacture. The remainder is remelted and poured into sand or iron molds. This is the cast iron of commerce and is also used mainly in engineering structures and machines.

Despite the fact that commercial carbon steels and cast irons contain many other elements in addition to carbon, metallurgists look upon them as alloys of the metal iron and the metalloid carbon because carbon has the greatest effect on their structure and properties. Depending upon the amount, form, distribution, and behavior of the carbon, the alloy will be hard or soft, tough or brittle, strong or weak, malleable or not. The increasing value of steel and cast iron to humanity over the past 50 or 75 years has resulted primarily from our increasing knowledge of the role played by carbon, and upon our ability to control its form, distribution, and behavior. Commercial carbon steels contain, in addition to carbon, varying amounts of manganese, silicon, sulphur, and phosphorus; frequently they also contain small amounts of as many as twelve other elements.

17. **Definition of Carbon Steel and Cast Iron**—For many years committees of metallurgists in English-speaking countries have been trying to define carbon steel, alloy steel, cast iron, pig iron, wrought iron, and other products of the industry precisely and concisely, but with little success. Some of these terms have been used for years, others have been applied to new products as these were developed; all of them have been used so loosely by the men who make and use steel that it is hardly likely that most of them will ever be defined both precisely and concisely.

It would be a waste of space, and probably even confusing, if the complex definitions for the numerous products of the iron and steel industry were all set down at once. We will, therefore, be content to distinguish here between carbon steel and cast iron and will hope that the definitions of the other products will become clear when they are discussed later.

Carbon steel may be defined as a commercial alloy of iron and carbon containing less than 1.7 per cent carbon, less than about 1 per cent manganese, less than 0.4 to 0.5 per cent silicon, small amounts of adventitious elements, and no intentionally added special element. If the alloy contains more than 1.7 per cent carbon and is poured direct from the blast furnace into cast iron molds of uniform size, or is used in the molten condition as an intermediate product, it is called *pig iron;* and if this pig iron (usually with the addition of scrap) is remelted and poured into a sand mold, thereby assuming the desired shape of the finished section, it is known as *cast iron.* This means that whether an iron-carbon alloy containing more than 1.7 per cent carbon is called pig iron or cast iron depends upon whether the material is an intermediate product or a finished product.

These definitions are probably as concise as possible without the use of such metallurgical terms as carbide eutectic, graphite eutectic and others; they are undoubtedly not precise enough to satisfy the more pedantic among metallurgists but should be sufficiently accurate for all practical purposes. In this connection an additional concise but not very precise definition of cast iron may be worth mentioning: "iron containing so much carbon or its equivalent that it is not malleable at any temperature."

Pig iron and cast iron have been differentiated here chiefly to indicate some of the necessary distinctions in formulating definitions of ferrous products. Pig iron is of little interest to the engineer; cast iron is an important engineering material and is discussed in some detail later.

It may be asked legitimately why the dividing line between carbon steel and cast iron is placed at exactly 1.7 per cent carbon. Although this percentage is fixed primarily for convenience, it has considerable scientific justification as 1.7 per cent is the carbon concentration represented by the point on the iron-carbon equilibrium diagram which marks the maximum solid solubility of carbon in iron at very high temperature and to the left of which graphite—a common form of carbon in cast iron—is not ordinarily present under normal conditions of treatment.

For convenience, the commercial iron-carbon alloys may be divided into four classes:

> Low-carbon steel ...... Less than 0.30 per cent carbon
> Medium-carbon steel ...... 0.30 to 0.70 per cent carbon
> High-carbon steel .... 0.70 to 1.70 per cent carbon
> Cast iron and pig iron ..... 2.50 to 4.50 per cent carbon

18. **Iron Ore and the Manufacture of Pig Iron**—The four essential raw materials of the iron and steel industry are iron ore, coke and coal, limestone, and scrap steel and scrap cast iron. The iron ore used in the United States is chiefly hematite, an

impure ferrous oxide, Fe_2O_3, containing between 45 and 55 per cent metallic iron and between 20 and 35 per cent earthy matter, known as gangue, which is made up of silica, alumina, calcium oxide, magnesium oxide, and water, plus varying small amounts of phosphorus and occasionally sulphur. Hematites and other usable iron ores are widespread throughout the world; the commercial ores in the United States are estimated at more than 10 billion tons, of which 90 per cent is located near Lake Superior and in Alabama. Iron ores are graded by phosphorus content into Bessemer and non-Bessemer (basic) ores. As phosphorus is not removed in the blast furnace, the ore must not contain more than approximately half the amount of this element permitted in Bessemer steel.

Iron ore is reduced by coke in the blast furnace, limestone being used to flux the gangue and the ash of the coke. The raw materials, in the approximate ratio of two tons of ore (frequently including some scrap steel or cast iron) to one ton of coke and one-half ton of limestone, are charged into the top of the furnace, and air preheated to 1000° F. (540° C.) or above is blown into the furnace through a number of nozzles (called tuyeres) near the bottom. The blast furnace, shown in cross-section in Fig. 6,[1] is a steel shell lined with firebrick, 90 to 100 ft. high, 17 to 20 ft. in diameter at the top and 24 to 28 ft. in diameter at the bosh (just above the tuyeres). Operation is entirely continuous: the raw materials, carefully weighed and analyzed, are charged into the top at frequent intervals and slowly settle to the bottom, the downward pressure being slightly greater than the upward blast pressure plus the friction of the burden on the walls of the furnace.

As the charge settles, the temperature increases (Fig. 6) until near the bosh the iron ore is practically all reduced and the spongy iron is heated to incandescence. Here it starts absorbing carbon, which lowers the melting point. The iron then becomes pasty, absorbs carbon more rapidly and finally melts, trickling down over the remaining unburned incandescent coke into the hearth. The calcium oxide in the limestone forms a fusible slag that is much lower in specific gravity than the iron and that floats on top of the molten metal in the hearth from where it is drained at

[1] Based on J. M. Camp and C. B. Francis, *The Making, Shaping and Treating of Steel*, Carnegie Steel Co., Pittsburgh, 4th ed., 1925, p. 159.

regular intervals. The molten high-carbon iron is drained from the hearth into ladles every 5 or 6 hr. and is then either poured into molds to solidify as pig iron or used in the molten condition in the manufacture of Bessemer or open-hearth steel. A modern blast furnace produces between 500 and 1000 tons of pig iron

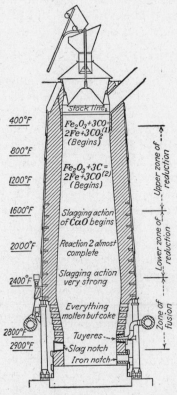

Fig. 6—Cross-section of a modern blast furnace showing temperature and chemical reaction levels (Based on Camp and Francis).

every 24 hr. and, barring shut downs for economic conditions, will operate continuously for years.

The average proportion of the raw materials entering the blast furnace and of the resulting products is shown graphically in Fig. 7.[2] The slag is mostly waste and must be disposed of, a con-

[2] H. M. Boylston, *Iron and Steel*, John Wiley & Sons, Inc., New York, 1935, p. 71.

siderable problem in some plants. As Fig. 7 shows, an enormous volume of gas is given off. This gas, which totals more than 100 million cu. ft. a day, contains 20 to 25 per cent carbon monoxide and has a heating value of 90 to 100 B.t.u. per cu. ft. It is, consequently, used to heat the blast and to generate power. Thermally the iron blast furnace is not efficient. Owing, however, to the value of the gas as a by-product and to the operation of

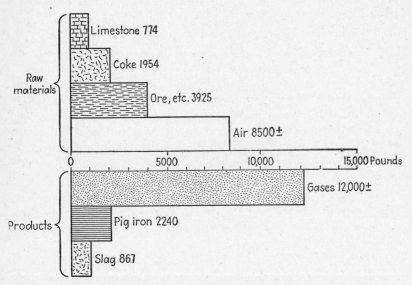

Fig. 7—Relative proportions by weight of the raw materials and products of the modern blast furnace (Boylston).

large units, the overall efficiency is relatively high, and pig iron is made cheaply.

19. Chemistry of the Blast Furnace—The preheated air, which is blown into the furnace under a pressure of 15 to 20 lb. per sq. in., in coming into immediate contact with incandescent coke forms large volumes of carbon monoxide gas. This gas, together with the carbon in the coke, reduces the iron oxide by two general reactions:

$$Fe_2O_3 + 3\ CO \rightleftharpoons 2\ Fe + 3\ CO_2 \qquad (1)$$

$$Fe_2O_3 + 3\ C \rightleftharpoons 2\ Fe + 3\ CO \qquad (2)$$

Both reactions are reversible and may proceed in either direction depending upon the temperature and other conditions prevailing at the various levels in the furnace. The net result, however, is reduction of the oxide to metallic iron. Both reactions are progressive: the Fe_2O_3 is reduced first to Fe_3O_4, then to FeO, and finally to Fe. Reaction (1) predominates in the upper part of the furnace (see Fig. 6), beginning at a temperature of about 400° F. (210° C.); reaction (2) begins at a temperature of approximately 1200° F. (650° C.) and is not completed until the iron oxide is completely reduced in the zone of the bosh.

The chemical reactions in the blast furnace are essentially reducing so that any easily reducible oxides in the iron ore or the coke (in addition to the iron oxide) are also reduced. Thus all the phosphorus and most of the manganese will be found in the iron. Oxides of silicon and sulphur are more stable but are partially reduced. The remaining oxides—of calcium, magnesium, and aluminum—are very refractory and are not acted upon by the carbon or carbon monoxide even at the highest temperature of the furnace. To flux these refractory oxides the necessary amount of limestone ($CaCO_3$) must be charged. This calcines in the upper part of the furnace and, together with the calcium and magnesium oxide in the ore, combines chemically with the alumina and with part of the silica to form a fusible slag composed of calcium, magnesium and aluminum silicates.

The pig iron, tapped from the furnace, contains about 4 per cent carbon, all the phosphorus and most of the manganese in the raw materials. The amounts of silicon and sulphur in the iron are controlled to some extent by a careful selection of raw materials but chiefly by regulating the chemical characteristics of the slag, that is, by controlling the proportion of calcium oxide to silica and by controlling the temperature. The latter depends upon the amount of coke, the temperature of the blast, the amount of water vapor in the blast (the humidity), and other variables. The operation of a modern blast furnace and the production of cheap pig iron of satisfactory quality is an art which demands long experience and skill of a high order.

20. Acid and Basic Processes—The reduction of iron ores and the manufacture of steel are chemical processes and are unique in large-scale industrial operations in that the chemical reactions involved take place at high temperatures, nearly always above 2000° F. (1100° C.) and usually in the range 2500 to 3500° F.

(1370 to 1925° C.). Few refractory materials withstand such temperatures. The only ones that are available cheaply are the oxides of silicon, calcium, and magnesium. These are relatively inert at normal temperatures but become active chemically at steel-making temperatures: silica (SiO_2) becomes an active acid, and calcium and magnesium oxides become active bases, reacting at high temperatures thus

$$CaO + SiO_2 \rightarrow CaSiO_3 \qquad (3)$$

$$MgO + SiO_2 \rightarrow MgSiO_3 \qquad (4)$$

It is characteristic of silicates such as these that they fuse at temperatures much lower than the fusing temperatures of the oxides.

Molten metals are refined by slags which are essentially silicates of calcium, magnesium, and iron and which are formed by a reaction between definite amounts of a basic oxide and the acid oxide silica. Depending on whether the basic or the acid constituent is in excess, the slag will have a basic or an acid reaction at steel-making temperatures. The character of the refractories used in the furnace—which is decided by economic considerations—determines the character of the slag and thus determines whether the process is basic or acid.

It is obvious that, if a furnace has an acid lining, the slag must be acid in character or it would attack and destroy the furnace lining. Thus, in an acid process the slag must contain an excess of silica, and in a basic process, where the lining is magnesium oxide, the slag must contain an excess of calcium oxide. The advantages and disadvantages of acid and basic steel-making processes may be summed up as follows:

(1) In a basic-lined furnace, using a basic slag, most of the phosphorus and part of the sulphur are removed by the slag; acid slags have no effect on either impurity. Basic refractories are more costly than acid refractories, but scrap and pig iron suitable for the basic process are cheaper than guaranteed low-phosphorus material.

(2) Acid slags contain less free oxide than basic slags. Consequently, if other things are equal, acid steel is cleaner and of higher quality than basic steel.

These characteristics of acid and basic processes are enlarged upon in the discussion of the chemistry of the steel-making processes later in this chapter.

21. The Basic Open-hearth and Acid Bessemer Processes—Of the large tonnage of steel produced annually in the United States, about 98 per cent is made by the basic open-hearth and the acid Bessemer processes (see Table 2). Twenty-five years ago, 25 to 30 per cent of the so-called tonnage steels were made in the Bessemer converter. The price differential in favor of Bessemer steel, averaging $2 to $4 a ton, disappeared some years ago owing to the increasing scarcity and higher cost of low-phosphorus ores. This, coupled with the disadvantage that Bessemer steel containing

Fig. 8—Cut-away model of 100-ton open-hearth furnace.

more than about 0.20 per cent carbon is considered by many metallurgists to be inferior in quality to steel of comparable carbon content made by the basic open-hearth process, has resulted in the decline of Bessemer-steel production to about 7 per cent of the total and in the virtual restriction of this material to low-carbon skelp for welded pipe, bars for wire, sheet bar for the manufacture of tin-plate and other flat products, and free-machining steels.

The modern basic open-hearth furnace is a brick chamber about 80 ft. long and 18 to 20 ft. wide. The hearth is shaped like an elongated saucer and is about 40 ft. long, 14 to 16 ft. wide and 20 to 24 in. deep at the center (Fig. 8). The furnace is fired with gas or oil and preheated air, and, if a lean gas is employed, this is also preheated. To attain the temperature necessary the regenerative principle is used. White-hot exhaust gases from the furnace are led through a series of brick checkerwork chambers on the way to the stack. After about 15 min., these exhaust gases are diverted to another set of checker chambers, and the cold air

Fig. 9—Bessemer converter in operation (Jones and Laughlin Steel Corporation).

and gas are led through the heated checkers on their way to the furnace. The direction of the exhaust and the incoming gases is reversed every 15 or 20 min. By this means the temperature attained by the gases as they burn and sweep across the hearth is about 3500° F. (1925° C.).

The charge is scrap steel and pig iron and varies according to the price from 75 per cent or more scrap and 25 per cent or less pig iron to 75 per cent pig iron and 25 per cent scrap. If the open-hearth is a part of a large steel plant, molten pig iron is used. The furnace is lined with basic refractories, and limestone is used for the slag. The average charge is 75 to 175 tons, which is melted in about 6 hr. Refining takes 4 to 5 hr. longer. When this is complete the metal is tapped into a ladle and teemed into large ingot molds. Carbon and alloy steels containing from 0.05 to 1.00 per cent carbon are made by the basic open-hearth process.

The acid Bessemer converter is a pear-shaped steel vessel lined with silica brick and mounted on trunions by which it can be tilted 180 deg. (Fig. 9). The bottom contains a large number of tuyeres to admit the blast. In making steel by the Bessemer process the converter is tilted forward, and 15 to 25 tons of molten pig iron are poured into the belly of the vessel. It is then turned upright, and at the same moment the blast is turned on. Refining begins immediately. No external source of heat is needed as sufficient is generated, by the reaction of oxygen with the carbon and other elements in the pig iron, to raise the temperature several hundred degrees. The progress of the chemical reactions is followed by observing the color and length of the flame shooting from the mouth of the vessel (Fig. 9). Refining is complete in 10 to 15 min., after which the converter is tilted forward and the metal is poured into a ladle from which it is teemed into ingot molds. The production from a Bessemer plant of three vessels is 5000 to 6000 tons in 24 hr. To produce the same tonnage of basic open-hearth steel a battery of twenty 100-ton furnaces is needed.

22. Chemistry of the Basic Open-hearth and the Acid Bessemer Process—The basic open-hearth and the acid Bessemer are oxidation processes. Oxygen in the air or in some form of iron oxide (iron ore) is used to oxidize the carbon, silicon, manganese, and—in the basic process—the phosphorus and a part of the sulphur in the charge. In the basic open-hearth process limestone, $CaCO_3$, is charged with the scrap and pig iron, and when the metal is melted this limestone, calcined to lime (CaO) by the heat, rises to the top of the molten bath to form slag. Iron oxide in the form of iron ore is added to augment the iron oxide which, in the form of rust, was on the scrap and pig iron. The iron oxide oxidizes the silicon and manganese first, according to the reactions:

$$Si + 2\,FeO \rightarrow SiO_2 + 2\,Fe \tag{5}$$

$$Mn + FeO \rightarrow MnO + Fe \tag{6}$$

$$MnO + SiO_2 \rightarrow MnSiO_3 \tag{7a}$$

$$FeO + SiO_2 \rightarrow FeSiO_3 \tag{7b}$$

The manganese and iron silicates, of low melting point and low specific gravity, rise to join the slag. The phosphorus is then oxidized:

$$2\,P + 5\,FeO \rightarrow P_2O_5 + 5\,Fe \tag{8a}$$

$$P_2O_5 + 3\,FeO \rightarrow (FeO)_3P_2O_5 \tag{8b}$$

$$(FeO)_3P_2O_5 + 3\,CaO \rightarrow (CaO)_3P_2O_5 + 3\,FeO \tag{8c}$$

The iron phosphate formed by reaction (8b) is unstable, but in the presence of an excess of lime, reaction (8c) takes place, and the more stable calcium phosphate is formed and also leaves the metal and joins the slag.

Reactions (5) to (8) are exothermic and take place at relatively low temperatures, as the charge is melting or just after melting is complete. The oxidation of carbon

$$C + FeO \rightarrow CO + Fe \tag{9}$$

by reaction (9) is endothermic and takes place only at high temperatures.

When all the impurities have been eliminated as far as possible or desirable, the molten metal usually contains less than 0.10 per cent carbon, less than 0.20 per cent manganese, less than 0.01 per cent silicon and usually less than 0.03 per cent phosphorus. Sulphur drops from about 0.04 or 0.05 to 0.025 or 0.035 per cent. As the result of these oxidizing reactions the molten metal also contains a relatively large quantity of dissolved iron oxide which, as discussed in the next chapter, is harmful. It also contains too little manganese to combine with the sulphur. To remove harmful oxide and to ensure the presence of sulphur as manganese sulphide, manganese is added to the molten metal in the furnace or as it is tapped from the furnace. This reacts with dissolved iron oxide

$$Mn + FeO \rightarrow Fe + MnO \tag{10}$$

to form manganese oxide which is insoluble in the molten metal and which rises to the top to join the slag.

The manganese is added as a ferroalloy containing 80 per cent manganese, 14 per cent iron and 6 per cent carbon, or as an alloy containing 20 per cent manganese, 75 per cent iron and 5 per cent carbon. Adding the manganese also adds a certain percentage of carbon to the metal. By using different grades of ferromanganese and, if necessary, adding carbon in the form of ground anthracite coal, steel of any desired carbon and manganese content can be made.

In the acid Bessemer process, the blast of air entering the converter forms large volumes of iron oxide as soon as it strikes the molten metal, which immediately oxidizes the manganese and silicon according to reactions (5), (6) and (7). The phosphorus is oxidized, but as there is no excess of lime, stable phosphate is not formed and none of this element is removed from the metal. Sulphur is also unaffected. Carbon is oxidized by the same reaction that occurs in the basic open-hearth. When the manganese, silicon, and carbon in the pig iron are reduced to a low percentage the converter is tapped, harmful oxides are eliminated as far as possible, and the proper amounts of carbon and manganese are secured by adding an alloy of iron, manganese, and carbon to the ladle exactly as in the basic open-hearth process. No slag-making materials are added. The slag formed is composed of compound silicates of iron and manganese—oxidized from the pig iron—plus some silica, eroded from the lining, and is acid in character. Owing to the rapidity with which the reactions occur and to the large volume of iron oxide formed, acid Bessemer steel usually contains more dissolved iron oxide than basic open-hearth steel.

In the basic open-hearth as well as in the acid Bessemer process it is impossible to control the oxidation of silicon and manganese; the oxidation of carbon can be controlled and stopped when desired. Usually, however, this is not economical so that in both processes the carbon is practically all oxidized and the heat is usually recarburized by a ferroalloy, by coal, or by molten pig iron.

23. **Manufacture of High-quality steels**—High-quality carbon and alloy steels are made by the acid open-hearth and the acid and basic electric processes (Table 2). Most carbon tool steels and special alloy steels are made in the basic-lined electric furnace. Selected steel scrap is melted in an arc or induction furnace.

The arc furnace, shown in Fig. 10, produces most of these materials, in lots of 5 to 25 tons; the induction furnace, with a capacity up to 5 tons, is used chiefly to melt high-alloy steel scrap without loss of costly alloying metals.

Fig. 10—Héroult electric furnace tilted for tapping, showing arrangement of electrodes (American Bridge Company).

If the scrap contains too much carbon and phosphorus, these elements are oxidized together with the silicon and manganese, under conditions similar to those outlined for the basic open-hearth process on page 43. When oxidation is completed the slag is removed and a new one is added, composed of lime, fluorspar and silica sand or crushed ferrosilicon. This slag, which consists principally of calcium silicate when melted, is deoxidized, and strongly reducing conditions are established in the furnace by scattering powdered coke or ferrosilicon over the surface. Since slag and metal tend to be in equilibrium, eliminating iron oxide from the slag also deoxidizes the metal. Furthermore, a strongly reducing slag will remove sulphur almost completely from the metal. Owing to the complete deoxidation of the slag and to the absence of oxidizing gases—a condition attained only in the basic electric process—much sounder steel can be made by this process than by either the acid Bessemer or the basic open-hearth process where gases and slag are strongly oxidizing at all times.

In general the quality of acid open-hearth steel is intermediate between basic open-hearth steel and basic electric steel. Acid open-hearth furnaces are like basic open-hearth furnaces but are usually smaller and are lined with silica refractories. The slag used contains excess silica, SiO_2, instead of excess lime, CaO. The atmosphere is as oxidizing as in the basic process. In the acid slag, however, the iron oxide is mostly combined with the silica as ferrous silicate. Consequently there is much less free oxide in the slag to migrate into the metal. Thus, acid open-hearth steel usually contains less oxide than does basic open-hearth steel and is used for armor plate and ordnance, large forgings and castings, and for other purposes where high-grade carbon and alloy steels are required in large quantities.

The acid electric process combines the non-oxidizing character of arc heating with the lining and slag of an acid process. Acid electric steel is usually not so well deoxidized as basic electric steel, but it is cheaper. The 6-ton acid electric furnace is especially suitable for intermittent operation and, owing to the high temperatures of the arc, is widely used for melting steel for small high-grade castings.

The general features of the various steel-making processes are summarized in Table 2. In connection with this summary and with the discussion in this chapter it must be emphasized that in steel melting, as in all metal melting and many other industrial arts, the personal equation is important. As an incompetent chef can spoil the best steak in the cooking, so can an unskillful or careless melter produce a heat of basic electric steel that is more unsound than a heat of basic open-hearth steel produced by a

TABLE 2. CLASSIFICATION OF STEEL-MAKING PROCESSES (UNITED STATES)

Process	Percentage of total production 1936-1940	Raw material used	Percentage present in finished steel		Furnace slags remove			Rank with regard to			Principal products
			Phosphorus	Sulphur	Phosphorus	Sulphur	Oxygen	Tonnage	Quality	Cost	
Basic open-hearth	90.7	Scrap and pig iron	0.020 to 0.045	0.030 to 0.055	Most	Part	Very little	1	4	2*	Structural shapes, plate, sheet, strip, rails, tubes, wire and large castings of carbon and alloy steel
Acid Bessemer	6.8	Molten pig iron	0.070 to 0.12	0.030 to 0.065	None	None	None	2	5	1*	Skelp for pipe, sheet bar for tin-plate, some wire and zinc-coated sheet, free-machining steels
Basic electric	1.4	Scrap	0.010 to 0.035	0.010 to 0.030	Most	Most	Most	3	1	5	Special alloy steels, high-grade carbon steels, special tool steels, and high-speed steel
Acid open-hearth	0.8	Scrap and pig iron	0.040 to 0.065	0.020 to 0.045	None	None	Part	4	3	3	Large castings, high-strength wire, large forgings, ordnance, and armor plate
Acid electric	0.3	Scrap	0.030 to 0.065	0.020 to 0.045	None	None	Part	5	2	4	Small carbon and alloy castings, and a few special alloy steels

* At present there is very little difference in the cost of acid Bessemer and basic open-hearth steel. See p. 40.

skillful melter. In modern steel making, skill can usually be taken for granted, which was not true in the "good old days" of 40 or 50 years ago. The carbon and alloy steels made today are nearly always of such high quality as the inherent limitations of the process will permit.

24. The Mechanical Treatment of Steel—As noted in the introduction to this chapter, 97 per cent of all the steel made is poured into cast iron molds to solidify as ingots. These vary in weight from as little as 100 lb. to as much as 100 tons. After the ingot has solidified it is transferred to a soaking pit or heating furnace to equalize the temperature and to heat it to a temperature at which the steel is very plastic. It is then hot worked by rolling, pressing or forging it into a finished or semi-finished product. A few special carbon and alloy steels used in very heavy sections, such as large guns, axle shafts, armor plate and the like, and a few tonnage products are worked from the ingot directly into the finished section. It is, however, considered better practice, whenever the size of the finished product permits, to reduce the ingot to a section known as a bloom, slab, or billet, which is reheated, either with or without intermediate cooling and inspection, and is rolled into finished products. These may be rails, structural shapes, plates, sheets, strip, pipe and tubes, bars, or rods of a wide variety of sizes and forms. Finished sections from the large rolling mill, especially bars and rods, may be fabricated further into a multitude of small articles.

Hot working has two primary objects: (1) to produce various shapes and sizes economically; and (2) to improve the structure and properties by breaking up the coarse crystal structure of the ingot.

A large tonnage of hot-rolled bars and rods is worked cold by drawing through a die to wire, or by rolling to sheet and many other products. Cold working also has two primary objects: (1) to produce sections, sizes, and shapes that cannot be produced economically by any other method; and (2) to produce certain combinations of properties, especially very high strength accompanied by considerable ductility, that also cannot be secured economically by any other process.

The mechanical treatment of steel is an art that has been perfected mechanically until it is now in a relatively high state of development. Hundreds of millions of dollars have been invested in rolling mills and forging plants that are marvels of mechanical efficiency and low-cost production. Modern rolling mills, such as the recently developed continuous strip mill, are, in fact, such marvels of costly perfection that when the steel industry is playing the role of pauper (as it frequently has in the past ten years) the overhead eats up months of profits gained when operations are on a princely scale.

Although the mechanical equipment used and the methods of hot and cold working are a fascinating field for discussion, they are of little concern to the engineer who uses steel and who does not care whether strip is rolled on a continuous or a hand mill so long as it has the properties he requires and is cheap enough for him to use economically. The discussion of hot and cold working is, therefore, cut off at this point as being of no further interest, but the effect of hot and cold working on the structure and properties, a subject of great interest to most engineers, is given more consideration elsewhere in this volume.

Steel and other metallic materials that have been hot or cold worked (or, in some instances, cast) frequently must be joined together to form the finished structure. The principal methods of joining are welding and riveting. The equipment and the methods used for joining are of much interest to engineers but are hardly within the scope of a book on elementary metallurgy, and are, therefore, not discussed further here.

CHAPTER 4

THE COMPOSITION OF CARBON AND ALLOY STEELS

MAN made fine steel for centuries before he knew or cared anything about its composition. Damascene swords, made by the Moslems in the Middle Ages from steel imported into the Near East from India, and by the famous families of Japanese sword makers between A. D. 500 and 1500, are the finest specimens of the early steel makers' art which have come down to us. They were made by welding alternate strips of high- and low-carbon steel into a bar, forging out this composite material, doubling it over and reforging again and again until a laminated strip of the finest quality resulted. This was drawn out into a sword or dagger blade, heat treated, sharpened, and finally etched with a dilute acid to bring out the laminations. Such a blade is shown in Fig. 11 in which the blade and scabbard are photographed against a background of the damask pattern near the dagger point, magnified eight times.

The use of chemical analysis for determining the composition of steel and cast iron did not become general until about 60 years ago, more than a decade after large-scale steel making by the Bessemer and the open-hearth processes had been introduced. Until its use became general, that is, until the opposition of the steel makers to something as radical as a chemical laboratory had been overcome, composition and general quality were judged by breaking a small piece and examining the fracture, and by forging a small block into a flat disc on an anvil and examining the edge for cracks. Steel melters became so expert in judging the amount of carbon from the fracture, and the amount of manganese and the completeness of the deoxidation from the forging test, that it has been only within the past 25 or 30 years that chemical analysis has been used to follow the progress of refining while the steel is in the furnace, and then only for electric-furnace steels and steels of special quality made in the acid and the basic open hearth.

Fig. 11—Damascus steel dagger. The background is a photograph of the etched damask pattern of the blade, magnified 8 times (Ziegler, *Mining and Metallurgy*, v. 20, 1939, p. 69).

For many years the analysis of steel and cast iron consisted of the determination of carbon, manganese, sulphur and phosphorus, silicon, if present, and alloying elements when these were specially added. Only in the past few years has it been realized that these common elements tell only a part of the story of the composition and that in addition some ten or twelve other metals, metalloids, and non-metals may be present. As a result, the chemical composition of unalloyed steel is no longer as simple as it seemed 15 or 20 years ago; on the contrary it is very complex and worthy of considerable attention.

Commercial carbon steels contain, in addition to carbon which is the most important element, varying amounts of manganese, silicon, sulphur and phosphorus, and small percentages of oxygen, nitrogen, and hydrogen. Occasionally they also contain small amounts of copper, nickel, chromium, molybdenum, lead, arsenic, aluminum, and tin. As indicated in the last chapter, some of these are added intentionally to improve the quality, but most of them are picked up from the raw materials used in the various processes. Steel men commonly divide these elements into three classes: harmful, beneficial, and neutral. This classification is convenient but is not very accurate because under certain conditions a harmful element may be neutral or even beneficial or a beneficial element may be neutral or even harmful. Thus, phosphorus, for example, may be harmful in its effect on toughness and beneficial in its effect on resistance to atmospheric corrosion.

25. Phosphorus in Carbon and Alloy Steels—The five so-called harmful elements present in all steels in varying amounts, but mostly in small fractions of 1 per cent, are: phosphorus, sulphur, oxygen, nitrogen, and hydrogen. There are many data on the effects of the first three; nitrogen and hydrogen are mystery elements, and very little is known about them.

In the amounts usually present in carbon and alloy steels phosphorus is combined with the iron as iron phosphide, Fe_3P, which dissolves in solid iron as sugar dissolves in coffee. Although metallurgical opinion is not wholly unanimous, most available data, plus many years of experience with acid steels containing 0.07 to 0.12 per cent phosphorus, indicate that this element makes steel "cold short," in other words, brittle when cold, particularly in its resistance to impact. This brittleness is more marked in high-carbon steels than in low-carbon grades and is apparent if the amount of carbon plus phosphorus is above 0.30 per cent. The static ductility is not appreciably affected.

Because of the brittleness caused by phosphorus the maximum

amount permitted is usually given in engineering specifications. This varies from a maximum of 0.10 to 0.12 per cent in low-carbon acid Bessemer steels to a maximum of 0.045 per cent in rails and railway materials, structural shapes, sheet, strip, and other products of the basic open-hearth process. In tool steels and other high-grade high-carbon and alloy steels, the maximum permitted is usually 0.03 and occasionally even 0.02 per cent. The average amount of phosphorus in various grades is shown in Table 2.

Despite the fact that, in general, phosphorus has a bad name and for nearly a hundred years has been considered a nuisance that should be kept as low as possible, it has been discovered lately that it has its good points. It raises the tensile and the yield strength and improves other properties including the resistance of steel to some varieties of corrosive attack. Some of the new low-alloy high-strength steels contain about 0.10 per cent phosphorus used together with small amounts of copper, nickel, or chromium. The carbon, however, is low.

26. **Sulphur in Carbon and Alloy Steels**—In a manner analogous to phosphorus, sulphur will combine with iron to form iron sulphide (FeS), which dissolves in molten iron. However, manganese, if present, having an affinity for sulphur which it does not have for phosphorus, will rob the iron of its sulphur to form manganese sulphide (MnS). This compound is insoluble in molten and solid iron. Consequently, when the iron solidifies, manganese sulphide is present in the mass of metal as discrete particles. These particles, together with oxides and silicates described in the next section, are known to the metallurgist as "solid non-metallic inclusions" or more simply as "inclusions," and to the man in the mill by the more expressive term "dirt." If insufficient manganese is present, some of the sulphur remains as iron sulphide. This compound melts at a temperature lower than the usual temperatures for rolling or forging, with the result that the steel is likely to crack during hot working. This brittleness or fragility at elevated temperatures is known as "hot shortness."

Practically all commercial steels contain plenty of manganese so that engineers who use steel at elevated temperatures need not worry about hot shortness caused by sulphur. Of much more interest to engineers is the fact that manganese sulphide particles are always present and that they may be present in large amounts if the sulphur is high. If these particles segregate in vital areas, they may have a deleterious effect on the ductility of the steel; in fact, impact resistance may be greatly reduced. Any particle of dirt in the metal, if large enough, if the shape is favorable, and if it is strategically located, may act as a stress raiser and cause failure, especially by fatigue, much sooner than would normally be expected. The appearance of manganese sulphide inclusions, which are readily detected by the microscope, is shown in Fig. 12.

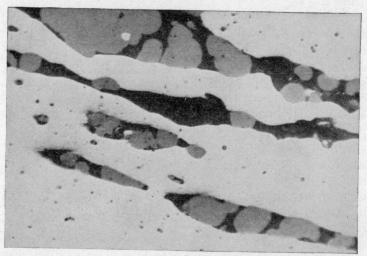

Fig. 12—Manganese inclusions (gray) and silicate inclusions (black); un-etched, 500×.

Sulphur has few virtues when present in steel. Compared with phosphorus it is a real nuisance and is, therefore, kept as low as possible. Its only benefit, so far as is known now, is that, if the manganese sulphide is present in the proper amount and is well distributed, it makes the steel easier to machine. Steels which are machined automatically at high speeds and which are used for parts that are not subject to high impact stresses contain 0.080 to 0.150 per cent, or even more, sulphur. With high sulphur percentages the manganese is frequently increased from the usual amount in low-carbon steels, namely 0.30 to 0.60 per cent, to 0.60 to 1.65 per cent to ensure that no iron sulphide is present. The average sulphur percentages for various grades of steels made by the different processes are shown in Table 2. In general, the higher amount of the range is the maximum permitted bv the usual specifications.

27. Oxygen in Carbon and Alloy Steels—All steel, except that made by some special variants of the basic electric process, is melted and refined by gases and slags which are essentially oxidizing. At the high temperatures used, oxygen combines avidly with iron, carbon, manganese, silicon, and some other elements which may be present, forming a variety of gaseous or liquid oxides. Some of these dissolve in molten steel and are thrown out of solution when the steel solidifies, others are deoxidized by later slags or by alloys added especially for this purpose. The result of these deoxidizing reactions, which are more effective in some processes than in others (see Table 2), is to produce a steel which is more or less free from oxygen and its reaction products. Even under the best conditions, however, the steel is never wholly cleansed; hence, all steels contain when solid a larger or smaller quantity of gas cavities or solid inclusions bearing oxygen in some form. These oxides or combinations of oxides (silicates) form, together with sulphur, the most common source of the solid non-metallic inclusions or dirt found in commercial steels (see Fig. 12). Like sulphide inclusions, oxides and silicates, if segregated or if present in large particles, may act as stress raisers or as loci of weakness where under favorable conditions failure may start.

Inclusions which are entrapped in the steel ingot (or casting) when it solidifies are usually in the form of small rounded particles varying in size from those which are submicroscopic to those which can be seen on a polished surface with the unaided eye. At high temperatures most of the inclusions are plastic. Consequently, when the ingot is rolled or forged, they elongate into stringers or threads, shown in Fig. 13. It should be emphasized that inclusions, once they are entrapped in the steel, may be distorted, elongated, or otherwise changed in form by hot or cold work, but they cannot be removed or even diminished in amount by any treatment. No commercial carbon or alloy steel is wholly free from dirt. The amount present and the degree of dispersion of the particles depend to a considerable extent upon the nature of the melting process. As indicated in Table 2, basic electric steel is inherently the cleanest, acid electric steel ranks next, and acid Bessemer steel ranks lowest. The process itself is, however, not the only factor. Also important are quality of the raw materials used and the skill of the man who makes the steel. These factors are discussed in more detail elsewhere.

It has been well known for many years that most ferrous materials exhibit directional properties, that is, some properties, notably impact resistance, are lower if determined on a specimen cut at a right angle to the direction of rolling than if determined on a specimen taken longitudinally. Elongated inclusions are an important factor in causing this difference in properties.

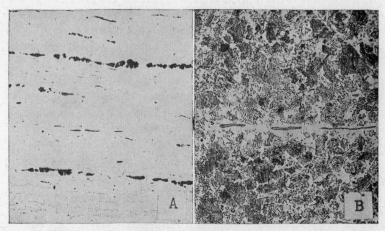

Fig. 13—Elongated slag inclusions in (A) rolled carbon steel, unetched, and (B) rolled alloy steel, etched, 100×.

Owing to the impure raw materials available to the iron and steel industry and to the necessity of using—except in a few restricted cases—oxidizing reactions to get rid of these impurities economically, one of the chief problems of steel men has been to eliminate the harmful effects of oxygen and its compounds by deoxidizing as thoroughly as possible. For more than 50 years one of the principal tenets of metallurgists has been "the more complete the deoxidation, the better the steel." Within the past 10 or 15 years, however, it has been found that the phrase "for certain steels" should preface this doctrine of deoxidation. McQuaid, Bain, and other investigators in this field have shown that a certain degree of oxidation may be very desirable in some carbon and alloy steels in which a control of the grain size is advantageous. This is discussed later.

The amount of oxygen in solid steel varies from a trace to as much as 0.02 per cent: few steels contain less than 0.005 per cent; the average amount in commercial carbon steels is probably between 0.01 and 0.015 per cent, with the higher amounts found normally in the lower carbon grades. Most of the oxygen—probably all of it in most steels—is present as an oxide or silicate. Small amounts of oxygen are difficult to determine accurately by

Fig. 14—Seams on the surface of a shaft, 2×.

chemical analysis, and it is even more difficult to determine in what form it exists in the metal.

28. Carbon Monoxide, and Rimming and Killed Steel—As a result of the reaction between oxygen and carbon in the molten metal large volumes of carbon monoxide gas are formed. Most of this gas is given off during refining; some of it, however, remains entrapped and, unless removed by silicon or other degasifier as described in section 30, will be still in the metal when it starts to solidify. Most of this remaining carbon monoxide escapes during solidification. Owing, however, to the viscosity

of the metal just before it solidifies, some of the gas remains entrapped to form cavities of varying size in the ingot or casting. These cavities—blow holes as they are commonly called—will usually weld in rolling or forging, especially in low- and medium-carbon steels, and will disappear. If, however, the inner surface of the cavity becomes oxidized, which frequently happens in heating for rolling when the cavity is near the surface, or if the steel is high in carbon, the surfaces of the cavity do not weld and the result is a defect known as a seam (Fig. 14). Seams are usually located on the surface of the rolled section where they can be detected and removed by machining, chipping, or grinding, but they may be internal and if so they may, like inclusions, act as loci where premature failure will start.

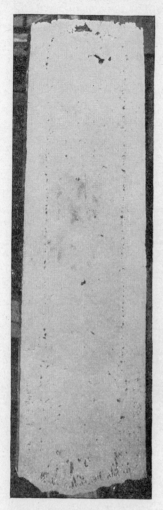

Fig. 15—Cross-section of an ingot of rimming steel, about $\frac{1}{20}$ natural size (American Rolling Mill Company).

Carbon steels are frequently classified according to the method of removing gas cavities or rendering them innocuous, as killed, or rimming. Killed steels, which nearly always contain more than 0.25 or 0.30 per cent carbon, are those which must be thoroughly sound and free from gas cavities. The descriptive adjective comes from the action of the molten metal when poured into the ingot mold: it lies perfectly quiet with no evolution of gas; there is neither bubbling nor churning of the upper surface of the metal. Killed steels are degasified by silicon, aluminum, or other degasifier. All plain carbon forging steels, all rails, all high-carbon tool and spring steels, and all alloy steels are thoroughly killed.

Rimming steel—so called from the rim of solid metal next to the mold wall (Fig. 15)—is low-carbon basic open-hearth steel in which deoxidation is partly completed in the furnace or in the ladle but which is not degasified. When the steel is poured into the ingot mold and begins to solidify, there is a brisk but controlled evolution of gas which results in an ingot having a sound gas-free surface and in locating the blow holes so far below the surface that there is no danger of their becoming oxidized when the ingot is heated for rolling (Fig. 15). The blow holes will weld completely in rolling, and the result is a material with a clean surface free from seams. Rimming steels are especially suitable for sheet and strip, notably for thin, deep-drawing stock used in large tonnages for automobile bodies and fenders. Close control of the slag composition, particularly the amount of iron oxide, slag viscosity and pouring temperature, is necessary to produce a steel that rims properly when it solidifies.

Most basic open-hearth steels containing less than 0.15 per cent carbon are made so that they rim; steels containing 0.15 to about 0.25 per cent carbon, used widely for structural shapes and plate, are killed or are partly killed.

29. Manganese in Carbon and Alloy Steels—Manganese is an essential and a beneficial element in nearly all grades of steel because it performs a vital dual role: it combines with sulphur to form manganese sulphide, a less obnoxious impurity than iron sulphide; and, as noted in the previous chapter, it deoxidizes the metal by reacting with oxygen to form an oxide which is less soluble in molten steel than iron oxide and which, therefore, will leave the metal more readily. The amount used varies with the grade of steel and with the amount of oxidation in melting: enough is added to most steels so that, after its purifying action has been completed, 0.30 to about 0.60 per cent, occasionally as much as 1.00 per cent, will be left in the metal.

A small amount of manganese also increases the strength of steel. Either alone or, preferably, in combination with relatively small amounts of other alloying elements, it produces such a favorable combination of properties that the so-called "intermediate-manganese" alloy steels are finding increasing use in some fields of engineering, especially for railroad rolling stock and in bridges. The amount of manganese in these steels ranges from about 1.00 to 1.90 per cent. There is considerable confusion, even among metallurgists, about the dividing line between these steels and carbon steels as some steels which are made and used as intermediate-manganese alloy materials may contain 1.00 per cent or even less, and a few steels which have for years been classed as plain carbon steels—rails are an example—contain as much as 1.00 per cent or even more manganese. If carbon steel and intermediate-manganese steel cannot be differentiated by their manganese content, they can sometimes be classed according to the industrial application for which they were made. This is a glaring example of the slipshod terminology which has grown up over the years in the iron and steel industry and which confuses maker and user, metallurgist and engineer, alike.

30. **Silicon and Other Degasifiers**—Like manganese, silicon is beneficial and is added to carbon steel as a purifier and, in larger amounts, as both purifier and alloying element. It is effective in removing oxygen and is, therefore, added to those grades of steels (usually containing more than 0.30 per cent carbon) in which gas cavities do not weld readily or are otherwise harmful. Silicon is so used in a few medium-carbon and high-carbon basic open-hearth steels (for example rails), in practically all acid open-hearth and acid electric steels, and in all basic electric steels. It is added rarely to such low-carbon basic open-hearth steels as structural material, wire, sheet, plate and strip, and to those low-carbon Bessemer steels which are used for pipe and tin-plate. The reaction product of silicon with carbon monoxide gas is silica (SiO_2), which reacts readily with manganese oxide and iron oxide, forming silicates. These are insoluble in the molten metal and are of such low specific gravity that they readily leave the steel. Silicon thus carries deoxidation further than manganese and is in addition an effective degasifier. Enough is added to complete the purifying reactions and leave 0.10 to 0.40 per cent in the finished steel.

There is occasionally some confusion—but not so much as in the case of manganese—in distinguishing between a silicon-treated carbon steel and a silicon alloy steel. Some specially deoxidized open-hearth steels used in bridge construction, containing around 0.25 per cent silicon, have been and still are termed silicon steels by civil engineers. This is unfortunate, and it is hoped that the tendency to call a material silicon steel only if the silicon is 0.50 per cent or more will become more widespread. Steels containing 1.50 to 2.25 per cent silicon and about 0.75 per cent manganese are used widely for springs, and steels containing 0.5 to 5.0 per cent silicon and small amounts of other elements are used in the construction of dynamos and other electric apparatus.

Small amounts of aluminum and titanium are added to some grades of carbon steel as final deoxidizers and degasifiers. It has been discovered recently that aluminum, probably through the agency of minute aluminum oxide particles, can be used to control the grain size of carbon and alloy steels. As this is one of the major recent developments in ferrous metallurgy, it receives detailed attention elsewhere in this volume. Both aluminum and titanium are also used, in much larger amounts than is necessary for deoxidation and degasification, as alloying elements.

31. Other Elements—Since the introduction of alloy steels some 40 years ago there has been a gradually increasing contamination of carbon steel by nickel, copper, molybdenum, and other alloying elements owing to the inadvertent mixture of alloy-steel scrap with the other scrap. In the case of elements which oxidize readily, for example chromium, vanadium, aluminum, titanium, and a few others, the contamination is not serious as they are largely oxidized and removed during melting and refining, leaving usually not more than traces in the steel. In the case of such alloys as nickel, copper, and molybdenum, which do not oxidize, the amounts present will normally increase slowly over a period of years. This is especially true for nickel and copper, which are used in steel more frequently than molybdenum. The amount of these elements in the scrap is not of such serious consequence for steels made by a process that uses also a large proportion of pig iron, which is normally free from nickel and copper, as it is in steel made wholly from scrap (Table 2). In the latter the scrap may contain an unsuspected 0.10 to 0.25 per cent nickel and 0.05 to 0.10 per cent copper, sometimes even enough to affect the properties materially. The chemical determination of nickel and copper in carbon steels is seldom made, but these elements are present just the same.

A recent development in free-machining steels is the addition of lead to low-carbon material. This element is insoluble in carbon steel, but by special methods of addition to the molten metal it may be incorporated as a suspension so finely disseminated throughout the metal that it is not easily visible in an unetched section with the microscope. These submicroscopic particles of lead apparently act as an internal lubricant and in addition cause the chips to break up readily. Recently reported data indicate that a lead content of 0.10 to 0.25 per cent greatly increases ease of machining but has no appreciable effect on mechanical properties.

Carbon steel may be contaminated with small amounts of arsenic, tin, and antimony, traces of which may be present in iron ores and may persist through melting and refining. These metals may also be picked up from scrap containing bearing metals or tin cans. The amounts present are small, rarely exceeding 0.05 per cent. Very little is known about the effect of small amounts of most of these adventitious elements. According to the present state of our knowledge, their effect, with the possible exception of that of antimony which is assumed to be harmful, may be called neutral.

Although the presence of oxygen, as oxygen-bearing inclusions or gases, has been fairly well studied, reliable data of the effect of the other two gases, nitrogen and hydrogen, are few. This is due primarily to the difficulty of determining accurately the amount present in steel. Unquestionably, nitrogen (from the air used in melting furnaces) and hydrogen (from the dissociation of water vapor) are both introduced into steel during melting and refining, but to the best of our knowledge the amount is small, probably less than 0.005 per cent. Within the past ten years, nitrogen has been found to be an effective hardening agent when introduced into solid steel by treating with ammonia. It has been suspected recently that hydrogen causes some troublesome defects in carbon and alloy steel, but nothing very definite is known about the effect of this gas as yet.

32. Ingot Iron and Wrought Iron—Ingot iron and wrought iron are two specialized products of the iron and steel industry, made in relatively small tonnages but important enough to be described briefly. Both are related to carbon steels. Ingot iron is a commercially pure iron. It contains between 99.75 and 99.90 per cent iron. The common elements, carbon, manganese, silicon, sulphur, and phosphorus, account for about half of the impurities; the occasional elements make up the other half. Ingot iron resembles carbon steel in that it is melted and refined

by the basic open-hearth process, but it is lower in carbon (about 0.02 per cent) than the lowest carbon steels made industrially, which range from 0.04 to 0.08 per cent. Ingot iron is used chiefly in the form of galvanized and enameled sheet.

Wrought iron is a low-carbon material made by a process which involves oxidation without actual melting. The nature of the

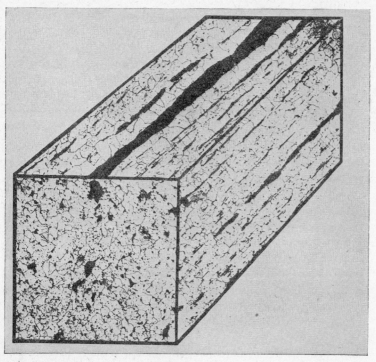

Fig. 16—Composite photomicrograph of wrought iron showing inclusions (black), etched, 100✕ (Sauveur).

refining is such that this material contains a larger proportion of solid non-metallic inclusions than low-carbon steel made by the usual processes (Fig. 16).[1] Owing to the nature of the process and the composition of the inclusions, wrought iron when rolled has relatively low strength but is ductile and tough and is easily welded. It is used for staybolts, rivets, some grades of pipe, boiler

[1] A. Sauveur, *The Metallography and Heat Treatment of Iron and Steel,* McGraw-Hill Book Company, Inc., New York, 4th ed., 1935, p. 56.

tubes, and especially for heavy chains and hooks. Wrought iron has well-marked directional properties.

33. **Low-alloy Steels**—There is no precise and concise definition of alloy steel, but practically there is seldom any difficulty in distinguishing between carbon and alloy steels. The practical criterion is: if an element, not used primarily for deoxidation or degasification, is added to carbon steel in the amount required to produce a desired specific effect, the resulting material is an alloy steel. A large number of metals (and some metalloids and non-metals) have been alloyed with carbon steel, either alone or in various combinations, and the resulting properties have been studied more or less completely. These include manganese, silicon, nickel, chromium, vanadium, tungsten, molybdenum, copper, and phosphorus as the more common alloying elements and cobalt, aluminum, zirconium, titanium, nitrogen, lead, uranium, and selenium as the less frequent additions. Steel may also be coated or plated with zinc (galvanizing), tin, lead, chromium, or nickel, but such products are not classed as alloy steels.

There are two general classes of alloy steels: (1) the low-alloy engineering steels and (2) the high-alloy tool and die steels, corrosion- and heat-resistant steels and special-purpose alloys. In tonnage, the first class is the more important; in value to man, both are probably of equal importance for both have played a vital role in the development of our present-day machine-age civilization.

There are several hundred low-alloy engineering steels, of which some 70 to 80 have been included in the Society of Automotive Engineers' specifications. The S.A.E. steels are divided into eight main classes: intermediate-manganese, silicon-manganese, nickel, nickel-chromium, molybdenum (including chromium-molybdenum and nickel-molybdenum), chromium, chromium-vanadium, and tungsten steels. There is also a large number of low-alloy structural steels, most of them a development of the past 10 years, which contain small amounts (usually less than 1 or 1.5 per cent) of nickel, copper, chromium, manganese, silicon, phosphorus, and molybdenum in various proportions and combinations. These were developed to satisfy a demand for a material of better properties than carbon steels but cheaper than the S.A.E. grades. These have been nicknamed "Irish stew steels" by Gillett, a happy and accurate designation.

The amounts of the various alloying elements in the low-alloy steels are roughly as follows:

Element	Percentage
Manganese	1.00 to 2.00
Silicon	0.50 to 5.00
Nickel	1.00 to 5.50
Chromium	0.25 to 3.50
Vanadium	0.15 to 0.25
Molybdenum	0.15 to 0.50
Copper	0.15 to 1.50
Phosphorus	0.065 to 0.150

34. The High-alloy Steels—There are almost as many varieties of the high-alloy steels as there are of the low-alloy grades. These special materials can be divided into three classes. The first includes the well-known high-speed steels and the closely allied die and valve steels. The primary requirement is hardness, especially at elevated temperatures, which is attained by large amounts (10 to 25 per cent) of tungsten, chromium, and occasionally cobalt, plus smaller amounts of vanadium, molybdenum, or silicon, together with relatively high carbon percentages.

The second class includes all the highly alloyed steels used primarily because of their corrosion resistance or scale resistance at normal and at high temperatures. The basic element in these steels is chromium, in amounts ranging from 10 to 35 per cent, either alone or together with varying amounts of silicon, manganese, nickel, copper, or molybdenum. The best known steels of this group are the cutlery steels, containing about 0.35 per cent carbon and 14 per cent chromium, and the soft stainless steels, containing low carbon, 15 to 25 per cent chromium and 6 to 20 per cent nickel, which are used widely for building trim, hardware and fixtures on buildings and automobiles, various kinds of utensils and, more recently, in the construction of railroad equipment and aircraft. Not so well known but just as important are the highly alloyed steels containing chromium, molybdenum, and other alloys, used in steam plants, oil refineries and for other applications where high pressures and high temperatures are encountered. Also in this second class are the alloys containing up to 65 per cent nickel, 15 to 20 per cent or more chromium, the remainder being iron. These are the heat-resistant alloys of high electric resistivity which are used for the heating elements of all our domestic and industrial heating appliances.

The third class includes a large number of alloys of highly specialized but important uses. They are the steels with special magnetic and electric properties, alloys with special expansion characteristics, steels with exceptional wear resistance, and many others. While these materials are not manufactured in large tonnages, some are of such importance that by means of them the communication and other industries have experienced a veritable revolution in the past 10 or 15 years.

Low-alloy steels may be manufactured by any process except the acid Bessemer. Some are melted in the basic or acid open hearth, many of the S.A.E. grades are made in the basic electric furnace. Nearly all the high-alloy materials are made in electric arc or induction furnaces. Alloy steels are much more costly than carbon steels so that care is exercised to keep the quality as high as possible. Selected scrap is used, deoxidation is carried farther, and sulphur and phosphorus are usually required to be lower than in carbon steels.

CHAPTER 5

THE CONSTITUTION OF STEEL

THE demands of industry for materials with which it can fashion its tools, machines, and structures have been growing more exacting year by year for the past 50 years or more. It is only in metallic materials that development has kept pace with this steadily increasing demand. Between 1875 and 1940 there was little change in wood, brick, and stone construction, but the change in metal structures has been enormous. This advance is plain if a locomotive of 1875 or even of 1890 is compared with the streamlined steam or Diesel-electric engine of today, and it is even clearer if our present-day automobiles and aircraft are compared with those of 20 or 25 years ago. In metal manufacturing, the iron and steel industry has shown outstanding development in the past half century, certainly surpassing the non-ferrous industries, with the possible exception of the aluminum industry. During this period, practically all the alloy steels have been developed. Moreover, for carbon steels and cast irons new standards of quality have been set up and met.

As indicated in a previous chapter, one of the principal reasons for this was the development of a science of the constitution, or internal structure, of metals and alloys known as metallography or physical metallurgy. Metallography has been valuable in the study of all metals, but it has been especially fruitful in the field of ferrous alloys, not only in providing a more basic knowledge of their constitution but also in the development of new steels and of new treatments of industrial importance. Despite this advance, much remains to be learned. The mountain top of complete understanding is high; the trail to the summit is long and steep, and we have gone but a short way. We will reach the summit more quickly if we do not stop so frequently to bicker about this or that stone along the path and if in the future we do not explore so many of the numerous bypaths which we hope are short-cuts but which in reality lead nowhere.

The properties of steels and cast irons, and the suitability of these materials for the many requirements of industry depend upon the amount of carbon and other elements alloyed with the iron. The amount, however, is not the only variable of importance. Equally essential, and even more so in some cases, are the distribution and behavior of these elements with respect to each other and to the iron present. Chemical analysis gives fairly exact information on the amounts of elements present but gives no clue on whether they combine with each other to form definite chemical compounds, or whether they form simple or complex mixtures, or whether these compounds or mixtures have any effect on each other or on the large amount of iron present. It gives no indication why ferrous alloys respond to heat treatment or why the properties are so greatly affected by such an operation. These important factors are the subject matter of ferrous metallography and are discussed in this and the next chapter.

35. **The Fundamental Structure of Carbon Steel**—At very high temperatures, iron and carbon react to form the definite compound iron carbide (Fe_3C). This compound, while thermodynamically unstable at temperatures of interest to engineers, is very persistent in alloys containing less than 1.7 per cent carbon, especially if appreciable amounts of silicon are absent. Carbon steels, therefore, while fundamentally alloys of the metal iron and the metalloid carbon, are in reality alloys of iron and the chemical compound iron carbide. Furthermore, since iron exists in two allotropic forms, carbon steel is an alloy of alpha iron and iron carbide at normal temperatures, and an alloy of gamma iron and iron carbide at elevated temperatures. To go one step further, since carbon (i.e., iron carbide) is insoluble in alpha iron and soluble in gamma iron,[1] slowly cooled carbon steel is a mixture of alpha iron and iron carbide at normal temperature, and a solution of iron carbide in gamma iron at elevated temperature.

By metallurgists alpha iron is known as *ferrite,* iron carbide is called *cementite,* and the solid solution of iron carbide (cementite) in gamma iron is known as *austenite.* These three metallographic constituents are the basic phases in the constitution of

---

[1] Metallurgists are not agreed whether iron carbide dissolved in gamma iron is in solution as molecules of Fe_3C or whether it has split into atoms of Fe and C. This is an academic question of no practical significance.

carbon steel; they are the primary building materials from which the whole complex edifice of carbon steels is constructed. Moreover, they are also the fundamental constituents in all alloy steels. The primary function of the alloying element is to alter the usual relationship that these three phases hold toward one another in carbon steels.

In commercial carbon steels, ferrite is not pure iron, but iron holding in solid solution the small amounts of silicon and phosphorus present, also nickel and copper, and a number of other elements if these are present. These small amounts of dissolved elements, together with traces of carbon which are also soluble in alpha iron, have, however, so little effect on the structure that they may, for the present, be ignored. The structure of ferrite, as it appears when viewed with the microscope, is shown in Fig. 18A. Ferrite is soft and ductile, of low strength and high resistance to impact, and has the ability to stretch as much as 50 per cent under static loads.

Cementite, on the contrary, is hard and brittle, probably much like glass in properties, and is responsible for the hardness and strength, and also for the brittleness, of steels containing considerable carbon. Austenite, like ferrite, has a structure of irregular polygonal grains. Owing to the difference in crystal structure of gamma iron, as compared with alpha iron, austenite is stronger than ferrite. In addition, if the austenite contains much dissolved cementite, it is still stronger. It is just as tough and probably even tougher than ferrite. Because austenite in unalloyed carbon steels is an entity existing only at elevated temperatures, its room-temperature properties must be inferred from the properties of steels which contain such a large amount of an alloying metal that austenite is preserved at room temperature.

36. The Iron-carbon Phase Diagram—The changes in the phase relations in any alloy system caused by variations in temperature can be followed most readily by means of the phase diagram of the system. Such a diagram is constructed by preparing a series of alloys of the highest possible purity and by various precise experimental methods determining the temperatures at which changes in phase and in structure occur. These temperatures are then plotted against composition.

The phase relations in iron-carbon alloys have been the subject of much investigation and, although some points are still obscure, the main details are fairly well established. That portion of the diagram which gives a picture of the phase changes in carbon steels is shown in simplified form in Fig. 17.[2] The

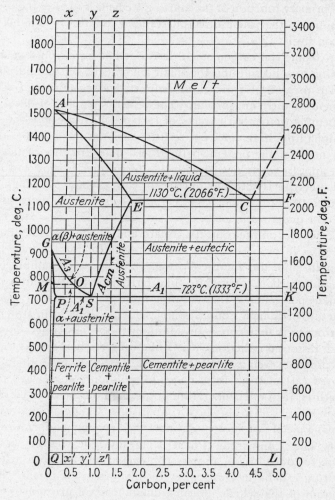

Fig. 17—The iron-carbon diagram (Epstein).

lines *GOS*, *SE*, and *PSK*, which are commonly known as A_3, A_{cm}, and A_1 respectively, are drawn through a series of points

[2] From S. Epstein, *The Alloys of Iron and Carbon*, Vol. I, *Constitution*, Fig. 13, p. 96, with the delta region omitted.

each one of which represents equilibrium of the phases in an alloy whose carbon content is indicated by the ordinate and whose temperature is indicated by the abscissa.

As ice and water will coexist indefinitely as long as the temperature remains at the freezing point, so at 1333° F. (723° C.) and with a carbon content of 0.80 per cent (point S) austenite, ferrite, and cementite will coexist indefinitely. However, if 0.80 per cent carbon steel containing these three phases at 1333° F. is heated very slightly above this temperature, ferrite and cementite will disappear and only austenite will be left; conversely, if it is cooled very slightly below 1333° F. and held at this temperature, austenite will transform completely into ferrite and cementite. Thus, the lines *GOS, SE,* and *PSK* represent temperatures at which phase changes are ready to start. The dashed line *MO* (known as A_2) represents the temperature where carbon steels containing from a trace to about 0.45 per cent carbon become paramagnetic (lose their magnetism) on heating or ferromagnetic (regain their magnetism) on cooling. This phenomenon is not a phase change in the ordinary sense.

A map of the Atlantic ocean is valuable because it gives the longitude and latitude of New York and London, despite the fact that it tells us nothing about the time necessary to go from one city to the other. In the same way, a phase diagram such as Fig. 17 is valuable as a map showing the temperature and composition where certain phases exist, despite the fact that it tells us nothing about the time required to effect changes in these phases. The phase diagram is an equilibrium diagram: the points and lines represent temperatures at which changes are ready to start and will start immediately if the temperature is changed slightly. In a few systems, the alloys are very sluggish when solid; changes take place so slowly with slight variations in temperature that it is virtually impossible to study the effect of time. Fortunately the alloys of iron and carbon are not in this class. Very slow heating or cooling initiate phase changes at temperatures close to the equilibrium temperatures. Hence, we can study these changes readily and can determine with equal facility the effect of varying the heating or cooling rate.

37. The Eutectoid and Structure of Pearlite—In many alloy systems there is one alloy of definite composition which solidifies at a lower temperature than any of the others. Such alloys are

often characterized by a laminated structure when viewed with the microscope. Metallurgists call such alloys *eutectic* (from the Greek meaning well-melting). In iron-carbon alloys there is one alloy, containing about 0.80 per cent carbon, which, when cooled slowly, undergoes transformation in the solid state at a lower temperature than any of the others. This alloy, moreover, if cooled slowly, has at room temperature a laminated structure resembling closely a eutectic alloy. Because it is formed in the solid state instead of from the liquid, it is known as *eutectoid*. This word and its significance should be remembered as it will appear frequently later in this book in connection with the discussion of carbon and alloy steels.

Steel of eutectoid composition (0.80 per cent carbon) contains 12 per cent cementite [3] (iron carbide) and 88 per cent ferrite. In other words, the eutectoid composition is 1 part of cementite to 7 parts of ferrite. As the composition of the eutectoid is always constant, steels containing less than 0.80 per cent carbon contain more ferrite than is necessary for the eutectoid ratio, and steels containing more than 0.80 per cent carbon contain an excess of cementite.

Because the laminated structure of a slowly cooled steel of eutectoid composition resembles mother-of-pearl when viewed with the microscope [4] (see Figs. 18D and 18F), this aggregate of cementite and ferrite is known as *pearlite*. The properties of pearlite vary with the size of the particles of cementite. If the steel has a laminated structure consisting entirely of plates of the size shown in Fig. 18F at 1000 diameters, it will have a tensile strength of 120,000 to 130,000 lb. per sq. in. and an elongation of about 10 or 15 per cent in 2 in.

38. Phase Changes in Slowly Cooled Low- and Medium-carbon Steels—The phase changes in carbon steels cooled slowly from a high temperature can be illustrated by three steels containing (A) 0.30 per cent carbon, (B) 0.80 per cent carbon, and (C) 1.30 per cent carbon. These are indicated in Fig. 17 by lines XX', YY', and ZZ'.

---

[3] $C : Fe_3C = 12 : 180$. Therefore $1 \ C = 15 \ Fe_3C$ and $0.8 \ C = 12 \ Fe_3C$. $100 - 12 \ Fe_3C = 88$ ferrite.

[4] The lamellar structure of pearlite is seldom so readily recognizable at a magnification of 100 diameters as in Fig. 18D. Usually a magnification of 200 diameters or more is necessary.

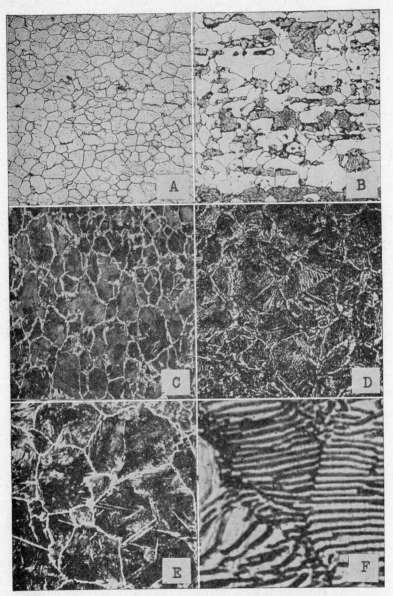

Fig. 18—Microstructures of slowly cooled iron-carbon alloys: (A) low-carbon iron, (B) 0.20 per cent carbon steel, (C) 0.40 per cent carbon steel, (D) 0.80 per cent carbon steel, (E) 1.3 per cent carbon steel, (F) pearlite at high magnification; etched; A to E, 100×; F, 1000×.

At 2820° F. (1550° C.), the first steel (XX') is a solution of iron carbide in molten iron. Upon slow cooling, there is no change until the solidification temperature 2770° F. (1520° C.) is reached. Here solidification of austenite begins; this is complete at 2685° F. (1475° C.). The white hot steel, which consists wholly of solid solution of cementite in gamma iron, cools unchanged until a temperature of 1470° F. (800° C.) is reached. At this point on line A_3 (GOS), the austenite is saturated with iron. If the temperature falls slightly, the excess iron is precipitated in the form of alpha phase. Since the austenite loses no carbon during the process, the loss of some iron as alpha phase by the austenite is equivalent to increasing the carbon content of the austenite. As the temperature continues to fall, precipitation of alpha iron and increase of carbon content of the austenite (since there is progressively less austenite for a constant amount of carbon) occur continuously. When the temperature reaches that of the line A_1 (PSK), the austenite is saturated with carbon also. Further cooling results in simultaneous precipitation of alpha iron and carbon (as iron carbide). This process goes to completion, which is to say that the austenite disappears completely.

If the cooling is very slow through the temperature interval from line A_3 (GOS) to just below line A_1 (PSK), the excess ferrite which is first formed assumes the shape of discrete polyhedral grains, and the remaining austenite, containing 0.80 per cent carbon, transforms to the pearlite aggregate in which the ferrite and cementite particles are in the form of relatively large laminated plates. The structure of the slowly cooled steel consists of 36 per cent pearlite and 64 per cent excess ferrite.[5]

If a piece of slowly cooled carbon steel is polished and etched with dilute acid and examined with the microscope, the relation between the carbon content and the amount of free ferrite (etches light) and pearlite (etches dark) is clearly evident. This is shown in Fig. 18. Micrograph A shows the structure of iron containing practically no carbon; it consists wholly of polyhedral grains of ferrite. In B, the steel containing 0.20 per cent carbon, the dark grains of pearlite are numerous, and in C, the material

---

[5] 0.30 per cent carbon is equivalent to 4.5 per cent Fe_3C. Since 1 part of Fe_3C is associated with 7 parts of ferrite to form pearlite, 4.5 per cent Fe_3C plus 31.5 per cent ferrite form 36 per cent pearlite.

containing 0.40 per cent carbon, they are still more numerous. The parallel plates of cementite and ferrite making up the pearlite aggregate are shown clearly at high magnification in micrograph F.

39. Phase Changes in Slowly Cooled High-carbon Steels— Referring again to Fig. 17 (line YY'), at 2820° F. (1550° C.) a steel containing 0.80 per cent carbon is a solution of iron carbide in molten iron. As the molten metal cools, it is unchanged until a temperature of 2700° F. (1480° C.) is reached where solidification of the austenite begins. This is not complete until a temperature of 2520° F. (1380° C.) is reached. It will be noted that with higher carbon the solidification range is wider.

After the steel has solidified completely, the solid solution of cementite in gamma iron cools unchanged until a temperature of 1333° F. (723° C.) is reached. Owing to the fact that the steel contains 0.80 per cent carbon and, therefore, the exact amounts of cementite (12 per cent) and iron (88 per cent) to form the aggregate pearlite, there will be no preliminary precipitation of alpha iron from the saturated austenite, as was the case with the 0.30 per cent carbon steel described in the previous section.

As the steel cools through the A_1 temperature, 1333° F. (723° C.), the austenite undergoes precisely the same change as was described for the last stage of transformation of the 0.30 per cent carbon steel, that is, simultaneous precipitation of alpha iron and iron carbide. There is no further structural change as the steel cools from A_1 to room temperature, and if cooling through the A_1 temperature is slow, the cementite and ferrite form well defined plates as shown in Fig. 18D and, at high magnification, in Fig. 18F.

In the case of a steel containing 1.3 per cent carbon (19.5 per cent cementite), represented by line ZZ' in Fig. 17, the changes taking place during slow cooling are fundamentally analogous to those taking place in a 0.30 per cent carbon steel. The essential difference is (in addition to a wider solidification range) that the A_{cm} line marks the preliminary separation of excess iron carbide rather than excess alpha iron. When a steel containing 1.3 per cent carbon cools slowly, at 1760° F. (960° C.) the austenite is saturated with carbide. Further cooling results in precipitation of this excess carbide from the saturated austenite, which continues as the temperature falls from 1760 to 1333° F. (the A_1

temperature). The remaining austenite, which now contains 0.80 per cent carbon (12 per cent cementite), here transforms to pearlite, as in the preceding case. At room temperature, the structure is made up of grains of pearlite (etches dark) with a net-work (or needles) of excess carbide (light). This structure is shown in Fig. 18E.

The discussion to this point has all been concerned with slow cooling. In heating carbon steels, the reverse changes take place. For example, a 0.30 per cent carbon steel which has been cooled slowly consists at room temperature of a structure of 36 per cent pearlite and 64 per cent excess ferrite. If this steel is heated slowly, no change takes place until a temperature of 1333° F. (723° C.) is just exceeded. Here, the alpha iron of the pearlite transforms to gamma iron and the cementite goes into solution. As heating is continued, the excess alpha iron changes to gamma iron and is absorbed by the austenite. At 1470° F. (800° C.), these changes are complete, and the steel, now a solid solution of 4.5 per cent cementite in gamma iron, remains unchanged to the melting point.

40. **Effect of Cooling Rate on Phase Changes and Structure—** As shown in Fig. 17, a steel containing about 0.8 per cent carbon is entirely austenitic at any temperature between A_1 (point S) and the solidification temperature. Heating or cooling in this range, whether fast or slow, causes no phase changes. If, however, this steel is held at a temperature of exactly 1333° F. (723° C.), although no phase change will ever occur, there is a tendency for the change to start. If, now, the steel is cooled very slowly, the phase change from austenite to ferrite and cementite starts just below A_1, at about 1300° F. (700° C.), and proceeds very slowly to completion. The result is a pearlitic structure of coarse plates of ferrite and cementite.

If the steel is cooled somewhat faster from 1333° F. or above, the apparent temperature of the phase change is depressed to about 1220° F. (660° C.), the speed at which the phase change occurs is higher, and the particles of ferrite and cementite which make up the pearlite are smaller. If the steel is cooled still faster, as by cooling small sections in air or large ones in oil, the apparent temperature of the phase change is depressed still more, for example to 1000° F. (540° C.). The reaction now takes place very quickly and the particles of ferrite and iron carbide are still smaller. These general effects are shown in Fig. 19 in which temperatures where the phase changes occur are plotted against time.

Thus, increasing the cooling rate has three important effects: (1) the apparent transformation temperature is depressed, (2) the rate at which gamma iron changes to alpha, and at which iron

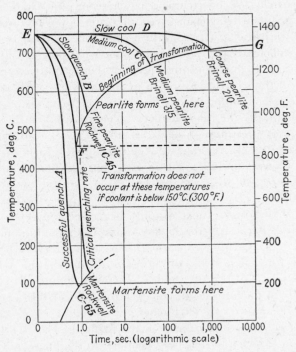

Fig. 19—Relation between time and temperature of transformation of 0.80 per cent carbon steel (Bain, *Trans. Am. Soc. Steel Treat.*, v. 20, 1932, p. 390).

carbide is precipitated, is speeded up, and (3) the particle size of the precipitated carbide and of alpha iron is decreased. In addition to these effects, increasing the cooling rate increases the hardness and strength of unalloyed steels and decreases the ductility.

For each cooling rate, therefore, and for every steel, there is a definite transformation-temperature range, and a definite speed with which the transformation occurs, and finally a definite structure that results, accompanied by definite properties. Thus, depending upon the cooling rate, the resulting structure may vary from one made up of coarse laminated plates of ferrite and cementite to one of such fine particles of these two constituents that they cannot be detected individually with the highest magnifications of the metallurgical microscope. Metallurgists have distinguished between these structures, have classified them by their particle size or etching characteristics, and have tagged them with identifying names. As they are, however, fundamentally all pearlitic structures with a difference in particle size, it will be sufficiently accurate for the present purpose to call all of them pearlitic, distinguishing, perhaps, between coarseness and fineness of the structure as shown by the microscope.

In steels containing less or more carbon than the eutectoid ratio, essentially the same changes occur, complicated, however, by the prior precipitation of excess iron or excess carbide from the austenite. Increasing the cooling rate of such materials not only lowers the temperature of A_1 but also lowers the temperatures (A_3 or A_{cm}) where these excess constituents are precipitated.

As is shown in the next chapter, heavy sections do not cool uniformly. Because of this, a 2-in. round bar cooled in air or oil may contain pearlite or ferrite in several degrees of fineness. Thus, the outside, which cools most rapidly, may have a structure of fine ferrite and pearlite; half way between center and surface, it may be of medium ferrite and pearlite; and at the center the structure may be coarse ferrite and pearlite.

41. Effect of Hot Working on the Structure—So far, the discussion in this chapter has been confined to the phase and structural changes in carbon steels when they are heated or, more important, cooled at varying rates between the temperature where austenite is stable and room temperature. It was stated that there is no change in the austenite if it is heated or cooled between the transformation temperature and the melting point. This is true. There is no change in the internal structure of the austenite grains, but there may be a great change in the size of the grains. If carbon steel is heated above the transformation temperature, the austenite grains grow, and the higher the temperature the larger the grains.

Small-grained steels are generally considered to have better properties than coarse-grained material of the same composition. Since grain size at room temperature depends largely upon the grain size of austenite when it is ready to transform, the grain size of austenite should be small. One of the important factors affecting the grain size of austenite, and of pearlite and ferrite, is mechanical working.

Fig. 20—Large columnar crystals in a steel ingot, natural size (Hanemann and Schrader, *Atlas Metallographicus*, Berlin, 1927).

When molten steel cools, solidification usually begins by crystallization at the wall of the mold, and if the temperature of the steel is high when it is poured, and if the ingot or casting is large and of favorable shape, these crystals may become very large (Fig. 20). Hot rolling or forging, which is ordinarily carried out at temperatures at which the metal is plastic, breaks up the large crystals and elongates the fragments in the direction in which the work is applied. These elongated grains, together with elongated inclusions, give carbon and many of the alloy steels their directional properties.

Austenite grains, even when plastically broken and deformed, have the tendency to grow together again. This tendency is the greater the higher the temperature. Hence, if the finishing temperature of hot working is much above the transformation temperature, grain growth may occur while the steel is cooling to the transformation temperature, especially if the section is so large that cooling is slow. For this reason, if hot-rolled or forged

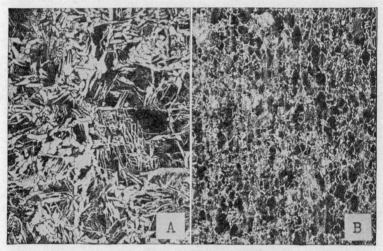

Fig. 21—Structure of a 0.20 per cent carbon steel (*A*) as cast and (*B*) as hot rolled; etched, 100×.

steels are to be used without subsequent heat treatment, and if a fine grain is desirable, the hot-working temperatures and the amounts of reduction are controlled so that the finishing temperature will not be much above the transformation temperature. Thus, the steel will cool below this temperature before appreciable grain growth has taken place. The effect of hot working in breaking up the coarse grain structure of cast 0.20 per cent carbon steel is shown in Fig. 21.

42. Effect of Cold Working on Structure—Cold working is usually defined as mechanical deformation of steel at temperatures below the transformation temperature. In practice it is generally carried out at room temperature. If steel is plastically deformed at these low temperatures—as in drawing wire, cold

rolling or extruding bars, or cold rolling sheet—the pearlite and ferrite grains are elongated in the direction in which work is applied. This mechanical distortion results in rapid increase of hardness and brittleness.

At atmospheric temperature, the rigidity of the steel is so great that the distorted grain fragments cannot rearrange tnemselves by recrystallizing into their normal equiaxed shape. Hence, if cold working is continued, the hardness and brittleness accompanying the fragmentation of the grains will increase with the amount of deformation until soon, unless the steel is annealed, it will fail. The amount of cold deformation that steel will stand depends upon its ductility, which, in turn, is related directly to chemical composition and prior heat treatment. Thus, annealed low-carbon wire will withstand more reduction by drafting before failure, or before reheating for recrystallization becomes necessary, than annealed medium- or high-carbon wire. The effect of cold working on the properties is discussed elsewhere.

The instability of structure of cold-worked steel and its accompanying hardness and brittleness are caused by the distortion of the ferrite and pearlite grains and not, as in quenched steel, by the presence of submicroscopic particles of carbide in a distorted alpha-iron lattice. But, as the stability of quenched steel can be increased by tempering (see Chapter 6), so can the stability of structure of cold-worked steel be increased by reheating below the transformation temperature. This is known as process annealing.

Structural changes which occur when cold-worked steel is reheated are not gradual. Cold-worked steel is softened by heating to 800 to 1200° F. (425 to 650° C.), the exact temperature depending on the composition, size of the section, and the amount of cold work. Reheating at the proper temperature effects complete recrystallization and restoration of the original structure and properties. The material can then be cold worked again until grain distortion and its accompanying brittleness have become so serious that another reheating is necessary. The effect of cold working on the structure of a 0.20 per cent carbon steel (whose structure as hot-worked is shown in Fig. 21B) is illustrated in Fig. 22A. The effect of reheating on the distorted grain structure is shown in Fig. 22B. Note that after annealing the grains are equiaxed and all indication of distortion has disappeared.

43. Effect of Alloying Elements on Structure—Alloying elements have important effects on the structure of carbon steels, in the slowly cooled stable condition as well as in the rapidly cooled condition. These are reflected in many of the properties. The alloying elements used in ferrous metallurgy may be divided into two classes according to their behavior when present in slowly cooled carbon steels. The first includes those elements which combine with carbon to form carbides; the second includes those elements which do not form carbides. All of the alloying ele-

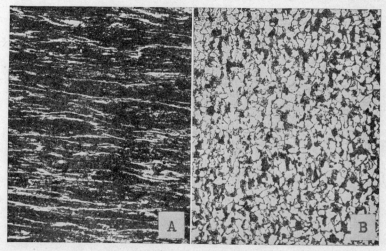

Fig. 22—Structure of a 0.20 per cent carbon steel (A) as cold worked and (B) as cold worked and annealed; etched, 500✕.

ments dissolve to a greater or less extent in the ferrite. Some of them exert a strong effect on the ferrite: they increase the strength, especially the yield ratio, and frequently make the steel tougher. The elements that form carbides increase hardness and affect those properties which are related more or less closely to hardness, such as wear resistance and machinability, also strength at elevated temperatures. Some alloying elements strengthen the ferrite and also increase hardness moderately. A general classification of the alloying elements is given in Table 3.[6]

6 Adaption of classification by E. C. Bain, *Yearbook,* American Iron and Steel Institute, 1934, pp. 87-128; modified in *The Alloying Elements in Steel,* American Society for Metals, Cleveland, 1939.

In addition to these effects, many of the alloying elements reduce the amount of carbon in the eutectoid. Thus, if 3.0 per cent nickel is added to a 0.40 per cent carbon steel, the structure after slow cooling consists entirely of pearlite; if no nickel is present, the amount of carbon necessary to form the same structure is 0.80 per cent. This has an important effect on the properties: it reduces the brittleness of some steels after heat treat-

TABLE 3. PRINCIPAL EFFECTS OF ALLOYING ELEMENTS ON MEDIUM- AND HIGH-CARBON STEELS

Alloying element	Effect in strengthening ferrite	Effect in forming carbides	Effect on transformation temperature	Effect on hardenability
Manganese	Strong	Weak	Lowers	Strong
Silicon	Strong	None	Raises	Moderate
Phosphorus	Strong	None	Raises	Moderate
Nickel	Strong	None	Lowers	Mild
Chromium	Weak	Moderate	*	Strong
Copper	Moderate	None	Lowers	Weak
Molybdenum	Weak	Strong	Raises	Strong
Vanadium	Weak	Strong	Raises	Strong
Tungsten	Weak	Strong	Raises	Moderate

* Raises or lowers depending on carbon content.

ment and raises the yield strength. If, for example, an 0.80 per cent carbon steel and a 0.40 per cent carbon steel containing 3 per cent nickel are both heat treated so that the tensile strength is 150,000 lb. per sq. in., the other properties will be as follows:

Property	Carbon steel	Nickel steel
Tensile strength, lb. per sq. in......	150,000	150,000
Yield strength, lb. per sq. in........	105,000	130,000
Elongation in 2 in., per cent.......	12	20
Reduction of area, per cent........	40	55

The effect of small amounts of the various alloying elements on the heat treatment of carbon steels is discussed in the next chapter. This is in accord with the statement previously made that the primary function of an alloying element is to modify the structure (and the properties) of a carbon steel. This is certainly true for the low-alloy steels. The economic value of any alloying element is judged solely by evaluating in dollars and cents the improvement in properties it is responsible for as compared with the unalloyed steels available. The high-alloy steels are in many cases unique materials; many of them cannot be thus evaluated. These are consequently a story in themselves and are properly discussed separately.

CHAPTER 6

FUNDAMENTALS OF THE HEAT
TREATMENT OF STEEL

To improve the cutting and wearing properties of his tools
and weapons, man has been quenching and tempering them for
at least 3000 years; but his use of all the operations of heat treatment to improve the other properties of steel so that it can be
used most effectively in engineering structures and machines is
comparatively recent. This more general use was the result of a
gradual accumulation of knowledge of what went on during the
change in the crystal structure of iron when it is heated or cooled
through the transformation temperature. Much of this accumulation has taken place in the past 50 or 60 years, some of it in the
last 10 years, and some is going on now.

Nothing is known about the first deliberate use of quenching
and tempering. It is reasonably certain, however, that it was long
before the Christian Era, because the application of heat to increase the malleability of copper alloys had then been practiced
for at least a thousand years, and it demanded no startling display
of intelligence to discover that iron also became more malleable
when it was heated. Charcoal was the universal heating agent,
and it was natural to quench the red hot piece into water to cool
it quickly after hammering it into shape. Thus, all the requirements for producing a hard weapon or tool were met: heating
low-carbon iron to a bright red heat in charcoal (whereupon it
absorbed carbon), and quenching the resulting medium- or high-
carbon steel from above the transformation temperature in
water. It did not take long to discover that iron so treated would
cut much better than iron which had not been treated at all;
hence, intentional repetition of these steps probably followed
quickly.

Being inherently inquisitive, *homo sapiens,* as early as the time
of Christ, doubtless tried to explain what happened when steel

85

became hard by quenching. Being also inherently superstitious and religious, and not suspecting that charcoal had anything to do with it, it was natural that he should attribute hardening to something necromantic in the quenching medium.

As a result, all sorts of mysterious rituals accompanied by awful incantations were developed in connection with the heat treatment of steel, some of which have persisted until fairly recently. Medieval literature is filled with the magic procedures developed by clerical and secular iron workers, especially for the treatment of swords upon which the owner's life depended. Thus, for example, the Spanish swords of Toledo gained world renown because of the supposedly mysterious properties of the water in which they were quenched; the famous swords of Damascus were heated to the color of the rising sun and were quenched by plunging them into the belly of a fat Nubian slave.

A favorite quenching medium of tenth- to nineteenth-century Europe was urine. The use of this liquid has considerable scientific justification as recent investigators have shown that sodium chloride brines and other salt solutions extract the heat from red hot steel 10 to 20 per cent faster than cold water. In most cases, however, the medieval smiths insisted that the urine be of special grade: from a three-year old goat which had been fed only on ferns for three days, or from a young red-headed boy.[1] Feeding the goat on ferns is understandable, but modern metallurgy cannot yet explain why the boy should be young or red headed.

The development of a science of the constitution of iron-carbon alloys in the early part of the twentieth century, followed by a better understanding of the role played by carbon, was responsible for the disappearance of practically all the hocus-pocus which had been connected with heat treatment for 2000 years. Only in a few backwoods blacksmiths' shops are quenching media with mysterious properties still used.

44. Grain Growth and Grain Size—Most of the operations of heat treatment are carried out at temperatures at which the crystal units have considerable mobility and at which, under the influence of heat, marked changes in structure occur. These changes have been of much interest to metallurgists, especially in the past 10 or 15 years, since they have been correlated success-

---

[1] Lynn Thorndike, *History of Magic and Experimental Science*, The Macmillan Co., New York, 1923, v. 1, p. 769.

fully with hitherto unexplained differences in properties in steels of the same composition and heat treatment. For this reason, it is necessary to review this elevated-temperature behavior in some detail.

When carbon steels which have been rolled or forged and cooled slowly to room temperature are reheated, there is no change in structure until the transformation temperature is reached. At this temperature, and accompanying the allotropic change of alpha to gamma iron and the solution of the carbon in

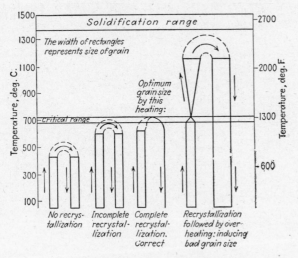

Fig. 23—Schematic representation of the grain size of carbon steel as affected by heating (Stoughton).

the latter, there is complete recrystallization with the formation of small austenite grains. If, now, the steel is cooled slowly, these small austenite grains will transform into small grains of pearlite, ferrite, or both. Moreover, these small grains will not change in size or structure between the transformation temperature and atmospheric temperature.

If, however, the steel is heated to the transformation temperature and heating is continued, the small austenite grains will grow larger, their final size depending upon temperature and time. If other things are equal, the higher the temperature and the longer the time, the larger will be the grains of pearlite or ferrite into which the austenite grains transform upon slow cooling. These changes are shown diagrammatically in Fig. 23.[2] The effect of heating to a high temperature on the structure of the steel is shown in Fig. 24.

It is evident, therefore, that there are two methods of securing fine grain in steel: the first, discussed in the previous chapter (section 41), consists of regulating the rolling or forging process so that the temperature of the steel when hot working is completed will be just above the transformation temperature; the

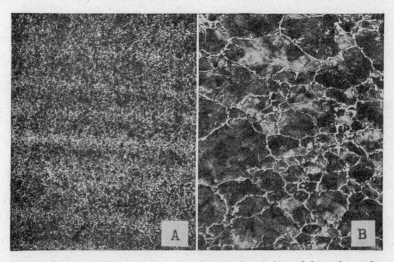

Fig. 24—Structure of 0.40 per cent carbon steel (*A*) heated just above the transformation temperature and slowly cooled and (*B*) overheated and slowly cooled; etched, 100×.

second consists of reheating to just above the transformation temperature and cooling again. If steels are rolled at such high temperatures that grain growth occurs in cooling from the finishing temperature of rolling to the transformation temperature—which usually happens owing to the lower cost of rolling at a very high temperature—the resulting large grains in those steels in which they are objectionable can be refined and made smaller by such reheating. Recrystallization and the production of small grains by reheating are commonly employed to refine the struc-

[2] B. Stoughton, *The Metallurgy of Iron and Steel*, McGraw-Hill Book Company, Inc., New York, 4th ed., 1934.

ture of castings upon which no mechanical work at elevated temperature can be done.

45. Control of Grain Size by Inclusions—Some heat-treating operations, for example carburizing (discussed in section 61), are carried out by heating for long periods at temperatures at which grain growth usually occurs. For many years it was noticed that some steels hardened uniformly after carburizing but others did not. No adequate explanation was advanced for this phenomenon until about 15 years ago, when McQuaid and Ehn discovered a relation between grain size and satisfactory hardening. The work of these two investigators, of Bain and Davenport, and of many others between 1925 and 1935 has furnished a new concept of heat treatment and has emphasized the importance of grain-size control in ferrous metallurgy.

It has been found that by adding definite small amounts of aluminum or other deoxidizers to carbon and alloy steels the tendency of the grains to grow at elevated temperatures can be controlled closely. Steels can thus be produced which, after heat treatment, have any grain size desired. It is thought that aluminum (or other deoxidizer) controls the grain-growth tendency by forming many minute, almost emulsified, aluminum oxide particles which perhaps act as nuclei for the formation of many small grains during recrystallization at high temperatures instead of the fewer larger grains which would form if grain growth were uninhibited.

For many years a coarse-grained structure was considered to be undesirable, and every precaution was taken in hot working and heat treatment to avoid it as far as possible. It is now known that this is wrong; for some steels, a coarse grain may be valuable. The properties of coarse- and fine-grained steels are discussed elsewhere. It is sufficient to state now that, compared with fine-grained materials, coarse-grained steels machine more easily and harden more deeply; on the other hand, fine-grained steels do not crack so readily when quenched and, in general, have greater toughness at low temperatures. Fine-grained steels, when carburized and quenched, are likely to show soft areas on the hardened surface; coarse-grained steels harden more uniformly.

46. Actual Grain Size and the Tendency for Grain Growth —It should be understood clearly that grain-size control by inclusions as discussed in the previous section is a different phenomenon from grain growth caused by overheating described in section 44. This can be shown by the following: Assume that steel *A* is an ordinary low-carbon steel not treated to control grain size and that steel *B* is a low-carbon steel of the same composition as steel *A* but treated with 0.10 per cent aluminum during melting. If these two steels are heated above the transformation temperature, held for the same length of time, and slowly cooled, the grain size will be as follows:

Steel	Grain size of slowly cooled specimens after heating to		
	1560° F. (850° C.)	1830° F. (1000° C.)	2100° F. (1150° C.)
A	Fine	Coarse	Coarse
B	Fine	Fine	Coarse

Grain-size control by inclusions is a restriction of the *tendency* of the grains to grow. This does not mean that the grains will not grow larger; it means that, compared with similar material which has not been so treated, the grains will not grow so fast nor so large. In other words, steel *B* has a restricted tendency for austenite grain growth at elevated temperatures, while steel *A* has not. If steel *A* is heated to just above the transformation temperature, it will recrystallize into small austenite grains which will transform into small pearlite and ferrite grains upon slow cooling; so will steel *B*. Heating to higher temperatures, however, causes the grains of steel *A* to grow faster and larger than those of steel *B*. As the actual grain size at room temperature depends upon the grain size of the austenite when it transforms to pearlite and ferrite, it follows that the aluminum added to steel *B* has affected the grain size at room temperature only insofar as it has affected the grain size of the austenite.

The tendency for grain growth and the size of the austenite grains are just as important—and perhaps even more so—in medium- and high-carbon steels which are quenched as in those which are cooled slowly, even if at room temperature all apparent differences in structure have been obliterated by quenching.

Grain-size control is an important recent development in ferrous metallurgy and is one of the few in which American metallurgists have forged far ahead of their European coworkers. Steels have been classified by austenite grain size (as evidenced in slowly cooled specimens) into eight classes (numbered 1 to 8). By controlling deoxidation in melting, steel makers are now able to supply coarse- or fine-grained material according to customers' requirements. The structures of class 2, containing 1.5 to 3 grains

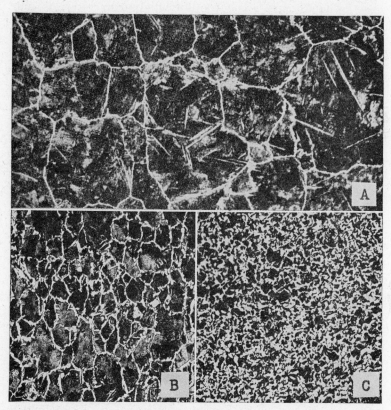

Fig. 25—Typical structure of slowly cooled carbon steel having (A) grain size 2, (B) grain size 5, and (C) grain size 8; etched, 100×.

per sq. in., of class 5, containing 12 to 24 grains per sq. in., and of class 8, containing 96 or more grains per sq. in., all at 100 diameters, are shown in Fig. 25.

47. The Mechanism of Quenching—As discussed in section 40 and shown in Fig. 19, increasing progressively the speed of cooling, *up to a certain rate*, lowers the A_1 transformation temperature

progressively from 1333° F. (723° C.) to approximately 1020° F. (550° C.). While this increase in rate affects the speed with which the gamma iron transforms, it does not affect the completeness of the transformation. Its chief result, therefore, is a reduction of the particle size of the precipitated ferrite and carbide. If, however, the cooling rate is increased still more, an important phenomenon occurs. The transformation temperature is suddenly depressed to 480° F. (250° C.) or lower, and the steel becomes very hard and brittle. The rate of cooling which is just fast enough suddenly to depress the A_1 temperature to 480° F. is known as the critical cooling rate (see Fig. 19) and is attained by quenching a high-carbon steel in water or (small sections) in oil.

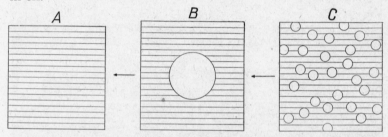

Fig. 26—Schematic representation of a crystal containing (A) no hard particles, (B) one large particle, and (C) many small particles.

The changes taking place when high-carbon steel is cooled at the critical rate or faster are in general simple, although some of the details are not wholly understood. In brief, the mechanism of quenching is as follows: At a temperature above 1333° F. (723° C.), the structure is austenite, the solid solution of iron carbide in gamma iron. In cooling more slowly than the critical rate, the face-centered gamma iron changes to body-centered alpha iron, and the carbide is thrown out of solution. If cooling is faster than the critical rate, the change of face-centered gamma iron to body-centered alpha iron is arrested and an intermediate crystal structure, the body-centered tetragonal, is formed. The carbide, instead of being wholly expelled from solution, is entrapped in the tetragonal lattice as a supersaturated solution. The result is a highly strained, very unstable crystal structure containing a multitude of entrapped submicroscopic particles of hard, brittle carbide.

Steel fails under stress by slipping or gliding along crystallographic planes of relative weakness (see p. 20); these submicroscopic hard particles of iron carbide act as keys and prevent easy slip (Fig. 26). The result is much higher strength and hardness, accompanied, however, by increased brittleness.

As an example of the effect of such a phenomenon the following properties of small specimens of a 0.70 per cent carbon steel may be cited:

Property	Slowly cooled	Quenched in oil
Tensile strength, lb. per sq. in........	95,000	230,000
Yield strength, lb. per sq. in........	50,000	165,000
Elongation in 2 in., per cent........	19	5
Reduction of area, per cent........	40	20

48. The Structure and Hardness of Martensite—The sudden lowering of the transformation temperature to 480° F. (250° C.)

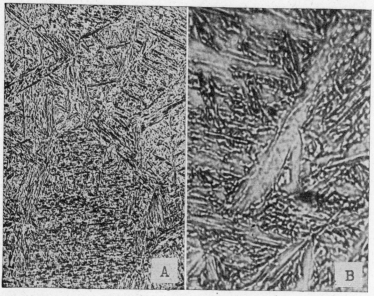

Fig. 27—Structure of martensite in high-carbon steel quenched in iced brine, (*A*) 500×, (*B*) 3000×; etched.

and the increased hardness and strength are accompanied by the formation of a structural constituent known as *martensite*, characterized by an angular, needle-like appearance (Fig. 27). The needle-like formation, while common in rapidly cooled high-carbon steels of small cross-section, is by no means universal. Martensite is a transition constituent; its composition, hardness, and appearance under the microscope depend primarily upon the amount of carbon, the size of the section, and the quenching treatment.[3] Depending upon the carbon content, the strength of steels which are chiefly martensitic in structure may vary from 150,000 to more than 350,000 lb. per sq. in., and such steels may be as brittle as glass or may show considerable toughness.

Metallurgists are generally agreed that the primary cause for the hardness of martensite (and drastically quenched medium- and high-carbon steels) is the precipitation of submicroscopic particles of iron carbide from the gamma solid solution and the retention of these particles as a supersaturated solution in the tetragonal alpha iron lattice, where they act as a multitude of keys effectively preventing slip. Some authorities, thinking that this explanation does not account for all the hardness, have postulated lattice distortion, internal strain, and fine grain size as contributing causes. The internal structure of martensite and the causes of its hardness are of much interest to the physical metallurgist but are of only passing interest to the engineer who wants a basic knowledge of heat treatment. Far more important is a realization of the instability of structure that results from quenching.

49. The Instability of Quenched Carbon Steels—When carbon steel is cooled slowly through the transformation temperature, all phase changes take place and the carbide is completely precipitated as large particles, resulting in a structure, laminated pearlite, that is very stable. If, however, the steel is cooled very rapidly, phase changes are arrested before completion, the carbide is entrapped in the crystal lattice as exceedingly minute particles, and the lattice is strained, resulting in a structure, martensite, which is very unstable.

As is characteristic of an extremely unstable condition, there is a very strong tendency for quenched steel to become more stable under the slightest provocation. Reheating to 500° F. (260° C.) or above will give the steel enough mobility so that instability

---

[3] For example, in quenching a 2-in. or larger round bar in ice water, the critical cooling rate may be greatly exceeded at and near the surface; it may be slightly exceeded ½ in. from the surface; and the cooling rate may be much lower than the critical near the center.

and the strained structural condition are relieved more or less completely, depending on the temperature and the time.

The instability after quenching is accompanied by high internal stresses, so high that frequently a small piece of water-quenched high-carbon steel, though undisturbed, will crack (Fig. 28) or will, occasionally, go to pieces with explosive violence hours or even days after quenching. To relieve these stresses and to produce at the same time a more stable structural

Fig. 28—Quenching cracks in the spline end of a shaft, natural size, etched.

condition, quenched steel is always reheated. This is known as *tempering* or, colloquially and somewhat inaccurately, as "drawing." [4]

50. Structural and Other Changes in Tempering—When a drastically quenched high-carbon steel is reheated, two things happen: The unstable tetragonal crystal structure of the martensite transforms to the more stable body-centered cubic lattice of the ferrite, and at the same time internal stresses are relieved. To produce such changes, it is only necessary to reheat to about

[4] The term "drawing" for tempering originated from the old blacksmith's expression "drawing the temper." Drawing in its correct sense means pulling a wire through a die to reduce the cross-section.

200 to 400° F. (100 to 200° C.); for many steels the temperature of boiling water is sufficient. Tempering at these low temperatures produces such a slight mobility in the steel that there is no detectable change in the size of the carbide particles, although they are precipitated from the supersaturated solution when the tetragonal structure transforms to body centered. Owing to the fact that there is no marked change in particle size, low-temperature tempering produces no appreciable change in hardness.[5] Tempering at 400° F. (200° C.) or lower is, therefore, commonly used for quenched high-carbon tool steels which must be very hard but should be free from internal stresses.

When drastically quenched carbon steel is tempered at 500° F. (260° C.) or higher, the particle size of the cementite increases. How far this return to stability proceeds depends upon the tempering temperature and to a lesser extent upon time. Most of the growth of carbide particles at any definite temperature occurs in the first few minutes; the reaction then slows down but continues for some time. In practical heat treatment the time for tempering is rarely less than 30 min. for each inch of cross-section.

As the carbide particles grow larger, it follows that there will be fewer of them to act as minute keys to prevent slip (see Fig. 26). Hence, hardness and strength decrease, and ductility, as measured by elongation and reduction of area, increases. The higher the tempering temperature, the larger the carbide particles and the more stable the resulting structure. Finally, when the tempering temperature is within a few degrees of the A_1 transformation temperature, the cementite has grown to particles so large that they are readily visible with the microscope at low magnifications, and the properties are practically the same as those of a steel of corresponding carbon content cooled slowly through the A_1 temperature.

Structural changes in tempering can be followed by microscopic examination of polished and etched specimens but not so closely as by dimensional changes and other methods. Martensite which has a structure similar to that shown in Fig. 27 is white after etch-

[5] Drastic quenching frequently causes small amounts of austenite to be entrapped and thus retained at room temperature. Tempering at low temperature results in the transformation of this residual austenite to martensite. As martensite is much harder than austenite, low-temperature tempering may cause an increase in hardness.

ing (i.e., etches slowly). Tempering at 575° F. (300° C.) produces, for the same degree of etching, a dark, almost black, structure indicating precipitation and considerable growth of the carbide particles. After tempering at 1100° F. (595° C.) the particles have increased in size so that they are visible in the microstructure. These two stages are shown in Fig. 29.

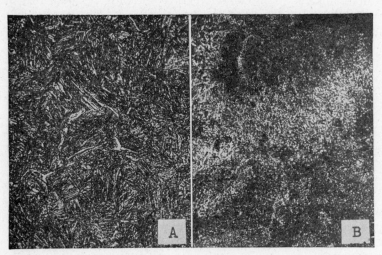

Fig. 29—Structure of high-carbon steel quenched in ice water and tempered (A) at 575° F. (300° C.) and (B) at 1100° F. (595° C.); etched, 500×.

51. Effect of Alloying Elements on Transformation Temperatures—The two most important effects of the alloying elements on steel—responsible in large measure for the large and valuable collection of special high-alloy steels available—are a change of the temperature at which austenite transforms to pearlite and, especially, a change of the rate of this transformation. One group of alloying elements raises the equilibrium A_1 temperature, another group lowers it (see Table 3, p. 83). It is generally true that increasing the amount of an alloying element increases the amount of lowering or raising as the case may be. For example, if enough manganese or nickel is added (and if the carbon percentage is carefully controlled), the transformation temperature is lowered until it is at atmospheric temperature or below. When this occurs, austenite, the solid solution of carbide in gamma iron, stable in carbon steels only at elevated temperatures, becomes more or less stable at atmospheric temperature. Such steels cannot be hardened by quenching, as no allotropic change occurs between room temperature and the melting point. Austenitic alloy steels form a group of important industrial materials.

Most of the elements which raise the alpha-gamma transformation temperature also do it progressively, with the result that, if enough is added (and if the carbon percentage is carefully controlled), this critical temperature may for all practical purposes disappear.[6] When this happens, the alloy undergoes no allotropic change, no austenite is formed, and alpha iron, the body-centered crystalline form of iron, is stable between atmospheric temperature and the melting point. As in the austenitic steels, no appreciable hardening by quenching is possible.

The most important role played by the alloying elements, especially in the low-alloy structural and engineering steels, is in slowing the rate at which austenite changes to pearlite. It is shown in detail in section 40 (see also p. 91) that austenite in carbon steels transforms to pearlite rapidly in the temperature range 1100 to 900° F. (595 to 480° C.), hence, very rapid cooling is necessary to suppress this change and form martensite. In fact, this change can be suppressed only in pieces of relatively small cross-section (i.e., large sections do not harden throughout). As indicated in Table 3, most of the alloying elements slow down the transformation from austenite to pearlite and thus increase the hardenability of the steel.

It is evident from this brief exposition of the principal effects of the alloying elements that by adding them in various combinations and by regulating the carbon percentage steels with a wide variety of properties can be made. Thus, it is relatively easy to produce low-alloy steels with properties so much better than corresponding carbon steels that they are considerably cheaper in some applications than carbon steels. It is also possible to make high-alloy steels which, by proper regulation of the alloy and car-

---

[6] Actually the A_3 temperature is raised and the A_4 temperature, which marks the change at high temperature from delta to gamma iron (see section 12), is lowered until the two meet, forming a loop at the left side of the phase diagram. Within this loop, the location of which depends on the carbon content, austenite is stable. This is a phenomenon of no importance to engineers except in the case of stainless steels.

bon contents, are harder at a red heat than hardened carbon steels are at normal temperature; or steels so tough that they stretch easily under load; or steels so resistant to rusting that they remain untarnished indefinitely; or steels with a coefficient of expansion that is zero or that is the same as that of glass or platinum; or steels of other desirable combinations of properties.

52. Hardenability—The hardenability or hardening power of a steel is a measure of its response to quenching as affected by its mass. The hardness of a quenched high-carbon steel tool, both on the surface and throughout the cross-section, is dependent

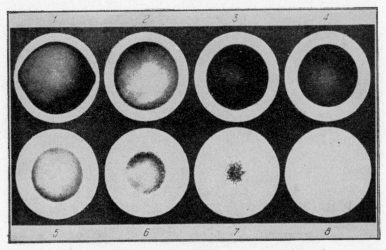

Fig. 30—Cross-section of eight water-quenched 1-in. round bars of 1 per cent carbon steel, polished and lightly etched (Bain).

upon a number of variables including the temperature from which it is quenched and the speed with which the heat is extracted by the quenching medium. This is discussed in the next chapter. Despite the rigid control of these variables, all high-carbon steels do not behave alike in their response to quenching; even steels of practically identical composition differ in hardenability. This is shown by Fig. 30, taken from a paper by Bain,[7] one of the pioneers in studying this phenomenon. Eight 1-in. bars of 1.0 per cent carbon steel were heated and quenched under identical conditions. They were then sectioned, polished, and etched with acid.

[7] E. C. Bain, *Trans. Am. Soc. Steel Treat.*, v. 20, 1932, p. 387.

The depth to which they hardened is shown (white) in Fig. 30. Specimen 1 hardened only at the surface; specimen 8 hardened completely throughout the section. Bain traced this difference in hardenability to a difference in the austenite grain size and found that the coarser the grain just before the steel was quenched the deeper was the steel hardened.

In a previous section (40) it was stated that increasing the cooling rate lowers the apparent temperature at which gamma iron changes to alpha iron and simultaneously rejects carbide, and that it also alters the rate of this change. With moderately fast cooling, the transformation is lowered to 900 to 1100° F. (480 to 595° C.), and the time required for transformation is decreased from around 20 min. to 1 or 2 sec. (see Fig. 19). It is also stated previously (section 47) that, in order to form martensite and thus have a completely hardened steel, it is necessary to cool at the critical cooling rate or faster, in other words, fast enough to suppress the rapid transformation of austenite to fine pearlite at 900 to 1100° F. For small sections of high-carbon steel, quenching in cold water completely suppresses this transformation, and the piece hardens throughout. In large sections, however, the diffusion of heat from center to surface is too slow; hence, although the surface of the piece cools fast enough to suppress the change to fine pearlite, this is not the case for the center. The result is shallow-hardening as shown in Fig. 30.

As it is impossible to speed up the diffusion of heat from the center to the surface of a large bar enough to suppress the change to fine pearlite, the only practical method of securing deep hardening is to decrease the rate of the change in the temperature range 900 to 1100° F. Metallurgy owes to Bain and his coworkers [8] a great debt for their study of the reaction rates of austenite transformation at various temperatures, especially at 900 to 1100° F., and for methods of controlling these rates.

53. Effect of Grain Size and Alloying Elements on Hardenability—The work of Bain and his associates has already had important ramifications in the art of heat treatment, especially in showing that increasing grain size increases the time necessary for the austenite to change to fine pearlite at 900 to 1100° F.

[8] E. S. Davenport, R. H. Aborn, W. S. N. Waring, E. L. Roff, J. J. B. Rutherford, G. E. Guellich, J. R. Anderson, and J. R. Vilella at the Research Laboratory, United States Steel Corporation.

(which is about 1 sec. for fine-grained high-carbon steels). It is unnecessary to discuss the actual mechanism of this change. The important fact is that the transformation is greatly slowed, hence, more easily suppressed, with the result that it is possible to quench relatively large sections and have the interior as well as the surface cool at the critical cooling rate or faster.

Table 3 of the previous chapter gives a classification of the alloying elements as they affect hardenability. Manganese, molybdenum, and chromium are very effective; silicon, phosphorus, and tungsten are moderately effective; and copper and nickel are little effective. Manganese and molybdenum are the most effective of all the alloying metals. As an example, Bain gives the time for a high-carbon steel to transform to fine pearlite at 1000° F. (540° C.) as less than 1 sec. for 0.5 per cent manganese, 10 sec. for 2.0 per cent manganese, and about 400 sec. for 4 per cent manganese. Vanadium and chromium are also effective.

Deep hardening is important for tools, which must be sharpened frequently, and for dies, for which high hardness is necessary but in which distortion caused by quenching must be prevented. By adding 1.5 per cent manganese to a 0.90 per cent carbon steel the transformation at 900 to 1100° F. (480 to 595° C.) can be suppressed entirely, and full hardness can be secured by quenching in oil instead of in water, thus minimizing the distortion which frequently results from quenching in the more drastic medium.

CHAPTER 7

THE OPERATIONS OF HEAT TREATMENT

THE value of heat treatment to mankind, emphasized in no uncertain terms in previous chapters, has little relation to the proportion of the world's steel tonnage which is treated. This amounts, in the United States, to possibly one or two million tons annually, certainly less than five per cent of the total amount of steel used. Heat treatment is most valuable for tools and dies which are in turn a very small proportion of heat-treated steel. Heat-treated tools and dies may be compared with the action of enzymes in the human organism. Like these minute organic substances which are responsible for the digestion and assimilation of large quantities of foodstuffs, heat-treated tools and dies are responsible for the economical digestion by industry of a hundred million or more tons of untreated steel.

Heat treatment is ordinarily an expensive operation, because costly furnaces, quenching baths, apparatus for controlling the atmosphere in the furnace, and temperature-recording and -controlling equipment are necessary. Some treatments cost as much or more than the steel itself, but this is no criterion of the value of the operation. Moreover, the cost of steel and of treatment is usually a very small part of the cost of the finished article and is even a smaller proportion of the value of the article to industry. One example will indicate this. The steel in a die may cost $2.00 and the heat treatment may increase this to $4.00. On this $4.00 die, the machine work frequently costs $100.00, but the completed die will turn out thousands of pieces of a finished product at a cost which is a very small fraction per piece of the cost of a similar product turned out, one by one, by hand.

Owing to the economic value of a properly heat-treated article and to the customary expense of the machine work to prepare this article for use, it is poor economy on the part of the engineer to take chances on the quality of the steel or the heat treatment so that a few cents may be saved. It is, furthermore, poor practice for the engineer to design expensive tools, dies, or other parts without requesting the metallurgist to advise whether the finished article will or will not survive the heat treatment satisfactorily. Thousands of dollars are wasted every year because tools and other articles, which cost much to machine, crack in quenching. Such waste can usually be prevented by the intelligent selection of the proper steel and by avoiding, in the design, sharp corners or reentrant angles where stresses concentrate. This factor is discussed in some detail later in this chapter.

The operations of heat treatment discussed in this chapter are those used for carbon steels, most alloy steels, and some non-ferrous alloys. Modifications of these, used for a few high-alloy steels, for certain other iron alloys, and for a number of non-ferrous alloys, are described in the chapters where these materials are discussed or in the chapter on precipitation hardening. The usual operations of heat treatment are divided into two classes: (1) varying the cooling rate and (2) surface hardening. The first class covers five industrial operations which depend upon the rate of cooling from above the transformation temperature or upon reheating a rapidly cooled steel to cause changes in the dispersion of the carbide. These are annealing, normalizing, spheroidizing, quenching, and tempering. The meaning of the last two should be clear from the discussion in the previous chapter; annealing is a softening operation and normalizing and spheroidizing are variants of the annealing process, used to produce a specific structural condition and special properties. There are two more operations: patenting, which is used extensively in wire manufacture, and "austempering," both of which are varieties of quenching and tempering.

54. Annealing—The primary object of annealing is to soften the steel so that it can be machined readily, and to refine the grain of castings and of hot-rolled products in which grain growth has taken place. In air cooling after rolling or forging, medium- and high-carbon steels frequently cool unevenly and are, therefore, heterogeneous in structure and hardness. Annealing equalizes the structure and makes the steel uniformly soft.

For annealing, the material is slowly and uniformly heated to a temperature above the A_3 transformation (Fig. 31),[1] held at

[1] American Society for Metals, *Metals Handbook*, 1939 ed., p. 993. The lower-case c when used with the A signifies that this is the transformation point in heating, which is somewhat above the equilibrium A temperature.

this temperature until heated through, and then cooled slowly to atmospheric temperature. Except for the spheroidization of the carbide discussed in the next section, this slow cooling results in the most stable structure possible to obtain in ordinary carbon steels, a structure in which the cementite and ferrite making up the pearlite are coarsely laminated plates and in which the excess ferrite, if much is present, is in the form of equiaxed polyhedral grains. These structures are shown in Fig. 18. Except for the spheroidizing treatment, ordinary annealing produces the lowest

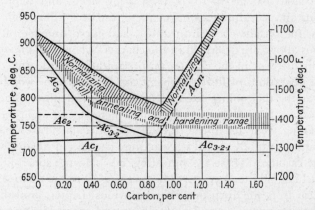

Fig. 31—Temperature ranges for the heat treatment of carbon steels (*Metals Handbook*).

hardness and strength, highest ductility, best machinability, and poorest wear resistance obtainable in carbon steels containing less than the eutectoid ratio of carbon (0.80 per cent). Annealing is described in detail in all elementary textbooks on metallurgy, and procedures governing heating, holding at the proper temperature, and cooling have been worked out and are tentatively standardized.[2]

As discussed in a previous chapter, cold working rapidly increases the hardness and brittleness of carbon steels. Hence, cold-drawn wire and cold-rolled sheet must be "process annealed" by heating to the recrystallization temperature before the material can be cold worked further. Process annealing consists (as noted on p. 81) of heating below the transformation temperature, the

[2] American Society for Metals, *Metals Handbook*, 1939 ed., p. 953.

exact temperature depending on the carbon content and the amount of cold work. For low-carbon material, there is a critical temperature, which also varies with the amount of cold work, which causes recrystallization to go too far, thus resulting in very large grains that impair the ductility. Low-temperature annealing is also used to relieve stresses, especially in welded structures.

55. **Normalizing and Spheroidizing**—In many steels containing more than 1 per cent carbon, slow cooling from a high temperature causes the excess carbide to form a network around the

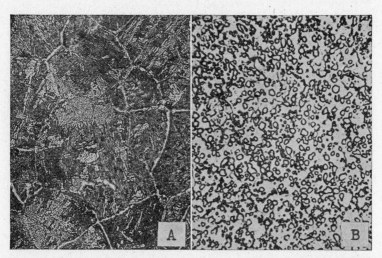

Fig. 32—Structure of high-carbon steel (*A*) normalized and (*B*) spheroidized; etched, 500×.

grains (Fig. 18*E*). This network is very stable and is unaffected by heating to the usual annealing temperatures (Fig. 31). If present, it increases difficulty and cost of machining and does not go entirely into solution when the steel is heated to the usual hardening temperatures. Such steels are, therefore, commonly normalized. This consists of heating to above the A_{cm} temperature (Fig. 31) to dissolve the excess carbide in the austenite, followed by cooling rapidly enough—for example in air—so that insufficient time is available for the excess cementite to form a network or for the cementite in the pearlite aggregate to form large plates. The structure after normalizing consists of very fine particles of carbides and ferrite (Fig. 32*A*). In this condition, the steel is somewhat harder, stronger, and less ductile than if it is annealed.

If, now, the normalized high-carbon steel is reheated to just below the transformation temperature (A_1), these fine particles of carbide coalesce into spheres (Fig. 32B) instead of forming plates. This process is spheroidizing. The steel is now very soft and readily machinable, and, when it is heated for quenching, more of these spheroids of carbide go into solution—provided the spheroids are not too large—than would be the case if the carbide were in the form of plates, and a harder material results.

An operation similar to normalizing and spheroidization in its effect on the properties of steel is the homogenization of heavy forgings of medium-carbon steel. Owing to large temperature gradients or unequal deformation in hot working, the structure, and properties, in various parts of the same piece (as hot-worked) may be heterogeneous. This is eliminated by normalizing (air cooling) followed by reheating below the transformation temperature (A_1). Compared with annealed steel of the same composition a normalized and reheated material has equal or slightly lower strength, but the elongation and reduction of area are considerably higher. Homogenization may be the same treatment as normalizing and spheroidizing, or it may differ in that the reheating temperature of the normalized forging may not be that at which spheroidization takes place.

56. **The Operations of Quenching and Tempering**—The discussion in the previous chapter of the principles underlying quenching and tempering included details of structural changes and related changes in properties. These may be summarized by stating that, for carbon steels, it is generally true that the faster the heat is extracted the harder and stronger and more wear-resistant is the material. This hardness is frequently accompanied by excessive brittleness: water-quenched high-carbon steels have been known to shatter like glass if dropped on the floor. Tempering lowers the hardness and strength and decreases wear resistance; it also increases ductility. These changes are discussed in Chapter 6, and it is not necessary to repeat them here.

Whether or not a high-carbon steel hardens throughout its cross-section depends on the size of the cross-section, the hardenability of the steel (see p. 99), and upon quenching temperature and quenching medium. For steels of the same cross-section and hardenability, the probability of deep hardening is generally greater the higher the temperature and the more rapidly the coolant extracts the heat. Hardening temperatures for carbon steels are the same as full-annealing temperatures (see Fig. 31). High temperatures favor homogenization of structural irregularities. Since they also cause grain growth, the ranges used (Fig. 31) are a compromise: they are considerably above the transformation temperatures to permit some equalization of the structure, but they are not so high that grain growth is serious.

Carbon steel is heated slowly and uniformly to the hardening temperature and is held at this temperature just long enough for the heat to become uniform throughout the cross-section. It is then rapidly removed from the furnace and quenched in the selected medium. To prevent the formation of an insulating film of gas on the surface of the hot piece, it is moved constantly in the liquid, or the liquid is circulated, until the piece is almost cold. As for annealing, the various stages in the operation of quenching have been worked out and are fairly well standardized.[3]

For tempering, the hardened steel is reheated—in a furnace, in heavy oil, in molten salts, or in molten lead—and held long enough for the heat to penetrate to the center. For most steels, the speed of cooling after tempering is of little consequence, provided the steel was not heated to the transformation temperature. In practice, the cooling after tempering is usually in air.

57. Quenching Media—Modern heat-treating operations are carried out under carefully controlled conditions. Pyrometers are used to measure and control the temperature, and for some products the steel is heated in a controlled atmosphere to prevent scaling and decarburization.[4] Before the day of the thermo-electric pyrometer and the automatic furnace with a controlled atmosphere, successful heat treatment depended primarily upon the experience and skill of the heat treater. The steel was heated to a "cherry" or "bright red" (see Fig. 33). After quenching, the scale was removed and the temperature of tempering was judged by the formation of colored oxide films (temper colors), ranging

[3] American Society for Metals, *Metals Handbook*, 1939 ed., p. 953.

[4] If the furnace atmosphere contains oxidizing gases, the carbon in the outer layers of the steel combines with the oxygen in the gas. The result is a decarburized outer zone which does not harden in quenching.

from yellow through straw and purple to blue, on the surface of the steel. Some of the older tool makers still use this method.

One of the most important factors to be considered in hardening steel is the mass effect. When a piece of red hot high-carbon steel is quenched, the speed with which it cools to a black heat or below depends upon two factors: the rate at which the quenching medium extracts heat from the surface and the rate at which the heat diffuses from the center to the surface. In small specimens,

Fig. 33—The simplest form of pyrometer (Courtesy of American Society for Metals).

the first is the more important, and if the quenching medium carries away the heat rapidly, the piece will be hardened uniformly throughout. In large sections, the second factor is of major importance, and since the diffusion rate is low compared with the rate at which heat is lost from the surface, such sections are rarely hardened uniformly. If deep hardening is of prime importance, alloy steels must be used for heavy sections.

There are three common quenching media: water, oil, and air. Water extracts the heat most rapidly; oil is only 20 to 40 per cent as effective; air is still slower. Water is used when very high surface hardness is desired, but its use is usually accompanied by the introduction of high internal stresses. For carbon steels, oil results in much lower surface hardness, but its use is accompanied by fewer internal stresses, and those introduced are of lower magnitude. When superhardness is required or when the steel is of such a nature that it does not harden uniformly, a spray of cold water under high pressure or a cold 5 to 25 per cent brine solution should be used.

58. Internal Stresses—The internal stresses introduced by quenching are the result of (1) dimensional changes in cooling, (2) large temperature gradients between surface and center, and (3) the change in volume accompanying the change from gamma to alpha iron. If the steel is ductile, these changes cause plastic flow of the grains which relieves the stress. In high-carbon steels where no plastic deformation takes place these stresses may build up to a high value.

Stress distribution in quenching is complex and difficult to analyze accurately. In many instances, it is certain that the sum of the induced stress and the working stress is near or above the tensile strength of the steel. Thus, it was found [5] that in hollow cylinders the stress at the inner surface of the hole introduced in quenching was about 150,000 lb. per sq. in. As the working stress on the cylinders was 100,000 lb. per sq. in., the total stress was 250,000 lb. per sq. in. or close to the actual tensile strength of the steel.

Internal stresses may affect the strength and ductility and frequently cause warping and cracking. The magnitude of these stresses is dependent on the size and shape of the piece, the kind of steel, the quenching temperature, and the coolant. When the stress builds up to a value higher than the tensile strength, the steel cracks. There are two types of such defects: local cracks, which are usually external and start at sharp corners or deep tool marks (see Fig. 28), and internal cracks, which follow the major axis of the piece. Quenching in water is more likely to cause cracking than quenching in oil or air. Coarse-grained steel cracks more readily than fine-grained material. Localized heating in grinding frequently causes cracking, as does increasing the quenching temperature.

[5] O. V. Greene, *Trans. Am. Soc. Steel Treat.*, v. 18, 1930, pp. 369-403.

The best methods of avoiding quenching cracks are: (1) use generous fillets where the contour changes and avoid tool marks which may act as a notch; (2) avoid rapid heating, especially through the transformation range, which may cause cracking due to uneven expansion; (3) temper immediately after quenching; and (4) quench in oil instead of water wherever possible.

59. Interrupted Quenching—One result of the study of reaction rates by Bain and his associates [6] was the discovery of "austempering," a process of interrupted quenching whereby high-carbon and low-alloy steels of suitable composition and cross-section can be hardened without cooling to atmospheric temperature, thus eliminating the possibility of introducing high quenching stresses with possible distortion or cracking as discussed in section 58. The process cannot be used if a very hard martensitic structure, as obtained by water quenching and tempering at 200 to 300° F. (100 to 150° C.), is desired, but it may be used to obtain a structure corresponding to tempered martensite of any required degree of fineness, such as is usually attained by cooling rapidly to room temperature followed by reheating to 400° F. (200° C.) or above.

At any temperature below the A_1 transformation the austenite transforms to pearlite of definite structure at a definite rate. If, therefore, small specimens of high-carbon steel are heated above the transformation temperature and are quenched very rapidly, transformation of the austenite is prevented. If the quenching bath is maintained at any desired temperature—for example 400 to 800° F. (200 to 425° C.)—and if the specimen is held in this bath for a definite time, the transformation of the retained austenite and the resulting structure may be controlled closely. Steels so treated are more ductile than similar steels cooled rapidly to room temperature and tempered at a temperature that produces a corresponding structure. The hardness and strength of the austempered steel are about the same as if it had been quenched and tempered in the usual manner, but elongation, reduction of area, and impact resistance are higher. The explanation advanced for the higher ductility in the austempered steel is its freedom from submicroscopic cracks which are caused by drastic quenching (to form martensite) and not subsequently healed by

[6] E. C. Bain and E. S. Davenport, U. S. Patent 1,924,099, Aug. 29, 1933.

tempering. Austempering is already used on a commercial scale in the heat treatment of wire.

60. Patenting—Patenting is a very old process used to heat treat medium- and high-carbon rods which are to be cold drawn into high-strength wire. The rods or the wire (if patenting is used as an intermediate stage in drawing coarse wire to finer sizes) are heated to a temperature considerably above the A_3 transformation temperature, so that some grain growth takes place, and cooled rapidly in air or quenched in a bath of molten lead maintained at 850 to 950° F. (455 to 510° C.). The object of patenting is to produce a fairly coarse austenitic grain which transforms in the air or at the lead-bath temperature to large pearlite grains which are made up of fine ferrite and cementite. Such a combination of controlled overheating and finely dispersed carbide and ferrite in the pearlite is essential for the steel to withstand the cold work to which the wire is subjected in drafting, and is also essential if satisfactory quality is to be secured.

Patented and cold-drawn wire for use in cables in suspension bridges is fairly high in carbon and has a final strength of around 225,000 lb. per sq. in. and an elongation of about 2 to 6 per cent in 10 in. Patented and cold-drawn wire is the only suitable material found thus far for suspension-bridge cables. A high-carbon wire, cold drawn and then quenched and tempered so that it has the same mechanical properties, is unsatisfactory. The reason for this is not clear, but the first attempt to use heat-treated wire instead of patented and cold-drawn material ended so disastrously that it is doubtful whether it will ever be tried again.[7] Patented and cold-drawn wire has been used for suspension-bridge cables for many years, and failures are unknown. The most that can be said is that apparently the equiaxed structure of the heat-treated wire does not resist so well as the elongated "fibrous" structure of the cold-drawn material the propagation of minute cracks on the surface, formed when the wire is bent around the anchorage shoes.

[7] The wire used in the construction of the Mt. Hope Bridge, at Providence, and the Ambassador Bridge, at Detroit, contained 0.80 per cent carbon and was oil quenched and tempered. Although the mechanical properties were satisfactory, the wires began to fail soon after the cables were spun; the bridges had to be dismantled and rebuilt with the usual patented and cold-drawn wires in the cables. See E. E. Thum, *Metal Progress*, v. 21, 1932, No. 6; v. 22, Nos. 1, 2, and 3.

61. **Carburizing**—Heat treatment also includes another important class of industrial processes: surface hardening. In this class are carburizing, nitriding, and flame and induction hardening. Carburizing is one of the oldest processes of hardening steel; nitriding, flame, and induction hardening are the youngest. The object of all four is to produce a finished steel article having a hard surface and a soft ductile core.

There are many important industrial products, such as gears, camshafts, piston pins, and the like, which should have a hard, wear-resistant surface and a tough core. Carburizing is the most widely used method of securing such a combination of properties. In this process, unalloyed low-carbon or low-carbon alloy steel is heated in contact with a carbonaceous material, from which the steel absorbs carbon. The depth of absorption depends on temperature, time, the alloying element present (if any), and the carburizing compound. With a commercial compound, a case $\frac{1}{16}$ in. deep is obtained by heating for 8 hr. at 1700° F. (925° C.).

Two general methods are in use: pack carburizing and gas carburizing. In the former, the steel article, fully machined and finished except for a small allowance for grinding, is packed, together with the compound, in a heat-resistant alloy box. The carburizing compound is coke or charcoal mixed with an "energizer," which is usually barium carbonate. At the carburizing temperature, the barium carbonate dissociates into barium oxide and carbon dioxide; the latter reacts with the carbon in the charcoal to form carbon monoxide gas $(CO_2 + C = 2CO)$. This gas reacts with the iron at the surface of the steel to form iron carbide. By diffusion, the carbon then penetrates below the surface. In the other method, used chiefly for small articles, the steel is heated in a retort furnace into which a gas composed of hydrocarbons or carbon monoxide is introduced. This method is more rapid than pack carburizing, and the case depth can be more closely controlled.

After carburizing for a sufficient time at the proper temperature (both of which have been standardized), the carbon at the surface varies from about 0.8 to about 1.1 per cent. This grades off uniformly with increasing distance from the surface, until at a depth of $\frac{1}{4}$ or $\frac{3}{8}$ in. the structure is unaffected. Typical structures of slowly cooled carburized steel, at the surface (A) and in the transition zone (B), are shown in Fig. 34.

Carburized steel is always heat treated to produce the required hardness of the case, and usually to improve the ductility of the core which may be too coarse-grained from the long heating at high temperature. The various heat treatments for carburized steel are standardized, and specifications have been issued covering the various operations.[8] After heat treatment, the case of carburized steel articles is martensitic in structure and very hard, and the core has the ductility of low-carbon steels. Even greater

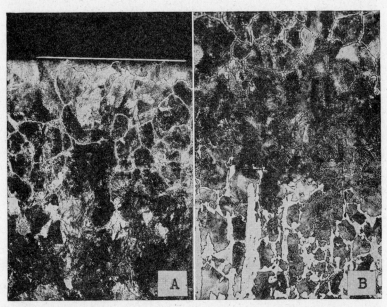

Fig. 34—Structure of slowly cooled carburized steel (*A*) at the surface and (*B*) in the transition zone between surface and core. The structure of the low-carbon core is shown at the bottom of *B*. Etched, 100$\times$.

toughness and shock resistance, combined with a hard surface, can be secured by carburizing a low-carbon alloy steel, especially one containing 3 to 5 per cent nickel.

Austenite grain size is important in carburizing steels. After carburizing and heat treatment, a coarse-grained material has a uniformly hard surface, but the core may not have such high impact resistance as is generally desired. Fine-grained steels, on the contrary, are prone to carburize irregularly and develop soft

[8] *Society of Automotive Engineers' Handbook*, 1939 ed., pp. 269-297.

spots on the surface after heat treatment. This can frequently be avoided by special quenching techniques, most of which use a spray of water under pressure, or by the use of alloy steel.

62. The Nitriding Process—Nitriding, a relatively new process for producing a hard surface on steel, uses nitrogen as the hardening agent instead of carbon. It was invented by Adolf Fry in Germany about 20 years ago and is already used widely in applications where a superhard surface combined with considerable corrosion resistance and resistance to softening at elevated temperatures is desired. It is used by the automotive and aircraft industries for valve seats and guides, gears, and piston pins of internal-combustion engines and in a number of applications in steam plants and oil refineries.

The process consists of heating the finish-machined article in a closed container into which ammonia gas is forced under pressure. At a temperature of 850 to 1000° F. (450 to 540° C.) the ammonia is mostly dissociated into nitrogen and hydrogen. The former combines with the iron and other elements in the steel to form complex nitrides which diffuse into the surface layers. This diffusion is slow: a case varying in depth from 0.0005 to 0.02 in. is obtained after 5 to 25 hr.

Unalloyed carbon steels cannot be nitrided successfully. Some alloying element which forms a stable nitride must be present. The steels used for nitriding, therefore, contain chromium, aluminum, molybdenum, and vanadium in various combinations. Aluminum and chromium are the effective elements in producing high hardness, while molybdenum and vanadium increase the toughness of the steel and also increase the depth of penetration of the nitrogen. Nitriding steels are usually heat treated before nitriding to obtain the desired mechanical properties, which are not affected by the treatment with ammonia.

63. Advantages and Disadvantages of Nitriding—The outstanding advantage of nitriding is high surface hardness and wear resistance. This surface hardness cannot be equaled by any other method known to ferrous metallurgy. It averages a Vickers hardness number of 1200 as compared with 650 to 700 for quenched high-carbon steel of maximum hardness.

Another advantage is that no subsequent heat treatment is necessary, as it is for carburized steel. Nitriding is, however, accompanied by an increase in the size of the section. This growth is dependent upon the time and temperature of the operation but is constant for a given set of conditions. It averages 0.001 to 0.002 in. for the usual temperatures and for nitriding periods of 15 to 20 hr. To allow for this growth, parts which are to be nitrided are machined so that they are undersize by the amount of the expected growth. If it is desired to prevent the absorption of nitrogen in certain areas, these are plated with nickel or coated with tin.

Nitriding is a relatively costly process. In the first place, special alloy steels are necessary; in the second, nitriding equipment is expensive. A nitrided camshaft, for example, costs from 5 to 15 times as much as a comparable article which has been carburized and heat treated. Since the cost depends largely upon the quantity treated, an appreciable reduction in cost is anticipated if the demand for nitrided steel would permit large-scale production.

Nitrided cases are very stable: the hardness is unaffected by long heating at temperatures as high as 750 to 850° F. (400 to 455° C.) and is not affected by heating for short periods at temperatures as high as 1000 to 1100° F. (540 to 595° C.). The surface is resistant to such corrosive agents as the atmosphere, alkalis, crude oil, tap water, salt water except when it is moving, ethyl gasoline, and many others. It is, however, not resistant to mineral acids. It has the highest wear resistance of any ferrous material and is finding increasing use in applications where this property is of prime importance.

64. Flame Hardening and Induction Hardening—There are a number of applications for steel articles which should be hard only in a relatively small area on the surface. For such uses, it is not economical to heat treat a section weighing a hundred pounds or more by the usual method of heating in a furnace followed by quenching and tempering, or by carburizing to harden the whole surface. In some cases, heat treating a complex section by the usual method causes too much distortion. Also, it is not generally economical to operate a furnace for the treatment of a single piece. For heat treatment under such conditions as these, flame hardening and induction hardening have been developed recently.

Flame hardening consists of heating above the A_3 transformation temperature any desired external spot of the finished steel article, as for example the teeth of a gear (Fig. 35),[9] with an oxy-

[9] R. L. Rolf, *Trans. Am. Soc. Metals*, v. 27, 1939, pp. 43-60.

acetylene torch. This is adjusted for flame composition so that the steel does not oxidize. The distance of the torch from the work and the time of heating are also controlled so that the steel does not become overheated to the point where grain growth is serious. As soon as the surface area is at the proper temperature,

Fig. 35—Flame hardening the teeth of a large gear (Rolf).

it is quenched and immediately tempered to relieve quenching stresses.

Two general methods are used. In the first, the steel piece is fixed and the torch moves across the area to be heated at a pre-determined rate. This must be controlled carefully as the temperature of the oxyacetylene flame is approximately 6300° F. (3500° C.), but the piece to be hardened should not be heated higher than 1475 to 1550° F. (800 to 850° C.). In the second method, the torch is stationary, and the steel piece moves slowly under the flame. The hot area is usually quenched in water which is conveniently conveyed through one tube of the torch and flows out of an orifice under pressure just behind the flame.

In addition to economy under certain conditions, flame hardening has other advantages. It does not scale or pit the surface,

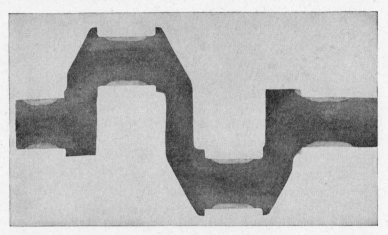

Fig. 36—Cross-section of a crankshaft showing hardened (white) bearing surfaces, etched (Tran and Benninghoff).

it has no effect on the chemical composition, it hardens only at the surface and to a depth of not more than $\frac{1}{4}$ in., and distortion is minimized. Its disadvantages are that it is more costly than the usual methods if large numbers of identical pieces are to be treated, and that high-carbon steels and very coarse-grained steels cannot be treated as they are likely to crack at the surface. Steels most suitable for flame hardening are carbon steels containing 0.35 to 0.60 per cent carbon and low-alloy steels containing 0.25 to 0.50 per cent carbon. Such articles as alloy-steel gears which have been heat treated so that they have optimum strength and toughness can be effectively hardened on the surface of the teeth by this method.

Differential hardening by induction is a recently developed method for securing high hardness on a relatively small bearing surface and is especially applicable to heavy-duty crankshafts.[10] The surface to be hardened is enclosed in a perforated induction

[10] The method is described in detail by M. A. Tran and W. E. Benninghoff in *Trans. Am. Soc. Metals*, v. 25, 1937, p. 935.

block which surrounds the steel but does not touch it. A high-frequency current, of perhaps 2000 cycles, is passed through the block inducing eddy currents which rapidly (in 1 to 5 sec.) heat the surface to be hardened to a temperature above the upper transformation temperature. As soon as this occurs, water under pressure is sprayed onto the hot surface through the holes in the induction block. The heating and quenching cycle and other conditions are controlled so that, if steel of the proper composition and grain size is used, the bearing surface will have a hardness of about 60 Rockwell C (600 Brinell) to a depth of ⅛ in. or more, and decarburization, grain growth, and distortion will be prevented.

One of the most difficult problems to solve in the manufacture of internal-combustion engine crankshafts is how to secure a combination of high hardness and wear resistance on the bearing surfaces, and ample toughness and relatively easy machinability for the rest of the shaft. This problem has been solved by induction hardening. The shaft can be heat treated by quenching and tempering at a high temperature, or even by normalizing, to secure a structure of fine pearlite, which has satisfactory toughness and ductility, and which can be machined fairly easily. Hardening by induction heating produces a bearing surface with ample hardness and wear resistance and leaves the fillets, where the stress concentrates, unaffected. Fig. 36 shows a section of a heavy-duty crankshaft with the bearing surfaces hardened (white) and the fillets unaffected.

CHAPTER 8

THE SIGNIFICANCE OF THE STATIC
PROPERTIES OF METALLIC
MATERIALS

THE properties of metallic materials are commonly divided into three general classes: (1) physical constants, (2) electric and magnetic properties, and (3) engineering properties. The first class includes elastic constants, density and related properties, thermal expansion, vapor pressure, emissivity, and thermal conductivity. These properties are of interest to the physicist as well as to the metallurgist. Usually, however, they are of interest to the physicist as a step in his study of theories of matter rather than as properties of metallic materials. Some of the physical constants are of interest to the engineer: the elastic constants surely are, because they are important in the design of structures; density is of interest if the strength-weight ratio must be considered, as in aircraft construction; thermal expansion and thermal conductivity may be of importance for some engineering applications and of none for others. The essential fact for the engineer to know about the physical constants as a group is that in general they are determined by standardized methods that yield fairly precise, readily reproducible values which can be used in engineering design without trepidation regarding their meaning and accuracy. Because of this, no further attention is paid in this book to their significance or to methods for their determination.

Electric and magnetic properties, which include thermoelectric properties, resistivity, saturation magnetization, induction, permeability, and coercive force, are of great interest to electrical engineers but are usually of little or no importance to engineers in other fields. Owing to their restricted applicability to engineering as a whole, and to the fact that in general the methods for their determination are precise, electric and magnetic properties need not concern us further.

From the standpoint of engineering in general, and those fields of engineering which deal specifically with the design, erection and maintenance of structures and machines, the last class, engineering properties, is of vital importance. These receive attention in this and the next two chapters. For convenience, they may be divided into three classes: static mechanical properties, dynamic mechanical properties, and miscellaneous.

It is not the purpose of this discussion to give complete details of the methods of making the various tests since engineers become familiar with these methods very early in their training. Moreover, a large number of authoritative books on the subject are readily available. Much more important to the engineer than how a test is made is what the test means, how accurate it is, and how he can use the value which the metallurgist reports to him. The discussion in this and the next chapters is, therefore, concerned mainly with these points. It summarizes from the point of view of the metallurgist the advantages and the shortcomings of the various tests and their worth in evaluating materials for use in engineering structures and machines.

65. The Relative Standardization of Static Tests—Static mechanical properties, which are a measure of the resistance of a material to a steadily applied load, include tensile strength, compressive strength, torsional strength, bending strength, hardness, and their related properties such as yield strength, elongation, and others determined incidentally to the first-named. The determination of some of these properties has been given considerable attention by testing societies in the principal metal-using countries with the result that methods and specimens are fairly well standardized.

The most important and the two most common tests for the evaluation of the static properties of metallic materials are tensile and hardness tests. The former are well standardized throughout the world. If the tensile strength of a certain steel is reported as 60 kg. per sq. mm. in Germany, it is certain that a standard specimen of the same steel will have a strength of about 85,000 lb. per sq. in. in the United States and that either value represents accurately the stress necessary to break a half-inch specimen of that particular steel. The tensile strength of a steel of certain composition, made by a particular process, and of otherwise satisfactory quality can be used in the design of a bridge in Japan, even if the steel was made and the strength was determined in France. Because hardness tests are made rapidly and cheaply and because they do not destroy the material, they are used widely. That hardness is not a definite property but a combination of several properties makes the interpretation of some of the tests difficult. Hardness tests are not standardized although the measure of a specific kind of hardness, namely resistance to indentation, is in a fairly advanced state of development.

Static tests used less frequently, and for which standardization has not proceeded so far, include compressive, torsion, and bend tests. None of these is used so universally as are tensile or hardness tests, although the transverse test, a form of bending, is the most widely used and is probably the most valuable single test for the evaluation of gray cast iron as an engineering material. With this one exception, none of these tests is standardized, and it is not always easy to interpret the values obtained or to apply them to the design of engineering structures.

66. **Tensile Strength**—The commonly determined tensile properties, including tensile strength, yield strength, proportional limit, elongation, and reduction of area, are obtained on a single test specimen (see Fig. 39). The accuracy and reproducibility of the results depend upon the dimensions of the specimen, the sensitivity of the machine, the alignment of the specimen in the machine, and above all on how accurately the specimen represents the whole section. Considerable attention has been paid to these factors by the testing societies and the builders of machines in all countries, with the result that reported values are about as accurate as for any engineering property.

As is well known, the tensile strength is the maximum stress on a standard specimen (point C, Fig. $37A$) which has been loaded to rupture, divided by the original cross-sectional area. It is reported in pounds per square inch, tons per square inch (England), or kilograms per square millimeter (continental Europe). Specimens and other variables have been standardized by the American Society for Testing Materials [1] so that further discussion is unnecessary.

Considering the heterogeneous distribution of structural constituents in most ferrous alloys, the absolute accuracy of tensile properties as determined on a modern machine is higher than

[1] *Standards Part I, Metals*, 1940, Spec. E8-40T.

necessary. Values may be determined with an accuracy of $\pm$20 to $\pm$100 lb. per sq. in., but to report the tensile strength of a 500-lb. bar of 0.38 per cent carbon steel as 75,330 or even 75,350 lb. per sq. in. is like gilding the lily. Metallurgical literature, however, contains many such values showing that metallurgists are much like other people in hinting omniscience if they think they can get away with it.

To report tensile-strength values to the nearest 100 lb. per sq. in. is postulating a relative accuracy which is rarely justified. In rolled carbon steels, 0.01 per cent carbon is equivalent to 600 to 1200 lb. per sq. in. tensile or yield strength. The accuracy of the chemical analysis for carbon in a steel containing 0.38 per cent of this element is not much greater than $\pm$0.01 per cent. Moreover almost any bar of steel varies 0.01 per cent or more in carbon from end to end or from surface to center. These variations in carbon are accompanied by variations, possibly 1000 lb. per sq. in. or more, in tensile strength. If, therefore, a single specimen from the center of a long rolled bar has a determined tensile strength of 75,350 lb. per sq. in., the most that can be hoped for is that the average strength of the bar is between 75,000 and 75,700 lb. per sq. in. Rounding the determined value to 75,300 or even 75,500 lb. per sq. in. is sufficiently accurate.

Owing to the inherent variations in structural constituents and in composition which may cause variations in tensile strength of as much as $\pm$1500 lb. per sq. in., there is a growing tendency to test full-sized structural members with large machines. This is especially valuable for structures which are riveted or welded.

If a tensile test is made on a larger or a smaller specimen than is commonly used (0.5 in.), the tensile strength may be considerably higher or lower than that obtained on the standard bar. For ductile materials, which includes most rolled, forged, or heat-treated carbon and alloy steels, the error is not great; for a brittle material, such as cast iron, it may amount to as much as 20 to 30 per cent. Three tensile specimens are used for cast iron, with diameters of 0.505, 0.8, and 1.25 in. Churchill[2] cited strength values for the same cast iron, as determined on these three specimens, as 52,500, 44,900, and 35,700 lb. per sq. in., respectively.

[2] *Physical Testing of Metals*. American Society for Metals, Cleveland, 1936, p. 20.

67. Elastic Limit, Proportional Limit, and Modulus of Elasticity—There is occasionally considerable confusion among engineers and steel men concerning the meaning of the terms elastic limit, proportional limit, yield point, and yield strength. The elastic limit is the maximum stress that a material withstands without permanent set. Although it is practically impossible to determine the elastic limit experimentally, it is possible with present-day extensometers to detect a relatively slight variation from Hooke's law,[3] and by careful testing the point of this variation can be fixed with considerable exactness on the stress-strain diagram (point *P*, Fig. 37*A*). The load which this point represents, divided by the cross-sectional area, is the proportional limit. It is frequently determined in testing laboratories but is seldom used in the design of structures. In most annealed and heat-treated carbon and low-alloy steels, the proportional limit is practically identical with the elastic limit and, as Fig. 37*A* shows, is slightly below the yield point. If the proportional limit of such steels is found to be much below the yield point, it is likely that internal stresses are present. The determination of proportional limit is frequently made to detect the presence of such stresses.

A word of caution is necessary here. Some engineers and metallurgists, even today, use the term elastic limit erroneously to mean yield point or yield strength. The elastic limit (i.e., the proportional limit) is difficult to determine accurately, and its value varies with the sensitivity of the testing equipment used. It is, moreover, primarily of academic interest, but the yield point or yield strength is important to engineers as it fixes the limit above which a material cannot be stressed without appreciable permanent deformation, i.e., without impairing its usefulness.

Modulus of elasticity in tension is the ratio of stress to strain within the elastic range. It is given by the slope of the stress-strain curve (see Fig. 37*A*) up to point *P*. For carbon and low-alloy steels of any composition and treatment, the value is approximately 29,000,000 lb. per sq. in.; for aluminum alloys, the modulus in tension is about 10,000,000 lb. per sq. in.; for copper

[3] Hooke's law states that in elastic materials stress is proportional to strain. It is generally held that in metallic materials the application of stress, within the range where deformation is elastic, actually produces some plastic deformation. The amount, however, is so small that for all practical purposes, and especially for engineering design, Hooke's law is valid.

and copper alloys, about 15,000,000 lb. per sq. in. Modulus of elasticity may be determined in compression as well as in tension; values are about the same for either method. Another important quantity is the shear modulus, or modulus of rigidity, which is

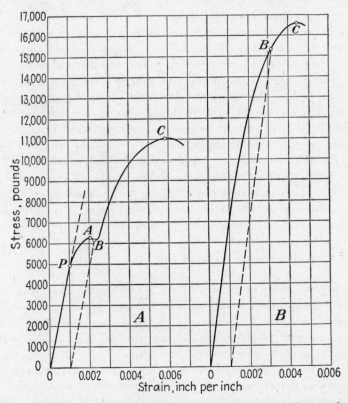

Fig. 37—Stress-strain curves in tension for (A) annealed low-carbon steel and (B) cold-worked low-carbon steel.

invariably smaller than the modulus of elasticity (Young's modulus).

There are some metallic materials—gray cast iron and austenitic alloy steels are outstanding examples—which when tested in tension have a stress-strain curve that is curved from the origin (Fig. 38). Such materials have no readily determinable proportional limit and yield point. Moreover, they have no true modulus of elasticity; reported moduli are arbitrary values that measure the relative stiffness under specified conditions of loading, usually with a stress equivalent to 25 per cent of the tensile strength.

68. **Yield Point and Yield Strength**—Engineering structures and machines subject to static loads are designed on the assump-

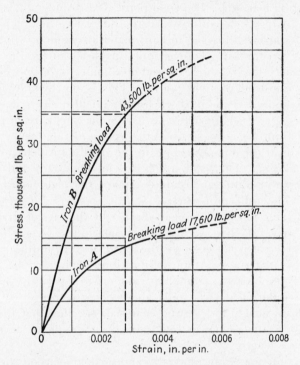

Fig. 38—Stress-strain curves for two gray cast irons tested in tension (**Bolton,** *Proc. Am. Soc. Test. Mat.,* v. 32, part II, 1932, p. 477).

tion that the stresses that must be withstood will not cause appreciable plastic deformation (permanent set). As plastic deformation probably starts in a large number of independent locations, it is difficult to determine where it actually begins. Plastic deformation does not become measurable until a large part of the section has been affected, and even then very sensitive equipment is necessary to locate this point—the proportional limit. Fortunately, practical experience has shown that, at ordinary temperature, the limit of usefulness of a metallic material is that stress which produces a plastic deformation which is readily detected. Higher stresses than this may cause considerable damage; with lower stresses the damage is negligible. This stress is the yield point. In ductile materials, it is indicated by a marked elongation of the specimen with no increase in load. It is readily detected with a pair of dividers or by the drop of the beam of the testing machine. The yield point is of considerable value to engineers in the design of structures, but it has the disadvantage that it is not well marked in hard materials, some of which have no true yield point. To overcome this disadvantage the American Society for Testing Materials recommends the use of *yield strength* instead of yield point.[4] This is the maximum stress which produces a specified set, usually 0.1 or 0.2 per cent of the gage length. In hard materials, the point can be readily determined from the stress-strain curve (point *B,* Fig. 37*B*); in soft materials, it corresponds closely to the yield point determined by drop-of-beam. The yield strength is an important and readily determinable value and should replace the yield point in all reports of tensile properties.

The value for yield point is affected by the rate of strain, i.e., by the speed of the cross-head of the machine. Generally, however, the error is not great for the speeds used in testing to determine if a material is within specifications. For example, increasing the rate of strain tenfold, as from 0.2 to 2 per cent per min., increases the yield point only about 2000 lb. per sq. in. The American Society for Testing Materials specifies that the cross-head speed should not exceed $\frac{1}{8}$ in. per min. (6 per cent) for a 2-in. gage length.

Very soft materials, especially annealed low-carbon sheet, frequently have two yield points: an upper point, at which there is a decrease in stress (*A* in Fig. 37*A*) marked by a sudden drop of the beam of the testing machine, and a lower yield point (*B* in Fig. 37*A*), where strain hardening begins and where additional stress is necessary to produce further strain. The difference between the upper and the lower yield point is considered to be an indication of the deep-drawing capacity of annealed low-carbon sheet. This is discussed in section 91.

69. **Elongation and Reduction of Area**—In the United States, the standard round tensile test specimen has a diameter of 0.505

---

[4] *Standards Part I, Metals,* 1939, Spec. E6-36.

in. (cross-sectional area 0.2 sq. in.) and a gage length of 2 in.
(Fig. 39, top). Elongation values determined on round specimens larger or smaller than the standard are directly comparable
with the standard if it has a gage length equivalent to

$$G \doteq 4.5 \sqrt{A}$$

where G is the gage length and A the cross-sectional area in square
inches. Unfortunately, since the standard tensile specimens used

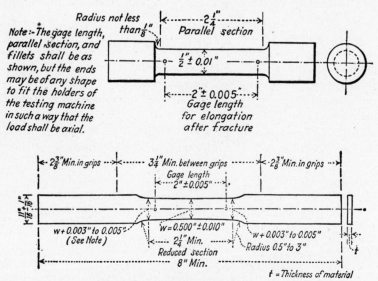

Fig. 39—Standard round and flat tensile specimens (Am. Soc. Test. Mat.,
Standards, 1940, part I, Spec. E8-40T).

in Great Britain, Germany, and France have a different relation
between gage length and cross-sectional area from that expressed
by the above formula, values obtained in those countries, while
always reproducible where determined, cannot be compared
directly with elongation values determined in the United States.

For some products, especially for plate and thin sheet, specimens are used that may differ in size and shape from the standard
(Fig. 39, bottom). Gage lengths for tensile specimens of such
products vary from 2 to 10 in., depending upon the material and
its size. As elongation is reported as a percentage of the original

length, the percentage elongation of a given material is the higher the shorter the gage, owing to the fact that most of the elongation takes place in the "necking-down" which occurs at the point of fracture. When tensile properties are determined on specimens which differ in dimensions from the standard, the gage length is always given. Even if a standard specimen is used, most metallurgists report the gage length (2 in.) so that there will be no misunderstanding. Reduction-of-area values are always reported as a percentage of the original area so that values for this property should be comparable.

Elongation and reduction of area give a rough, but usually a fairly clear, idea of the ductility of the metal tested. Although engineers generally demand a relatively high elongation, metallurgists place more emphasis on reduction of area as a criterion of ductility and believe that the importance of elongation is usually overemphasized. It is doubtful if there are any applications for which an elongation of more than 8 or 10 per cent in 2 in. is needed. As an example of the exaggerated importance sometimes given to ductility, the crankshaft of the internal-combustion engine may be cited. For years crankshafts were made from highly alloyed steels which were carefully heat treated so that they would be as ductile as possible coincident with the high hardness required. The cast-iron crankshaft now used successfully in some automotive engines shows practically no elongation in the tensile test and has very little resistance to single-blow impact.

It is generally true that in carbon steels high strength values are accompanied by low values of elongation and reduction of area and vice versa. This general relation does not always hold for alloy steels. One of the principal reasons why alloy steels are used in place of carbon steels is that a better combination of yield strength and ductility—as shown by elongation and reduction of area (and impact resistance)—justifies their higher cost for many applications.

70. **Hardness**—Physicists do not recognize hardness as ordinarily determined as a fundamental property of matter; to engineers it is a property of great importance. Everyone thinks he knows what hardness is, but no one has been able to define it satisfactorily. Probably as good a definition as any is that hardness is resistance to permanent deformation. Hardness is complex. First and most important, it is the resistance of a material

to indentation.   It is also the resistance to cutting with a tool, which involves resistance to indentation plus tensile strength and toughness.   It is also resistance to abrasion, which likewise involves indentation resistance, strength, and toughness.

There are at least eight methods for the determination of hardness, of which two—Brinell and Rockwell—are the more fre-

Fig. 40—Brinell hardness testing machine (Tinius Olsen Testing Machine Company).

quently used.   The literature on hardness testing is extensive. Since standards for making Brinell and Rockwell tests have been set up by the American Society for Testing Materials,[5] the methods for making these tests can be dismissed with a few words.

[5] *Standards Part I*, Metals, 1936, E10-27, E18-36.   Also American Society for Metals, *Metals Handbook*, 1939 ed., pp. 112-116.

In the Brinell test, a definite load is applied to the piece to be tested by means of a hardened steel (or tungsten carbide) ball. The diameter or the depth of the resulting impression is measured, and the Brinell hardness number is calculated by dividing the load applied (in kg.) by the area of the impression (in sq. mm.), which is assumed to be spherical. Owing to a slight deformation of the steel ball and to the fact that the impression is not truly spherical, the hardness number varies somewhat with the load applied and with the diameter of the ball. These have been standardized in this country: a 10-mm. steel ball and a load of 3000 kg. are used for steel and a few non-ferrous alloys; and the same ball and a load of 500 kg. are used for soft materials. The load is applied for 20 to 30 sec., the diameter of the impression varies from about 6 mm. for soft materials to about 2.5 for hard materials and is measured with a micrometer microscope. The Brinell machine is shown in Fig. 40.

The Rockwell hardness machine (Fig. 41) is designed to test materials of widely varying hardness by interchangeable indenters. For hard materials, a diamond cone is used; for softer metals and alloys, $\frac{1}{16}$-in. and $\frac{1}{8}$-in. hardened steel balls are employed. In the Rockwell test, a minor load of 10 kg. is applied to force the penetrator below the surface of the material. The major load is then applied. The hardness, which is proportional to the depth of penetration, is read directly on a scale, several of which are used. A Rockwell hardness number is meaningless unless the scale symbol accompanies the value. Loads and scales used with the Rockwell machine are as follows:

Scale	Penetrator	Major load	Materials tested
A	Diamond cone	60 kg.	Tungsten carbide and other very hard materials. Thin, hard steel such as razor blades, nitrided steel, etc.
B	$\frac{1}{16}$-in. ball	100 kg.	Soft steels, hard non-ferrous alloys.
C	Diamond cone	150 kg.	Steels of 90,000 to 350,000 lb. per sq. in. tensile strength.
D	Diamond cone	100 kg.	Materials with thin, hard surface layer; case-hardened and nitrided steel.
E	$\frac{1}{8}$-in. ball	100 kg.	Soft materials, aluminum alloys, bearing metals, etc.

Other hardness tests, which are as yet unstandardized, include the Vickers test in which a diamond pyramid is pressed into the surface of the material; the scleroscope, which determines hardness by measuring the rebound of a diamond-pointed weight falling from a fixed height; and a number of scratch tests in which needles of definite hardness, or diamond or sapphire points, are

Fig. 41—Rockwell hardness testing machine (Wilson Mechanical Instrument Company).

dragged over the polished surface. Scratch tests are sometimes useful in the research laboratory to detect differences in the hardness of the various constituents in an alloy but are rarely used industrially. A practical qualitative method widely used for the determination of hardness is the file test. In the hands of an experienced man, relatively slight differences in hardness can be detected by rubbing the material with a file of known hardness.

Thus a steel with a Rockwell *C* hardness of 64 can be differentiated from one which has a Rockwell hardness of 67 *C*. Obviously too much depends upon the personal equation for the file test to be useful except in the hands of an experienced man.

71. **Comparison of the Various Hardness Tests**—In making hardness tests by any method a number of precautions are necessary. In the first place, the specimen must be rigidly supported, and the load must be applied perpendicularly. In the second place, the surface tested must be flat and relatively smooth, and any surface scale or decarburized area must be removed. In the third place, specimens must be thick enough so that the indentation does not affect the metal which rests on the anvil. In general, hardness impressions on thin sections are not accurate unless the material has a thickness equivalent to 10 times the depth of the impression.

All tests for hardness by indentation cause strain hardening to some degree. The Brinell test is as close to an ideal test as possible as it distributes strain hardening over a relatively wide area, but it has the disadvantage that the amount of strain hardening may not be uniform and, further, that the method is too restricted in application. With a 500-kg. load, the Brinell test is quite satisfactory for aluminum alloys and for brass and bronze; with a 3000-kg. load its use is restricted to steels with a tensile strength between 45,000 and 250,000 lb. per sq. in. When the test is used on steels that are harder than 600 Brinell (tensile strength greater than 300,000 lb. per sq. in.), there is apt to be some permanent deformation of the steel ball which causes all subsequent hardness determinations made with this ball to be inaccurate.

The Rockwell machine is designed to overcome some of the limitations of the Brinell test. It is flexible and can be used for hard materials, it makes a small impression which is not likely to spoil the appearance of the piece, and it can be used to measure the hardness of relatively thin sections. For example, on steel of 150,000 lb. per sq. in. tensile strength the minimum thickness which can be tested accurately by the Brinell method is 0.15 in.; with the Rockwell diamond cone (*C* scale), it is 0.06 in. The Rockwell machine also has the advantage that hardness numbers are read directly from the scale; it is unnecessary to measure the width of an impression. The Rockwell machine is, therefore, widely used for routine testing.

The Vickers hardness test, which is rapidly becoming standardized, is the most flexible of all hardness tests and can be used without change of penetrator on materials of widely varying hardness by varying the load applied. The impression is small and, owing to its shape, can be measured very accurately. The Vickers test, ideal as a laboratory tool, at present is not so well adapted to routine testing as the Rockwell.

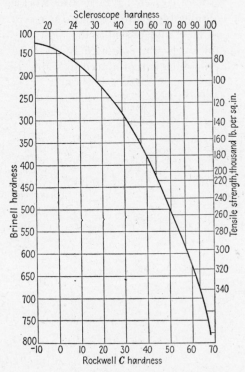

Fig. 42—Relation of hardness values to each other and to tensile strength (French and Sands).

72. Relation among Hardness Tests and between Hardness and Tensile Strength—All indentation hardness methods fail to measure the hardness of the undeformed metal. An exact mathematical correlation of the various hardness numbers is therefore impossible as the amount of strain hardening varies from test to test and, furthermore, varies from metal to metal. A large amount of time and effort has been expended in studying the relation among the hardness numbers as obtained by the Brinell, Rockwell, Vickers, and scleroscope machines. One of these correlations for carbon and low-alloy steels is shown in Fig. 42.[6] A word of caution is necessary regarding such a correlation. Brinell values may be converted to Rockwell C values or vice versa with an expected error of not more than 10 per cent except for hardness numbers over 500 Brinell where the uncertainty becomes greater. The error in converting Brinell or Rockwell to scleroscope may be considerably greater than 10 per cent. The most recent conversion table and probably the most accurate for carbon and low-alloy steels was compiled by H. Scott and T. H. Gray,[7] a portion of which is reproduced in Table 4.

TABLE 4. HARDNESS CONVERSION CHART FOR CARBON AND
LOW-ALLOY STEELS

Vickers hardness number, 50-kg. load	Rockwell hardness, diamond cone		Sclero-scope hardness	Brinell, 10-mm ball, 3000-kg. load		Approximate tensile strength, lb. per sq. in.
	C scale, 150-kg. load	A scale, 60-kg. load		Diameter, mm.	Hardness number	
210	16.7	57.6	33.5	.17	210	102,000
240	21.7	60.7	37.9	3.91	240	113,000
270	26.2	63.2	41.5	3.70	269	127,000
300	30.0	65.3	45.2	3.53	297	140,000
330	33.6	67.1	48.8	3.38	324	154,000
360	36.9	68.7	51.9	3.26	349	168,000
390	39.9	70.3	54.9	3.14	377	183,000
420	42.6	71.8	57.6	3.05	401	200,000
450	45.0	73.2	60.3	2.96	426	214,000
480	47.1	74.4	62.8	2.89	449	228,000
510	49.2	75.5	65.4	2.81	473	244,000
540	51.1	76.4	68.0	2.75	495	260,000
570	52.9	77.3	70.5	2.69	517	275,000
600	54.7	78.2	72.9	2.65	534	290,000
630	56.2	79.1	75.3	2.61	552	305,000
660	57.7	79.9	77.6	2.57	570	
690	59.2	80.8	79.8	2.53	585	
720	60.7	81.6	82.0			
750	62.0	82.4	84.3			

The resistance to indentation is directly related to compressive strength. For most carbon and low-alloy steels there is a fairly

[6] H. J. French and J. W. Sands (editors), *Nickel Alloy Steels*, The International Nickel Co., Inc., New York, 1934.

[7] *Trans. Am. Soc. Metals*, v. 27, 1939, p. 363.

close relation between compressive strength and tensile strength; hence, indentation hardness values for such steels can be converted into tensile strength with reasonable accuracy. Results of a large number of investigations on this relation indicate that the ratio of tensile strength (in units of 1000 lb. per sq. in.) to Brinell hardness number varies from 0.45 to 0.58. The ratio obtained most frequently is 0.47 to 0.50. Thus, if the Brinell hardness number is given, tensile strength can be calculated by multiplying the hardness number by 480; the result should be accurate within ±5000 lb. per sq. in. The relation between the various hardness numbers and the tensile strength is shown in Fig. 42 and in Table 4. Although this relation is fairly accurate, there may be considerable variation in individual specimens. The actual ratio depends upon structure and heat treatment, with composition a possible complicating factor, and, although in most cases the conversion may be made with an error of ±5000 lb. per sq. in., errors as great as ±12,000 lb. per sq. in. may be encountered.

If the proper precautions are observed, indentation hardness tests are accurate and readily reproducible, and if judgment is used, they give a reasonable approximation of the tensile strength and a rough idea of machinability and wear resistance. Their greatest value lies in their speed and cheapness, which make them ideal for checking uniformity of heat treatment and as an acceptance test for hardened steels, especially tools and dies.

73. **Shear, Compression, and Bend Tests**—The determination of the resistance of a material to failure by shear or torsion is important for many engineering applications, especially for shafts subjected to twisting, for rivets holding two plates together, for keys in shafts, and many others. Neither specimens for such tests nor the methods of making the tests are standardized. Stress-strain diagrams may be plotted from a torsion test, from which the maximum torque (torsional or shearing strength), yield point or proportional limit, and the modulus of elasticity in shear (modulus of rigidity) may be determined. There is no accurate relation between torsional strength and tensile strength, but for carbon steels, the torsional strength is generally about 75 per cent of the tensile strength.

Compressive strength can be determined accurately on brittle materials which fracture; on ductile materials, which flatten without fracturing, it can be determined only when a limiting amount of deformation is specified. Compressive strength is a common test for cast iron, as this metal is frequently used in compression, but is rarely made on steel. The compressive strength of cast iron is 3 to 4 times its tensile strength.

Bend tests are becoming increasingly valuable for some of the new low-alloy steels. These steels are used in structures primarily to save weight, and the bend test is useful to determine the relative stability of these materials under load. When ductile materials are tested, the specimen does not fracture when bent; hence, the test can also be used to detect deep-seated flaws and other internal defects, or to discover brittle areas in and around a weld. A variety of the bend test—the transverse test—is a useful measure of the quality of cast iron and has been used so widely for this purpose that virtual standardization has been effected.

Transverse tests of cast iron are made on standardized bars. As discussed in Chapter 12, the results are reported as the load necessary to fracture a specimen of definite diameter held on supports a specified distance apart. In the United States this is usually reported as transverse strength in pounds; abroad, and to some extent in the United States, it is reported as modulus of rupture in pounds per square inch. The test is usually made on a cast bar without machining; removing the surface layers of the bar may cause a slight change in values. The deflection in inches (i.e., how much the bar bends before breaking) is also reported. The transverse test gives an indication of toughness, flexibility, surface condition, and even machinability and is the most valuable single test for cast iron.

CHAPTER 9

THE SIGNIFICANCE OF THE DYNAMIC
PROPERTIES OF METALLIC
MATERIALS

THE design of engineering structures and machines that are subject to static loads is based upon tensile strength and yield strength with an ample factor of safety. Few failures of such structures and machines occur unless they are subjected to an accidental overload of considerable magnitude. This, however, is not the case with moving parts of machines which fail so frequently that it has been estimated that 95 per cent of all metal failures are caused by dynamic loads. For this reason, metallurgists and engineers are now paying more attention than ever before to the resistance of ferrous and non-ferrous materials to dynamic stresses and to methods of determining the dynamic properties. This is evidenced by the increasing number of technical committees working on the problem and by the number of papers dealing with these properties presented in the last few years to metallurgical, testing, and engineering societies.

The principal dynamic properties—impact resistance, endurance (fatigue) limit, and damping capacity—measure the ability of the material to withstand suddenly applied or pulsating loads. Endurance limit has been the subject of much study and might even be called a standardized property. Impact resistance and damping capacity are not standardized, hence the values obtained by impact and damping tests may mean very little unless the method and the specimen used are known. Such tests are more valuable as a method for comparing various materials, or various grades or classes of the same material, than as a means to obtain values which can be used in design.

The increased brittleness of many metals and most alloys when notched has been well known ever since some ancient but smart blacksmith discovered that the easiest way to break a metal bar was to nick and bend it. Fatigue is much younger: credit for discovering that metals and alloys fail under repeated stresses which are much lower than when the stress is slowly applied is due to Wöhler whose pioneer investigations were made in Germany nearly 100 years ago.

Interest in damping is relatively new. Although the acoustic properties [1] of steel were investigated 30 years ago, little attention was paid to the work. The realization that damping capacity is

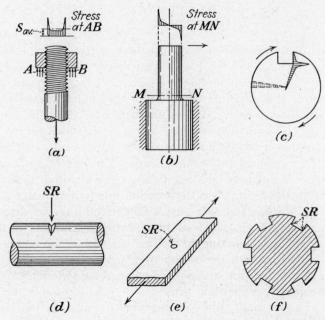

Fig. 43—Stress raisers (a, b, c) occurring in normal design of machines and structures and (d, e, f) as "imposed" by machining (Moore).

an important property of ferrous and non-ferrous alloys is due to the work of Föppl at the Wöhler Institute in Germany, between 1920 and 1925. Many a crankshaft in an airplane engine failed mysteriously before it was realized some 10 or 15 years ago that certain heat-treated alloy steels of otherwise excellent properties had little capacity to damp out vibration, and that in some engines these vibrations would build up to such a magnitude that

[1] The duration of sound from a vibrating body corresponds to that portion of the damping curve in which the vibrations are audible.

failure was accelerated. A few automotive engine builders have discovered recently that some grades of cast iron with high damping capacity make very good crankshafts, notwithstanding their low strength and impact resistance when compared with heat-treated alloy steels.

74. **Notch Brittleness and Notch Sensitivity**—It seems almost platitudinous to state that a notch in a material sets up such a

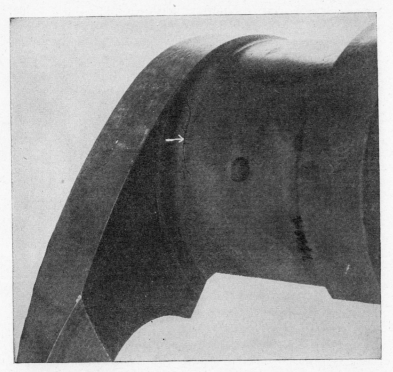

Fig. 44—Failure of the bearing of a crankshaft starting in a sharp fillet.

highly localized concentration of stress at the root of the notch (Fig. 43) [2] that the material fails by impact, fatigue, or bending under loads much lower than would be necessary to fracture it if it were unnotched. This fundamental bit of knowledge should be possessed by every engineer; perhaps it is, but that it is not used is clear from the large number of failures that all metal-

[2] H. F. Moore, *Trans. Am. Inst. Min. Met. Eng.*, v. 120, 1936, pp. 31, 32.

lurgists encounter, which have started at a sharp corner, usually the base of a spline or tooth, in a keyway, or in a sharp fillet as shown in Fig. 44.

Steels differ widely in their toughness when notched: a steel which is normally ductile in tension may be brittle when notched and subjected to impact; another steel with exactly the same tensile properties may be so tough when notched that it breaks with difficulty or even bends without breaking under the same conditions. This property is known as notch sensitivity and is a characteristic of most steels and a few non-ferrous alloys.

The notch sensitivity of metallic material is unpredictable and has never been explained. The best hypothesis to date was put forward in Germany by Ludwik about 10 years ago and was amplified later by Kuntze.[3] The latter made tensile tests on a

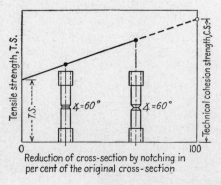

Fig. 45—Kuntze's method of determining "technical cohesive strength" (Piwowarsky, *Allgemeine Metallkunde*, Berlin, 1934).

series of steel specimens with constant diameter but with a central notch machined to different depths. As the notch becomes deeper, plastic deformation above the yield point becomes more and more restricted, and the tensile strength calculated on the minimum section increases. By extrapolating to zero cross-section (Fig. 45), a value is obtained which Kuntze called "technical cohesive strength" (Trennfestigkeit). He thinks that this is a fundamental property of metals and that there is a direct relation between the

[3] The work of these two investigators has been discussed recently by McAdam and Clyne and by Hoyt in "Symposium on Impact Testing," *Proc. Am. Soc. Test. Mat.*, v. 38, part II, 1938.

cohesive strength and ordinary tensile strength which explains notch sensitivity. This is an important and almost virgin field in the engineering properties of ferrous materials which should be of increasing interest to both metallurgist and engineer. Hoyt[4] stated that:

If one knew the two controlling properties, cohesive strength and resistance to deformation, and if he thoroughly understood the laws of the notch effect he would be able to predict by calcu- lation whether a given steel would deform when notched or would open up a crack.

75. **Value of the Notched-bar Impact Test**—It is evident from the foregoing discussion that the chief value of the notched-bar impact test is in classifying materials by their notch sensitivity. It is rapid and cheap and gives information which no other test gives at present, provided common sense is used in its evaluation. In the present state of development of impact testing it has a num- ber of disadvantages: (1) it is not standardized; (2) full-sized structures cannot be tested as no machines are available; (3) as it is a very sensitive test, specimens must be made accurately and the size and shape of the notch must be controlled carefully; and (4) values obtained with one specimen and one type of notch cannot be compared with those obtained on different specimens or with different notches. It sometimes happens that a series of steels placed in one order of merit by one type of specimen will be placed in different order if a different specimen is used. It also has the disadvantage that it is not a reliable test for such inher- ently brittle materials as aluminum alloys, cast iron, hardened tool steels, and the like, even if unnotched specimens are used.[5]

Despite these disadvantages, the metallurgist has found the notched-bar impact test to be a valuable tool. He uses it pri- marily as an "exclusion test" to detect steels of high notch sensi- tivity, thus avoiding the cost of fabricating such materials. It is also used to show up variations in heat treatment, brittleness caused by aging, marked differences in grain size, temper brittle- ness in alloy steels which are susceptible to this defect, cold work- ing, or the presence of internal cracks, segregates, or inclusions,

[4] See footnote 3.

[5] American Society for Testing Materials, Report of Subcommittee XV on Impact Testing, *Proc. Am. Soc. Test. Mat.*, v. 33, part I, 1933, pp. 87-137.

if these are strategically located where they will act as an internal notch.

In industry the notched-bar impact test is used by manufacturers of ordnance, aircraft, and automobiles, who have found, as the result of experience, that steel which has a high impact resistance as determined in the laboratory gives satisfactory service in applications where shock loads are likely to be encountered.

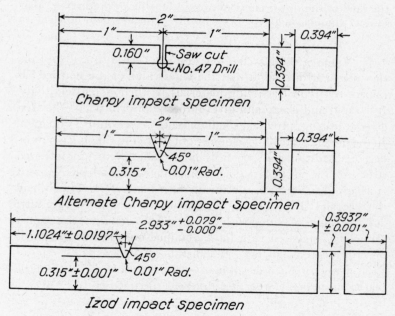

Fig. 46—Impact specimens (American Society for Testing Materials).

Of the several impact machines the Charpy and the Izod are the most commonly used in the United States. They usually have a capacity of 120 ft-lb. and break specimens 10 × 10 mm. square with notches shown in Fig. 46.[6] The falling tup of the machine breaks the specimen at the notch and swings on. From the distance it swings the energy absorbed by the specimen can be calculated. Values are nearly always reported in foot pounds of energy absorbed. As specimens must be machined accurately for

[6] American Society for Testing Materials, *Tentative Standards*, 1938, E23-34T.

reliable results, it is unnecessary to convert the impact resistance to terms of unit cross-section.

76. **The Mechanism of Fatigue**—Ever since man has used metal for moving parts, he has noticed that after a period of satisfactory service such a part would sometimes fail even though the stresses were relatively low.   Usually the failure would be sudden: an axle which had been forged from steel of excellent ductility would snap off short as if it were brittle.   Examination of the fracture would show a dull area usually surrounding an oval-shaped area of bright crystals (Fig. 47A).[7]

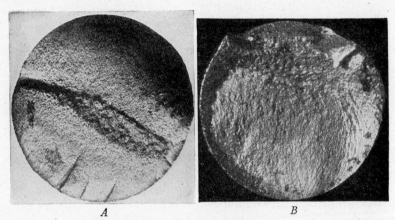

A   B

Fig. 47—Fracture of fatigue specimens with undistorted area (A) in center
(Moore) and (B) at side (Johnson).

Such a fracture was naturally considered to be *prima facie* evidence that repeated twisting, bending, or vibration had caused part of the normal "fibrous" structure of the metal to "crystal-lize."   This was a simple explanation, so simple that it became so firmly ingrained in the mind of everyone using metals that garage mechanics to this day—and some engineers as well—explain a fatigue failure by saying "the metal crystallized."   Nearly 50 years ago, it was shown by Ewing, Rosenhain, and Humphrey in England that, except for a splitting of the grains in the "crystal-lized" area, there is no change in the structure of steel when it fails by fatigue.   The work of these investigators has been con-

[7] H. F. Moore, *Manual of Endurance of Metals under Repeated Stresses,* The Engineering Foundation, New York, 1927, 63 pp.

firmed repeatedly, and the mechanism of fatigue failure is now thoroughly understood.

Under repeated stress the metal yields at one or more local areas of weakness. Slip breaks the atomic bonds, resulting in sub-microscopic cracks at the end of which there are frequently high concentrations of stress. As the working stress on the piece is repeated, the cracks spread, usually inward from the surface or from near the surface of the section. After a time there is so little sound metal left that the normal stress on the piece is higher than the strength of the remaining material, and it snaps.

The appearance of a typical fatigue failure is thus easily explained. As failure proceeds, the severed surfaces rub and batter each other crushing the grains and producing the dull appearance; the remaining unfractured portion preserves the normal grain structure up to the moment of failure. Although Fig. 47A shows a typical fatigue break, the undistorted portion is not always in the center. If the reversed stresses are not of equal intensity, the bright area may be located considerably off-center or even close to one surface (Fig. 47B).[8]

77. The Endurance Limit—Fatigue is an unfortunate word to describe this type of failure, but it has become so firmly entrenched in metallurgical and engineering terminology that it can hardly be dislodged now. Metals do not get tired and do not recover when rested; hence, endurance is a better term, especially for the value frequently reported as fatigue limit.

The endurance limit of a metal or an alloy is the stress below which the material will not fail if subjected to an infinitely large number of cycles of stress. It is determined in a number of ways, the most common of which is by alternate flexure, usually known as the rotating-beam method. A polished specimen of suitable size, which is rotating rapidly in a specially designed machine (Fig. 48),[9] is subjected to alternate tensile and compressive stresses, which are at the maximum at the surface and zero at the center of the bar.

A number of identical specimens are prepared (6 to 16 for steel, many more for non-ferrous alloys) from a single material. The first is run at a stress which is considerably higher than the expected endurance limit, and the number of cycles causing fail-

8 Courtesy of J. B. Johnson, Wright Field.
9 Courtesy of J. B. Johnson, Wright Field.

ure is noted. The stress is reduced for the next specimen; this is continued until, for steel, there is no failure after 10^7 cycles of stress. The stress (S) for each number of cycles (N) is plotted;

Fig. 48—R. R. Moore high-speed machine for endurance testing (Johnson).

the result is the familiar S-N diagram (Fig. 49). The value for S, in pounds per square inch, which the horizontal portion of the curve represents is the endurance (fatigue) limit.

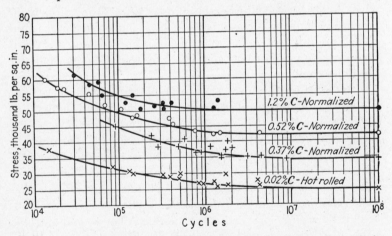

Fig. 49—Typical S-N curves for carbon steels (Moore and Kommers, Univ. of Illinois, Exp. Sta., *Bull.* 124, 1921).

Nearly all metals and alloys have a definite endurance limit which is probably a basic property of the material. For most steels this can be determined by running the test for 5 or 10 million cycles. Some non-ferrous alloys do not have a limit so easily determined; for these it is necessary to run the test for 100 million or even a billion cycles. This is the case for duralumin and other alloys of aluminum. Until recently, there was some question whether these alloys had an endurance limit. Oberg and Johnson,[10] however, have found a well-defined endurance limit for duralumin after 100 million cycles.

The importance of determining the endurance limit, even though the test takes a long period of time, is evident when it is recalled that airplane propellers and some turbines may easily run a billion cycles during their useful life. Until a few years ago endurance testing was time consuming. Using five or six machines with a speed of 1725 r.p.m., the endurance limit of steel could be determined in two or three days. For some non-ferrous alloys, however, it took two to four months, even if enough machines were available to run all the specimens simultaneously. One of the outstanding developments of the past few years in endurance testing was the perfection of machines operating at 10,000 r.p.m. which give as reliable results [11] as the older and slower machines.

78. Relation of Endurance Limit to Other Properties—If the endurance limit is determined by the rotating-beam machine using carefully polished specimens of proper design, the value obtained for most carbon and alloy steels is about one-half the tensile strength; in other words the endurance ratio (endurance limit divided by tensile strength) is about 0.5 (Fig. 50). As there is a fairly close relation between tensile strength and indentation hardness, it follows that there is also a close relation between endurance limit and hardness; the former is about 250 times the Brinell hardness number (Fig. 50). There seems, however, to be no possible definite correlation between endurance limit and any other property of ferrous alloys although further work may show some relation to damping capacity.

This relation among endurance, tensile strength, and hardness holds for carbon and alloy steels of any composition and heat treatment except those treatments which produce very high hard-

[10] T. T. Oberg and J. B. Johnson, "Fatigue Properties of Metals Used in Aircraft Construction," *Proc. Am. Soc. Test. Mat.*, v. 37, part II, 1937, pp. 195-205.
[11] Oberg and Johnson. op. cit.

ness. The endurance ratio of 0.5, or preferably 0.4, can be used in design if endurance is not the most important factor. If it is, the actual endurance limit of the material must be determined as this may in individual cases vary between 35 and 65 per cent of the tensile strength. In very hard steels the endurance limit may be affected by the presence of internal stresses. Steels having a tensile strength of 300,000 lb. per sq. in. or higher are common, but no endurance-limit values higher than 125,000 lb. per sq. in. have

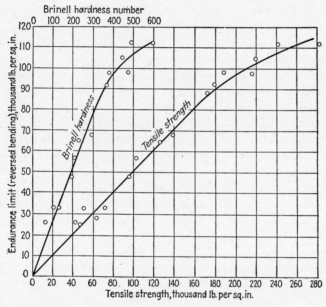

Fig. 50—Relation of endurance limit to tensile strength and Brinell hardness
(Moore, *Yearbook Am. Iron Steel Inst.*, 1929, p. 304).

ever been reported. An approximate relation among endurance limit, tensile strength, and hardness of the steels of higher strength is also shown in Fig. 50.

H. F. Moore and other investigators have shown that, in general, cast steel (not heat treated) has an endurance ratio of about 0.4, somewhat below the average for all steel. Cast iron has a ratio of 0.3 to 0.35. Non-ferrous alloys are a law unto themselves: their endurance limit may be less than 25 per cent or more than 50 per cent of the tensile strength.

79. The Effect of Notches on Endurance Limit—Two factors have a great effect on the endurance limit: notches and under- or overstressing. The endurance limit of a carefully polished specimen may be reduced as much as 50 per cent by a notch. The effect varies with the kind of notch, its location, and the notch sensitivity of the material. In a ductile material the effect of the notch cannot be estimated: only if the notch is very sharp is the endurance limit lowered as much as mathematical theory would indicate. This is probably associated with a property called "crackless plasticity" by Moore [12] and defined as the ability to resist occasional overstress.

In most ferrous materials all kinds of notches reduce the endurance limit. These vary from rough surfaces and tool marks, holes of various kinds, internal defects such as inclusions and gas cavities which may act as local stress raisers, and internal stresses produced by violent quenching, to sharp corners and surface corrosion. One of the most effective means of lowering the endurance limit (discussed in the next section) is by corroding the surface, especially while the part is under stress and in motion. The effect of a number of different surface conditions is shown by Fig. 51.

As a general rule the damaging effect of a notch in carbon and alloy steels and in some non-ferrous alloys increases with its sharpness, i.e., with increase in the ratio of its depth to the radius of its root. Usually a notch becomes harmful if this ratio exceeds 28 or 30. When shallow notches are present, hard steels with their relatively high endurance limits are superior to low-strength steels. If the notch causes a severe concentration of stress, a soft steel with low notch sensitivity is superior to a high-strength, high-endurance steel with high notch sensitivity. Gray cast iron, although inherently brittle, is relatively insensitive to notches.

Notches, unless they are very sharp, have little effect on the endurance limit of steels with a tensile strength of less than 60,000 or 70,000 lb. per sq. in. When the exigencies of design make it necessary to use a square or V-notch or to omit a fillet at a change of section, and when endurance limit is important, there is no advantage in using a high-strength steel as its endurance limit usually does not exceed 30,000 to 40,000 lb. per sq. in.

[12] H. F. Moore, "Crackless Plasticity—A New Property of Metals," *The Iron Age*, v. 128, 1931, pp. 674-677, 721.

even with tensile strength values of 150,000 to 250,000 lb. per sq. in.   Another important fact for the engineer to remember is that a decarburized surface, while not acting as a notch, lowers the endurance limit of the whole section to that of a steel whose carbon content is represented by the surface layer.

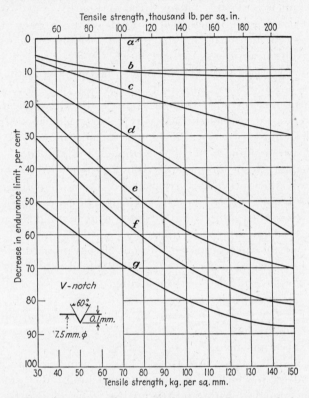

Fig. 51—Relation between endurance limit and tensile strength for carbon and low-alloy steel specimens having the following surfaces: (*a*) polished, (*b*) ground, (*c*) roughened, (*d*) circumferential V-notch, (*e*) rolling skin, (*f*) corroded in tap water, and (*g*) corroded in salt water (Z. *Ver. deutsch. Ing.*, v. 77, 1933).

Chafing or fretting the polished surface of steel or non-ferrous alloys, which sometimes occurs in bearings or in other moving parts that fit tightly and are subject to vibration, reduces the endurance limit.   Sachs, who studied this,[13] found that chafing

[13] G. Sachs, *The Iron Age*, v. 146, 1940, Sept. 12, p. 36.

produces a notch effect which reduces the endurance limit of cast steel as much as 25 per cent, of rolled or forged steel as much as 50 per cent, and of non-ferrous alloys 30 to 60 per cent.

80. Corrosion Fatigue—It has long been known that if a polished metal specimen becomes corroded before testing, the endurance limit is lowered. This is caused primarily by reduction in cross-section, as the roughened surface or the corrosion pits are generally of such character that they are seldom responsible for stress concentration.

About 15 years ago D. J. McAdam, Jr., working at the Naval Research Laboratory, Annapolis, discovered that if a polished specimen was corroded simultaneously with the application of repeated stress, a different and very disturbing phenomenon occurred. This discovery aroused widespread interest and led to much investigation in the United States and abroad.[14] It was found that, except for special ferrous and non-ferrous corrosion-resistant alloys, all metals, regardless of their composition, heat treatment, or original static or dynamic properties, fail under a low stress when subjected to corrosion while testing. In general, carbon and low-alloy steels fail under a stress of 20,000 $\pm$ 5,000 lb. per sq. in. when subjected to simultaneous reversed stress and corrosion; but a number of workers in the field believe that these materials have no true corrosion-fatigue limit; that if they are run long enough (100,000,000 cycles or more), they will fail at stresses as low as 5000 lb. per sq. in. The corrosion-fatigue limit of most non-ferrous alloys is likewise only a small fraction of their endurance limit in air.

For high resistance to corrosion fatigue a material must have an oxide skin which is tightly adherent and at the same time flexible enough to withstand repeated stressing without breaking. Of ferrous alloys only the high-chromium stainless steels normally have such a skin. Corrosion of carbon and low-alloy steels results in corrosion products which, being brittle, fracture readily, thus exposing the underlying surface to further attack. Since all ferrous materials, except some highly alloyed steels, are reduced by simultaneous corrosion and repeated stressing to a

[14] McAdam has published 15 papers on the subject. Gough in England has also worked on the problem. See Sisco, *The Alloys of Iron and Carbon*, Vol. II, *Properties*, McGraw-Hill Book Company, Inc., New York, 1937, pp. 420-422.

common low level of resistance, there are only two things to be done in such applications: use a stainless steel or protect the surface by plating with some metal that will form a continuous uniform corrosion-resistant coating. According to our present knowledge, electroplated zinc or cadmium coatings are best.

81. The Effect of Over- and Understressing on Endurance Limit—A peculiar and important phenomenon is the effect of understressing. If a specimen of steel is subjected for a few million cycles to a stress slightly lower than the endurance limit, the material becomes stronger. This strengthening is expressed by an increase in tensile strength and endurance limit and is much like the strengthening that occurs on cold working with the notable difference that the size is not changed. After such treatment, the material withstands many millions of cycles of stresses at loads which would cause early failure if it had not been so improved. Increases of the endurance limit up to 30 per cent have been reported.

If a highly polished specimen is stressed above the endurance limit, even for as short a period as a few thousand cycles, damage may result and, if so, the specimen will fail at stresses much below the endurance limit. Such damage by overstressing, which may occur in a few seconds or a few minutes in service, is important to the engineer who must know the actual stress rather than the design stress and must be sure that it is not high enough to damage the material. The presence of such stress raisers as holes, scant fillets, notches or grooves, screw threads and tool marks (see Fig. 43) should be considered from the point of view of whether they will raise the actual stress to the extent necessary for damage to occur, or whether the material will have enough crackless plasticity so that occasional overstress will do no harm.

It is likely that 75 or 80 per cent of all fatigue failures are caused by the presence of an actual stress so much higher than the design stress that it causes damage and thus reduces the endurance limit.

82. Significance of the Endurance Limit—Endurance limits obtained under controlled laboratory conditions on polished specimens carefully designed so that tensile and compressive stresses are equal are valuable in the design of machines and structures subject to repeated stresses, but they should be so used only with full realization of their significance. Such endurance data give information of one kind only; conditions in service are rarely so simple that these data can be used without considering other factors.

In service, tensile and compressive stresses may not be equal. If, for example, a moving part is stressed 40,000 lb. per sq. in. in tension and 30,000 lb. per sq. in. in compression, or if torsional and other stresses are present, the effect of such unbalanced stresses on the endurance limit is not known and cannot even be guessed.

Another important factor is surface condition. Since rotating parts in service are rarely as highly polished as are laboratory fatigue specimens, full consideration should be given to the character of the surface, including the possibility of corrosion, and to how much a roughened surface may reduce the endurance limit. This in turn is related directly to the notch sensitivity of the material. It is generally preferable to use a tougher steel with low notch sensitivity and with a lower endurance limit than to use a high-tensile, high-endurance material in which a minute surface imperfection may be readily propagated into a crack. Thus, wrought iron, which is soft and tough, and which has relatively low notch sensitivity, is very satisfactory for staybolts in boilers. Another factor to be considered is the presence of notches and irregularities which may cause a momentary over-stressing, resulting in damage and a lowering of the endurance limit. Still another factor is the possibility of occasional abuse by shock or otherwise.

Endurance data as now determined give little or no information on these possible complicating factors. It is, therefore, just as necessary to use a factor of safety with endurance data as with tensile and yield strengths. Above all it must be remembered that in the design of machines and structures subjected to rapidly repeated stresses the endurance limit is only part of the story; with it should be considered a number of other properties, especially impact and damping capacity, and such important complicating factors as surface condition, unbalanced stresses, external or internal stress raisers, notch sensitivity, and a number of other variables which are usually included under the general term quality of the material.

83. **Damping Capacity**—If a metal or an alloy bar is supported at one end and if the free end is struck with a hammer, the bar

will vibrate for varying lengths of time depending upon the composition, the stress imposed, and other factors, but at a uniformly decreasing rate owing to the internal friction of the material which dissipates the energy as heat and sound. The amount of internal friction and dissipation of energy per unit volume of the material for one cycle of stress is the *damping capacity* and can be determined by cyclic bending tests or by alternate torsion tests. It may be reported as inch-pound per cubic inch, or as centimeter-kilogram per cubic centimeter, per cycle. The usual measure of damping capacity is the area of the stress-strain hysteresis loop; the ratio of this value to the work of deformation is the *damping ratio*. This increases with the capacity of the material to damp out vibration and is usually reported in percentage and plotted against the maximum fiber stress.

Von Heydekampf,[15] one of the pioneers in investigating damping capacity, stated that it is independent of the method of determination and the size of the specimen. There is apparently no direct relation between damping and any other mechanical property. In most cases the ability of a steel to damp out vibration decreases as the tensile strength increases. It is shown elsewhere that of ferrous materials the strong alloy steels usually have the lowest, and cast iron and low-carbon steels the highest damping capacity. There are, however, many exceptions to this generality as steels of the same composition and tensile strength may have very different capacities to damp out vibration. The non-ferrous alloys are a law unto themselves; many of them, however, including aluminum alloys and most brasses and bronzes, have as low a damping capacity as the alloy steels.

Damping capacity may be measured in a variety of ways. The most common is by the Föppl-Pertz machine developed at the Wöhler Institute where most of the work on damping has been done. This machine measures the free vibration damped only by the internal friction. Typical curves for cast iron, carbon steel, and duralumin are shown in Fig. 52 from a paper by Pohl.[16] It was thought formerly that endurance limit could be predicted from damping capacity. According to von Heydekampf, this

[15] G. S. von Heydekampf, "Damping Capacity of Materials," *Proc. Am. Soc. Test. Mat.*, v. 31, part II, 1931, pp. 157-175.

[16] W. M. Pohl, "Vibrations of Structure and Materials," *Product Engineering*, v. 4, 1933, pp. 91-94.

cannot be done. There is, however, much evidence that damping capacity is related to notch sensitivity. For example, cast iron has a high damping capacity and is relatively insensitive to notches; duralumin, with a high notch sensitivity, has a very low capacity to damp vibrations.

The damping capacity of a material is an important criterion for its usefulness in many applications. For example, in crankshafts in internal-combustion engines resonant impulses may occur frequently. If a steel with high damping capacity is used, the energy of these impulses is dissipated quickly by internal fric-

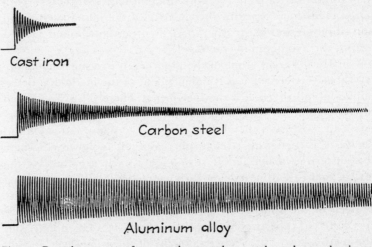

Cast iron

Carbon steel

Aluminum alloy

Fig. 52—Damping curves for cast iron, carbon steel, and an aluminum alloy (Pohl).

tion. If the crankshaft has low damping capacity, "high resonance stresses exceeding the fatigue range will be more likely to occur since there is no self-protection by internal damping of the material." It is not known yet whether internal friction can by itself prevent resonance failure. It is, however, advisable in such applications as the crankshaft to use a high-damping material if possible or practicable. Another example of engineering interest, cited by Föppl,[17] is the influence of damping capacity on the fatigue failure of high-tension wires and cables. Copper has a higher damping capacity than aluminum alloys. Despite the fact

[17] *J. Iron Steel Inst.*, v. 134, 1936, p. 393P.

that the light alloys possess higher tensile strength and endurance limit than copper, they fail prematurely by fatigue while copper does not, owing to the inability of the light-metal wire to damp out the resonant vibrations caused by the wind. Föppl also states that the life of airplane propellers, which often vibrate violently at critical speeds, depends more upon the damping capacity of the material than upon its endurance limit.

CHAPTER 10

MACHINABILITY, WEAR RESISTANCE AND DEEP-DRAWING PROPERTIES

THE properties discussed in this chapter have been responsible for many metallurgical and engineering headaches. The cause of these headaches is not hard to find; the cure, however, is more difficult. All these properties are important in one or more fields of engineering, and the engineer has much justification for requiring definite, if not complete, information about them when he considers a ferrous or non-ferrous alloy for a particular job. The metallurgist, however, encounters considerable difficulty in supplying such information.

Ten or fifteen years ago a metallurgist was much embarrassed if an engineer inquired concerning the expected service of a ferrous or non-ferrous alloy when exposed to high temperatures and high stresses, or to repeated stress, or to wear, or to corrosion, or corrosion and repeated stress. The metallugist's face is still red when he is asked such a question, but the deep crimson of ten years ago has faded to a delicate pink more becoming to one who, where metal is concerned, is supposed to know all the answers. Resistance to repeated stress is no longer a major bugbear, and we have learned much about corrosion, corrosion endurance (corrosion fatigue), and high-temperature strength. But some of the other properties are almost as much of a puzzle now as they were ten years ago.

There are several reasons for this. In the first place, many of these properties cannot be measured quantitatively. Unlike tensile strength and endurance limit, which are specific basic properties, wear resistance, machinability, and deep-drawing capacity are each the weighted average of a group of separate properties; hence, unless the various components affecting the average are known and are accurately appraised, the property itself cannot be evaluated precisely. With our present state of knowledge this is difficult. In the second place, the problem of evaluating these complex properties has been made more difficult of solution because until recently metallurgists—and many engineers as well —insisted that they are basic properties which can be determined readily by a suitable laboratory test, and failed to realize that such terms as machinability, wear resistance, and deep-drawing capacity are meaningless unless they are coupled with a description of the environment. It is impossible, for example, for the metallurgist to supply a material that resists wear unless the engineer gives full details about the service for which the material is intended, and, on the other hand, it is certainly misleading if the metallurgist tells the engineer that a certain steel machines readily because it was superior to other steels in laboratory tests. Similarly, the metallurgist should not recommend a material for tail skids on airplanes just because it showed high wear resistance in the Amsler machine.

There is a third reason why relatively little is known about these properties. Fortunately, machining, wearing, and deep drawing are operations which go on before our eyes—or ears— hence, sudden failures rarely occur. Metallurgists have, therefore, not given so much time and thought to these properties as they have to corrosion and to deformation at elevated temperatures, which are frequently so well hidden that a disastrous failure may occur before it is realized that anything is wrong.

It is the object of the discussion in this chapter to outline what is known about the components entering into machinability, wear resistance, and deep drawing and to describe in considerable detail the effect of the environment so that no misapprehension will exist when the engineer considers specific data later in this volume and elsewhere. Most attention is paid here to the problems encountered with ferrous alloys as these are the most important and have been the subject of the most extensive study.

84. Variables Affecting Machinability—To remove metal by machining the tool must penetrate below the surface of the metal to be machined. The facility with which this occurs depends upon the relative indentation hardness of the tool and of the metal to be machined. In general, for machining with carbon-steel tools, the Brinell hardness number of the metal cut should not exceed about 250, equivalent to a tensile strength of 120,000 lb. per sq. in. With some of the high-speed tools now available, and especially with some of the new cemented carbide tools, steels with much higher hardness can be machined readily.

Also important are the strength and toughness of the metal to be machined. After the tool has penetrated below the surface, it must break off the chip; hence, for easy machinability the material should be brittle and relatively weak, or it should contain a brittle constituent which will act as a "chip breaker." If other things are equal, it needs less power to machine a low-carbon steel than it does to machine high-carbon material. This is not to say that, because a steel is soft, it is easy to machine; it may be so tough that the chips are separated with difficulty, or in extreme cases they may weld to the point of the tool. Some metallurgists recommend that for automatic machines the minimum Brinell hardness number of a steel should be 180 to 200.

The third and last factor is the structure of the steel being cut. It is usually considered that of annealed medium- and high-carbon steels, those with completely spheroidized cementite are easiest to machine. Opinion on this point is not unanimous as many engineers claim that if there are some islands of pearlite scattered through the spheroids of carbide, the material is machined more readily than if the cementite is completely spheroidized. In quenched and tempered steels, hardness decreases and machinability increases as the tempering temperature is increased. Grain size is also an important factor. It is usually true that higher cutting speeds can be used for coarse-grained steels than for fine-grained steels of the same analysis and hardness and still produce a satisfactory surface finish. If, however, the finish is the most important factor in the machining operation, a fine-grained steel is best.

These metallurgical influences, while very important in determining machinability, are only part of the story. Equally important are the mechanical factors: the hardness, size, and shape of the tool, the angle and rake of the cutting edge, the speed, feed, and depth of the cut, and the nature of the cutting fluid, or coolant, used. In most instances, these overshadow the metallurgical factors. Much attention has been paid to the variables included under the general term machinability, but much remains to be cleared up. The literature is extensive and is growing rapidly; this has been covered to 1934 by the bibliography compiled by Boston [1] which pays special attention to the mechanical details.

1 American Society of Mechanical Engineers, *A Bibliography on the Cutting of Metals*, (compiled by O. W. Boston). Part I, A.S.M.E. Research Publ. 1930, 63 pp.; part II, publ. by the compiler, Ann Arbor, 1935, 202 pp.

85. Evaluation of Metallic Materials for Machinability— Owing to the number and complexity of the factors involved, it is impossible to evaluate the machinability of ferrous or non-ferrous materials by a single laboratory test. It is readily possible

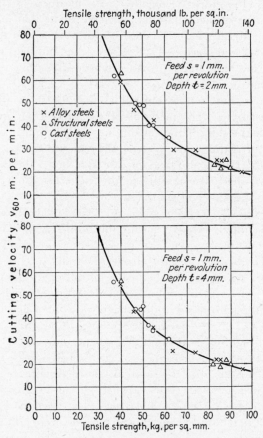

Fig. 53—Relation of cutting speed for a tool life of 1 hr. to tensile strength, for cuts of 0.08 and 0.16 in. (Wallichs and Dabringhaus, *Maschinenbau*, v. 9, 1930, p. 257).

to classify a series of steels for rough turning, but the order of merit into which they fall for this operation may not be the same if surface finish is important. Moreover, the order of merit for a series of materials as determined by a laboratory test may not be the same as in production. Laboratory tests under carefully controlled conditions, plus years of experience, however, have shown that there is a relation between machinability and some of the other properties of metallic materials. Fig. 53, for example, shows that machinability decreases with increasing tensile strength. This property, together with hardness, is probably a good criterion of machinability. It is also true that, under controlled conditions, there is very little difference in the machinability of cast and hot-rolled steels, of carbon and low-alloy steels, or of acid and basic steels, provided tensile strength and hardness are the same.

Cast steels and non-ferrous alloys may be more difficult to machine than wrought material of the same composition and structure if the skin of the casting has cooled rapidly enough to harden it, or if the sand has not been removed thoroughly from the surface. This is also true for cast iron, but if the skin of cast iron is soft, the machinability of this material also varies with the tensile strength and hardness.

Many efforts have been made to devise a laboratory test to indicate accurately relative machinability in service, but without success. The most recent attempts have been concerned with the work-hardening capacity of the material cut. It is known that when a tool cuts, the metal just ahead of the tool is strain hardened. Experiments are being made with the object of using the maximum hardness so induced as a measure of machinability.

86. **Free-machining Steels**—Despite the impossibility of evaluating machinability accurately, experience has shown that the machinability of some materials can be improved by certain treatments and, further, that there are alloys of certain compositions which can be machined more easily at high speed than other alloys of the same general type. Such materials, are, therefore, used extensively in automatic machines for the mass production of machined parts.

The machinability of those low-carbon steels which are too soft and tough to machine easily is improved by heat treatment and, especially, by cold working. Quenching a low-carbon steel to increase the Brinell hardness number from 90 or 100 to 170 to 210 improves its machinability (provided, of course, that no martensite is formed by quenching). Cold working is even more effective in increasing the hardness and at the same time decreasing the toughness; hence, most low-carbon steels which must be machined economically are cold drawn or cold rolled. This operation also has the advantage that it produces a smooth surface.

The best and cheapest method of improving the machinability of low-carbon steels is adding sulphur, or lead, or both. High-sulphur steels are widely used for automatic screw machine work, and suitable compositions have been standardized by the Society of Automotive Engineers. However, owing to the high sulphur (plus, for some of the steels, high phosphorus), these "free-machining" or "free-cutting" steels have much lower impact resistance than low-sulphur steels of the same carbon content and should be employed, therefore, only where low impact resistance is not a handicap. Leaded steel is a development of the past five years. The addition of lead improves the machinability of low- as well as of high-sulphur steel. Leaded steel is also more resistant to impact than high-sulphur material. The relative machinability of the free-machining steels compared with three low-sulphur steels is given in Table 5.[2]

TABLE 5.   APPROXIMATE MACHINABILITY RATING OF COLD-WORKED FREE CUTTING STEELS

S.A.E. No.	Composition, per cent				Machinability rating, per cent
	C	Mn	S	P	
X1112	0.08 to 0.16	0.60 to 0.90	0.20 to 0.30	0.09 to 0.13	140
1112L*	0.08 to 0.16	0.60 to 0.90	0.10 to 0.20	0.09 to 0.13	140
1112	0.08 to 0.16	0.60 to 0.90	0.10 to 0.20	0.09 to 0.13	100
X1314	0.10 to 0.20	1.00 to 1.30	0.075 to 0.150	0.045 max.	90
X1315	0.10 to 0.20	1.30 to 1.60	0.075 to 0.150	0.045 max.	87
1115	0.10 to 0.20	0.75 to 1.00	0.075 to 0.150	0.045 max.	81
1120	0.15 to 0.25	0.60 to 0.90	0.075 to 0.150	0.045 max.	78
X1330	0.25 to 0.35	1.35 to 1.65	0.075 to 0.150	0.045 max.	76
X1335	0.30 to 0.40	1.35 to 1.65	0.075 to 0.150	0.045 max.	72
X1340	0.35 to 0.45	1.35 to 1.65	0.075 to 0.150	0.045 max.	70
1020	0.15 to 0.25	0.30 to 0.60	0.055 max.	0.045 max.	63
1040	0.35 to 0.45	0.60 to 0.90	0.055 max.	0.045 max.	60
1010	0.05 to 0.15	0.30 to 0.60	0.055 max.	0.045 max.	53

* Contains 0.20 to 0.25 per cent lead.

Iron carbide particles, if favorably located and of favorable shape, act as chip breakers; thus unalloyed carbon steels containing 0.20 to 0.40 per cent carbon, when properly annealed, machine

2 Adapted from a tabulation by H. W. Graham. *Metal Progress*, July 1939, p. 53.

much more easily than those containing carbon below 0.15 per cent (Table 5). The best chip breaker is manganese sulphide (MnS). In high-sulphur steel, inclusions of MnS, when well distributed as small particles, break up the chips very effectively and, as Table 5 shows, greatly improve machinability. Despite their low impact resistance large tonnages of high-sulphur steels are used.

The action of lead in improving machinability is not wholly understood. It was noted in Chapter 4 (page 61) that, when 0.10 to 0.25 per cent of this element is added to low-carbon steels, it cannot be detected in the structure of the solid metal; it apparently is present as well·distributed submicroscopic particles that act not only as chip breakers but as an internal lubricant as well.

87. Relative Machinability of Steel and Non-ferrous Alloys —An approximate evaluation of the relative machinability of some common ferrous and non-ferrous materials can be made by averaging the data reported by Boston[3] for drilling, milling, and planing tests. They were reported as the horsepower required to remove one cubic inch of metal per minute. The order is as follows:

Material	Horsepower per cu in. per min.
Magnesium alloys	0.30
Bearing bronze	0.35
Aluminum alloy, 8% Cu	0.35
Free-cutting brass	0.38
Manganese bronze	0.60
Hard cast iron	0.60
Malleable iron	0.75
Yellow brass, unleaded	0.85
Free-cutting steel, cold drawn	0.90
Forged carbon steel, 0.20% C	1.12
Nickel steel, 0.40% C	1.20
Annealed copper	1.35
Tool steel, high carbon	1.60
Low-carbon, high-chromium steel	1.70
Monel metal	1.70

This is not an infallible evaluation, and the order might be changed for some of the alloys if the conditions of the tests were changed slightly. It does, however, show that it requires much more power to machine the free-cutting steels than is needed for some of the magnesium and aluminum alloys, some of the free-cutting brasses and bronzes, or cast or malleable iron.

[3] O. W. Boston, *Proc. Am. Soc. Test. Mat.*, v. 31, 1931, II, pp. 388-421.

Soft gray cast iron, containing no hard excess carbide or phosphide particles, and malleable iron are the most readily machinable of all ferrous materials, usually ranking higher than high-sulphur steel. The ease with which these materials are cut is due primarily to the softness of the ferrite plus the numerous small particles of graphite which act as chip breakers and as a lubricant.

In general, copper- and aluminum-base alloys are easy to machine. There is, however, enough difficulty with these alloys so that special compositions are used for material that is cut in automatic machines. Free-cutting brass and bronze contain 1 to 4 per cent lead; their machinability is 70 to 100 as compared to 20 to 30 for the same alloys containing no lead. Automatic machine work on aluminum alloys was difficult until four strong aluminum-copper alloys rated as free-machining were made available recently.

88. Types of Wear—The importance of wear resistance needs no amplification. Wear occurs in machines when shafts rotate, when pistons and valves operate, when a gear meshes and drives another, when steel or cast-iron wheels start, run, or stop on rails, when brakes are set, when excavating, conveying, crushing or mixing machines handle sand, clay, rock, coal, or minerals, when agricultural implements are used, and in a multitude of other engineering applications. Some of the most destructive wear of metals is caused by rapidly moving soft materials; for example, the wearing of hardened steel parts by cotton or silk thread in textile machinery.

The wear of metals may be divided broadly into metal-to-metal wear and abrasive wear. Another division is possible: into wear under rolling friction or under sliding friction and, further, according to whether lubrication can or cannot be used. The latter is, of course, most important in the metal-to-metal contact of machine parts. Lubrication may be omitted from detailed consideration because, although it greatly influences the rate of wear, it probably has little or no effect on the type of wear. Wear resistance is an important property of metals used in machines even if lubrication is of the best, because perfect lubrication is more of an ideal than a reality. Moreover, even if lubrication is so thorough that it prevents a metal-to-metal wear, it frequently happens that extraneous grit in the lubricant causes severe abrasive wear. Another important factor entering into the wear of machines is corrosion of the wearing surfaces caused by condensed moisture or acids in gases and lubricants.

Wear involving a single type is rare; in most machinery, both abrasive and metal-to-metal wear occur. This is the case in such parts as shafts revolving in bearings, where abrasive wear occurs until the shaft and bearing are "run in" and worn to a mirror finish, after which metal-to-metal wear predominates. Since in such service wear can rarely be avoided completely even with the best lubrication, it is common to use a hard metal and a relatively soft one together, the softer material being used (as in a bearing) for the part which is most economical to replace. In some kinds of excavating and material-handling equipment, abrasive wear is the principal type involved.

89. **Variables Affecting Wear Resistance**—Like machinability, wear resistance depends upon two factors, the metallurgical and the mechanical. The latter has been discussed briefly in the previous paragraphs and may, consequently, be dismissed with the statement that wear of metal depends as much, or even more, on the conditions of service as upon the metal used. The metallurgist cannot recommend a material for use involving wear unless he knows with some exactness all the factors which enter into that particular application.

From the metallurgical standpoint, wear resistance is inversely proportional to machinability and, in general, directly proportional to hardness. Hardness, however, is not the only metallurgical factor of importance. Wear by abrasion, like machinability, involves tearing off small particles of the metal. Consequently strength and toughness are important factors in resisting wear.

The wear resistance of the various carbon and alloy steels receives attention elsewhere; it can be dismissed here with a brief mention of the general types of ferrous material used for wear resistance. The first and most common, especially for metal-to-metal wear, is a cast iron or a steel with a surface of high hardness. Usually, in an application requiring high surface hardness, considerable toughness, especially of the core, is also required. This combination of properties is attained by quenching and tempering an alloy steel or by case carburizing or nitriding a carbon or alloy steel and heat treating to produce high surface hardness combined with considerable ductility in the core.

For abrasion resistance, two kinds of materials are used: (1) an austenitic steel which is relatively soft but which, under the severe cold working of the abrasion, transforms to martensitic; and (2) a carbon or alloy steel on which a hard surface layer of some special alloy is deposited by electric arc or other method.

90. **Evaluation of Steel for Wear Resistance**—The evaluation of the wear resistance of steels is one of the most difficult problems a metallurgist is called upon to solve. Simulating actual service conditions by a laboratory test—the most important phase of this problem—can be accomplished only rarely and then only if wear in service occurs rapidly and if it is possible to design a machine which duplicates service conditions exactly. Wear is usually a slow process. Shidle [4] notes that, when a 5-ton truck has finally worn out, it has lost only 5 pounds of metal. The useful life of the average automobile engine is probably 100,000 miles, hence the difficulty of devising a test which will simulate such service conditions accurately.

Several types of laboratory machines have been developed that determine the wear resistance of a material fairly rapidly and under relatively closely controlled conditions. For determining metal-to-metal wear, the most common is the Amsler machine, which tests a specimen under pure sliding or pure rolling friction, or a combination of the two. Pressures can be varied at will, and wear can be determined at any temperature, with or without lubrication. Some data on metal-to-metal wear at room temperature of carbon steels, together with Rockwell hardness, are shown in Fig. 54. [5]

For the determination of abrasive wear, two machines are commonly employed: the Brinell and the Spindel (used widely in Germany) which use sand or emery as the abrasive. Much care is necessary in the selection of the abrasives as these may not be uniform. The order of merit of a series of steels and alloys with one abrasive may change completely if another abrasive or a different lot of the same abrasive is used. It has been said with considerable justification that machines for determining resistance to abrasive wear are a better test of the abrasive than of the metal.

The important fact to be recognized is that any wear-testing

[4] N. G. Shidle, *Automotive Industries*, v. 66, Mar. 19, 1932, p. 449.

[5] S. J. Rosenberg, *The Iron Age*, v. 128, 1931, pp. 1366, 1367.

machine determines the relative resistance of a series of metals or
alloys under a few carefully regulated conditions, but that the
results obtained, while valuable for comparing the materials,
cannot be translated quantitatively into probable life in service
unless the test used duplicates in all respects, including time, the
conditions of service. A valuable discussion of the factors in wear

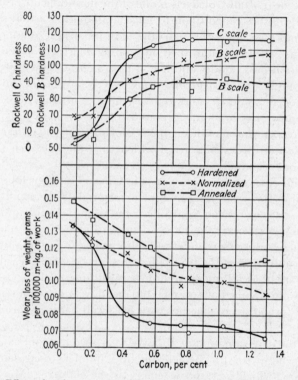

Fig. 54—Effect of carbon content and heat treatment on metal-to-metal wear
of carbon steels (Rosenberg).

resistance and of the wear of metals in automotive, power-plant,
and textile-plant equipment, together with a bibliography on
wear, has been published recently by the American Society for
Testing Materials.[6]

91. Importance of **Deep-drawing Properties**—Practically all
steels and most of the non-ferrous alloys can be deformed cold,

[6] Symposium on Wear of Metals, Philadelphia Meeting, April 1937, 105 pp.

but how much deformation they will withstand without failure, or without annealing to restore ductility, varies greatly, depending upon composition, structure, and other factors. In general, the higher the ductility as shown by the tensile test, and the lower the hardness, the more a material can be deformed without fracture. Thus, low-carbon wire can be drawn through a die to a smaller size than high-carbon wire without intermediate annealing to restore the original ductility and softness.

As cold forming by pressing or stamping is cheap and readily adapted to large-scale production, this method is used widely, especially by those industries producing automobile fenders and bodies and a variety of small stamped utensils for domestic and other uses. With the exception of aluminum and stainless steels, practically all deep-drawn products are coated—galvanized, tinned, painted, enameled, lacquered, or nickel- or chromium-plated. High tensile strength is usually not important, consequently, the materials most widely used are those with the least tendency to harden when cold worked. The principal ferrous materials are, therefore, ingot iron, unalloyed basic open-hearth steels containing 0.04 to 0.10 per cent carbon, and the soft stainless steels, all in the form of thin annealed sheets.

As the manufacture of deep-drawn products, such as of fenders and bodies by the automotive industry, is a continuous low-cost operation, it is common practice for consumers of this grade of sheet to arrange their various operations so that the material is worked until it strain hardens almost to the breaking point before annealing is necessary. Steel with a ductility just slightly below the standard will, therefore, show excessive breakage.

Consumers' requirements have become more severe year by year. It is only necessary to compare the automobile fender of the last year or two with those of 10 years ago to prove how the steel industry has kept up with this demand by raising the quality of its deep-drawing stock. There is still much room for improvement, both on the part of the steel maker and on the part of the consumer of deep-drawing sheets. What is needed most urgently is a test giving a reliable indication of drawability and a standardization of consumers' requirements.

92. **Evaluation of Steel for Deep Drawing**—As just stated, there is no single test for evaluating steel for deep drawing. Drawability is a weighted average of a large number of compo-

nents which include, among others, yield ratio in tension, hard-ness, elongation, reduction of area, and possibly impact. Draw-ing different shapes involves a different relation of the compo-nents; hence, even if all the components were known and could be weighted accurately, it would be necessary to change the weighting for different drawing operations. The difficulty of weighting even the known components accurately is increased by the virtual impossibility of determining reduction of area—prob-ably the most important component—accurately on thin speci-mens. Some users of deep-drawing stock have arrived at certain combinations of tensile strength, elongation, and hardness for different thicknesses of sheet to indicate satisfactory drawing properties, but such correlation is worthless to others who draw their product under slightly different conditions.

To overcome these difficulties, and in the hope that a single test could be devised to measure drawability, much time and effort have been devoted to the cupping test. Several varieties have been developed, chief of which are the Erichsen, used in Europe, and the Olsen, used chiefly in the United States.[7] Essen-tially, the test consists of supporting a specimen of the sheet between two dies, while a ball or a plunger is brought down against the specimen forcing it into the shape of a cup. The flow of the metal can be followed in a mirror, and the first fracture can be observed. The depth of the cup, or the pressure neces-sary to cause failure, is measured. The test gives some informa-tion on how the material deforms but not enough invariably to predict how it will deform in service. Metallurgical opinion on the value of cupping tests is divided; some metallurgists consider them not only unreliable but actually misleading.

Because the structure and the hardness of steel are important factors in deep drawing, great care is exercised in the melting, rolling, annealing, and finishing of the sheet so that the grain size will be controlled accurately and the hardness will be within certain limits. A fine-grained steel can be deformed to a greater extent and has a much better surface after deforming than coarse-grained material. This is shown in Fig. 55. The surface of the fine-grained steel is smooth after cupping; the coarse-grained ma-terial, on the contrary, has a crinkled "orange peel" surface.

[7] American Society for Metals, *Metals Handbook*, 1939 ed., pp. 524-525.

It is stated in section 68 that some annealed low-carbon steel sheet of the grade used for deep drawing (0.04 to 0.10 per cent carbon) has two yield points, an upper and a lower one. A great difference between the two is considered to be an indication of poor deep-drawing capacity. When such annealed material is deep drawn, strain lines—known as "stretcher strains"—appear on

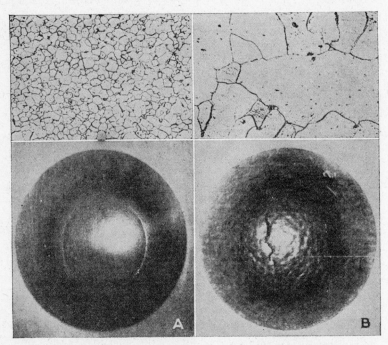

Fig. 55—Structure and Erichsen cupping tests of (*A*) fine-grained and (*B*) coarse-grained low-carbon sheet steel (Körber, *Stahl u. Eisen,* v. 47, 1927, p. 1158).

the surface (Fig. 56). This defect is analogous to the orange-peel surface caused by large grains (Fig. 55). The double yield point and the tendency of annealed low-carbon steel to show stretcher strains can ·be eliminated by subjecting such sheet to a small amount of cold rolling, which raises the hardness slightly and stiffens the material enough so that no distinct jog is evident in the stress-strain curve at the yield point.

There is still much to be learned about deep-drawing steels and their behavior under extreme deformation. In general, microscopic examination, Rockwell *B* hardness and yield ratio, plus some form of cupping test, give about as much information on drawability as can be secured at present. The steel maker is sometimes greatly puzzled because a certain lot of sheet, of the best quality he can produce, will be rejected as unsatisfactory by one user but if shipped to another consumer, will give splendid

Fig. 56—Stretcher strains in cold-drawn low-carbon sheet (Winlock and Kelley, *Trans. Am. Soc. Steel Treat.*, v. 18, 1930, p. 241).

results. Such experiences lead the steel maker to suspect that his customers do not know much about drawing sheet steel. On the other hand, consumers have found that out of a shipment of ten lots of steel, identical by all known tests, nine would draw satisfactorily, but the sheets of one lot would show excessive breakage. This leads the consumer to wonder if the steel man knows how to make good steel. Such differences of opinion need reconciliation.

CHAPTER 11

CARBON STEEL AS AN ENGINEERING MATERIAL

FOR a thousand years before 1850 man's entire stock of ferrous metals consisted of cast iron, wrought iron laboriously made in small quantities at high cost, and a few high-carbon steel tools made even more laboriously and at still higher cost. These were valuable materials and represented a long step forward from the metals of the bronze age, but they were too costly or too low in quality to be used in building railroads, bridges, buildings, and ships. As a result, industrial civilization stagnated until the discoveries of Henry Bessemer in England and William Kelly in the United States between 1850 and 1860 ushered in a new era. These discoveries announced the birth of the "steel age"; they resulted in the development of a process for making carbon steel in quantities large enough and at a cost low enough to make it available for every use.

It did not take man long to put the new metal to work. In 1870, he used about 800,000 tons; 30 years later, he used 28 million tons.[1] Carbon steel is still the most important metallic material; in 1939, approximately 95 per cent of the steel produced in the United States (50 million tons) was carbon steel.

About 3 per cent of the carbon steel produced annually is poured into castings which are used in the form the metal assumed in the mold with no further mechanical treatment. The remaining 97 per cent is poured into ingots that are hot worked by rolling, forging, or pressing into a large variety of finished or semifinished products. Most finished wrought sections receive no further treatment; .a few are subjected to some form of heat treatment before use. Some semifinished wrought products are processed further by additional hot working; the rest are fabri-

---

[1] Estimate by Sir Robert Hadfield, *Collected Papers*, vol. 7.

cated into the desired form by cold working (see section 24). Cold-worked steels may or may not be heat treated before being used.

There are, therefore, four major classes of finished products of carbon steel: castings, hot-worked products, cold-worked products, and heat-treated products. It is impossible to decide which of these four classes is the most important in present-day economic life since each plays a definite role for which there is no understudy. Without hot-rolled I-beams there would be no skyscrapers; without heat-treated tools they could not be built; without cold-drawn wire for elevator cables they could not be used; and without castings for steam and water lines they would not be habitable. It is the same in most other industries: each class of carbon steel is indispensable, and the cost or tonnage is no criterion of its value to man.

93. Carbon-steel Castings as Engineering Materials—Unalloyed steel castings have many industrial uses. Despite the fact that their mechanical properties are generally inferior to those of hot-worked steel of the same composition, the proportion of castings to rolled or forged material remains substantially unchanged year after year. The reason for this is twofold: (1) sections which are so complex that it would be difficult or even impossible to fabricate them by rolling or forging can be produced readily at low cost by casting; (2) castings are cheaper than forgings if a few pieces of a fairly intricate shape are desired. The economical production of such articles by forging is possible only when a large number of pieces of a single shape are produced thus spreading thinly the cost of the expensive forging dies.

Steel for castings may be melted by any of the processes enumerated in Table 2. Most of it is made by the basic or acid open-hearth or the acid electric process. The open-hearth process is used for melting steel for large castings; the acid electric process, owing to its flexibility and to the high temperatures obtainable, is favored for small castings, especially those of intricate shape. Steel castings are used for railroad equipment, especially for underframes of cars, for agricultural and excavating equipment, various parts of machines, electrical equipment, and a large variety of small parts and fittings.

There are three grades of steel castings for which specifications have been issued by the American Railway Association, the

United States Government, and a number of technical societies. These have the following *minimum* properties:

Grade	Tensile strength, lb. per sq. in.	Yield strength, lb. per sq. in.	Elongation in 2 in., per cent	Reduction of area, per cent
Hard......	80,000	36,000	17	25
Medium...	70,000	31,500	20	30
Soft......	60,000	27,000	24	35

Most specifications also show the maximum amount of sulphur and phosphorus permitted. This may be 0.050 or 0.080 per cent depending on whether the steel is made by a basic or an acid process. Manganese and silicon percentages vary widely, from 0.30 to 1.00 per cent for the former, and from 0.15 to 0.55 per cent for the latter. Some specifications give limits for these elements, most do not. The amount present in a steel depends on the process by which it was made and how thoroughly it was deoxidized. Carbon ranges from about 0.10 to 0.50 per cent; the amount is usually not specified, so the foundryman is permitted to vary this element to obtain the required properties.

94. Factors Affecting the Properties of Carbon-steel Castings —Since the properties of carbon-steel castings are greatly improved by heat treatment, many castings are now annealed, normalized and annealed, or normalized and spheroidized. Quenching and tempering, of castings of such shape that distortion is not likely to be serious, are used more and more frequently.

Large castings cool so slowly in a sand mold that a very coarse angular structure results (Fig. 57A).[2] If the casting is not too large, simple annealing will refine the grain and improve the properties (Fig. 57B); but such treatment does not effect complete homogenization in large castings. These are subjected to high-temperature normalizing followed by a grain-refining treatment. Quenching and tempering produce the finest structure (Fig. 57C) and the best combination of properties.

As is evident from Fig. 57, the smaller the grain size the better the properties. Grain size is directly related to the rate of cooling from the solidification temperature to the A_3 transformation temperature. It follows, therefore, that a small casting usually

[2] Micrographs by courtesy of Bonney-Floyd Company. **Mechanical** properties based on data by H. A. Mitchell, *The Iron Age*, v. 126, 1930, pp. 914-917.

has smaller grain size and better properties than a large casting; moreover, if the casting is not heat treated, it is also true that in

T.S.   74,000
Y.S.   37,000
El.   19.5
R.A.   31.0
Izod   16

T.S.   75,000
Y.S.   41,500
El.   24.5
R.A.   46.0
Izod   20

T.S.   83,000
Y.S.   57,000
El.   31.5
R.A.   69.5
Izod   42

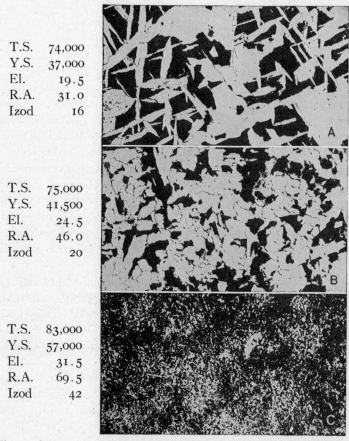

Fig. 57—Structure and typical mechanical properties of cast steel containing 0.30 per cent carbon and 0.79 per cent manganese. T.S. and Y.S. are tensile strength and yield strength in lb. per sq. in.; El. and R.A. are elongation, in 2 in., and reduction of area in per cent; Izod is Izod impact value in ft-lb. (A) as cast; (B) annealed at 1650° F. (900° C.); (C) water quenched from 1650° F. and tempered at 1300° F. (705° C.); etched, 100×.

large castings the properties are better near the surface than at the center.[3]

[3] Owing to the mass effect, it is frequently a serious problem to cast a test specimen that has properties truly representative of the casting.

The factor of greatest importance to the properties of cast carbon steel is carbon content. If other things are equal, increasing the carbon increases the tensile and the yield strength and decreases elongation, reduction of area and impact resistance. When the carbon is higher than 0.50 per cent, the casting is usually so brittle, even after heat treatment, that it is used only for a few specific applications—for example, rolls and dies—where hardness and wear resistance are the most important properties.

In general, carbon-steel castings of satisfactory mechanical properties can be made readily by regulating the carbon content and by using a simple annealing or normalizing treatment. The minimum properties given on p. 173 are conservative and are easily attained in commercial production.

Cast carbon steels containing 0.20 to 0.40 per cent carbon have an endurance ratio of between 0.40 and 0.50. In the cast condition the ratio is usually between 0.40 and 0.43. Heat treatment (i.e., annealing, normalizing, or quenching and tempering) improves it, but it is usually somewhat lower than the endurance ratio of a comparable steel which has been hot worked. Heat treatment also improves the yield ratio, elongation, and reduction of area of cast carbon steel and increases the resistance of the material to single-blow impact (Fig. 57). The added cost of heat treatment is usually justified if castings are to be subjected in service to stresses of considerable magnitude.

95. Hot-worked Carbon Steels as Engineering Materials— Most hot-rolled or forged carbon steels contain between 0.05 and 0.30 per cent carbon and are used for sheet, plate, strip, tubes, pipe, various structural sections, tin-plate and other coated sheets, and a large number of semifinished sections that are hot or cold worked into bars, wire, sheet, and tubes. Also included in this class is the well-known "machine steel" which is used for a wide variety of low-stressed machined parts, and which is the mainstay of every crossroads blacksmith shop in the world. Medium-carbon steels containing between 0.30 and 0.70 per cent carbon are used for railway materials, especially rails, for a large number of forgings, and for high-strength wire. The higher carbon grades, containing 0.70 to 1.30 per cent carbon, are used largely for tools and cutlery and to a lesser extent for springs and wire. Low-carbon steels are heat treated rarely; the medium-carbon grades may or may not be heat treated depending upon their use;

the high-carbon steels are always used in the hardened and tempered condition.

The properties of hot-worked carbon steel are affected by (1) the composition, (2) the several variables present in hot working, and (3) the rate of cooling from the rolling temperature. Except for deep-drawing sheet, this third factor is not important for low-carbon steels; in the case of small sections of medium- and high-carbon steels, air cooling may cause enough hardening to mask any effect of moderate changes in composition or of variations in the hot-working operation. The effect of composition is discussed in the next section. Of the three variables inherent in hot working—direction of work, amount of work, and finishing temperature—the first is the most important. In general, specimens cut longitudinally and transversely to the direction of hot working have about the same tensile strength and yield strength, but the elongation, reduction of area, and impact resistance of the transverse specimens are lower than those of the longitudinal specimens. This difference in directional properties is present even in clean steels, but it is accentuated by inclusions which are plastic at hot-working temperatures and which are thus elongated into fibers by the mechanical work.

96. Effect of Composition on Static Properties of Hot-worked Carbon Steels—The effect of carbon on the tensile properties of hot-worked basic open-hearth steels containing between 0.30 and 0.60 per cent manganese and between 0.02 and 0.04 per cent phosphorus is shown in Fig. 58.[4] The center line of the hatched area represents the properties to be expected most frequently. The top and bottom boundaries of the hatched areas give the limits of the properties to be expected at least 95 per cent of the time in the testing of commercial rolled or forged basic open-hearth steel of these carbon percentages. The data used for plotting Fig. 58 were obtained mostly by statistical analysis. It is safe, therefore, to conclude that of 1000 specimens of 0.20 per cent carbon steel about 700 will have a tensile strength of between 63,000 and 65,000 lb. per sq. in., and about 970 will have a tensile strength (60,000 to 68,000 lb. per sq. in.) which falls within the

[4] The values in Fig. 58 are a summary of all the data given in *The Alloys of Iron and Carbon*, Vol. II—*Properties*, Chapter 4, section A, and include not only laboratory investigations and other data but also the data obtained in Germany by statistical analysis of more than 100,000 individual tests.

hatched area for steel of this carbon content. There will, however, be about 30 specimens, or 3 per cent of the whole, with a strength falling above or below the limits shown. These proportions should hold for steel of any carbon content between 0.05 and 0.70 per cent.

The elongation values used for Fig. 58, if not originally determined on a 2-in. gage length, were converted to this gage. In

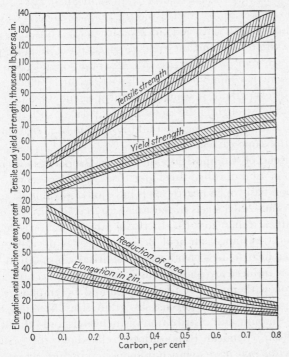

Fig. 58—Effect of carbon on tensile properties of hot-worked carbon steels.

connection with the elongation it should be noted that the usual flat specimen for plate, sheets, and similar products has a gage length of 8 in., hence values given in Fig. 58 are some 20 to 30 per cent higher than would normally be obtained on an 8-in. gage.[5] The increase in Brinell hardness with increasing carbon

[5] If standard flat specimens of basic steel of about 60,000 lb. per sq. in. tensile strength and with gage lengths of 2, 4, and 8 in. are tested, the respective elongation values will be approximately 45, 35, and 30 per cent respectively (see section 6g).

approximately parallels the increase in tensile strength: each 0.10 per cent carbon raises the hardness 20 numbers, from about 100 for 0.10 per cent carbon steel to 220 for 0.70 per cent carbon steel.

Although both manganese and phosphorus affect the tensile strength, the influence of the former is unimportant in most carbon steels. For example, if a basic open-hearth steel containing 0.20 per cent carbon and 0.50 per cent manganese has a strength of 65,000 lb. per sq. in., increasing the manganese to 0.80 will increase the strength only 3000 to 4000 lb. per sq. in. Phosphorus increases the tensile and the yield strength about 1000 lb. per sq. in. for each 0.01 per cent present. In basic open-hearth steels, this element is commonly so low that it has little effect; in acid steels, however, there is usually enough present so that it exerts considerable strengthening action. Thus acid steel is usually stronger, with lower elongation and reduction of area, than basic steel of the same carbon content.

97. **Effect of Composition on Other Properties**—Increasing the carbon of hot-rolled steel decreases the impact resistance: low-carbon basic open-hearth steels have an Izod value of 50 to 60 ft-lb.; for hot-rolled steels containing 0.50 to 0.80 per cent carbon, it is usually less than 20 ft-lb. Increasing the phosphorus decreases the impact resistance; an acid Bessemer steel is not so tough as basic open-hearth steel of otherwise identical composition. The brittleness induced by phosphorus is discussed in section 25. In connection with impact resistance it should be emphasized that this property is greatly affected by grain size, direction of hot working, amount and distribution of inclusions and other factors (aside from chemical composition) related to the structure. These factors may have so much influence on the impact resistance that the effect of variations in composition may be completely obscured.

The endurance limit of hot-worked carbon steels increases with the tensile strength (see section 78). Owing, however, to the fact that high-carbon steels have less plasticity under load than low-carbon steels, and are more likely to contain internal stresses, the endurance ratio is usually between 0.35 and 0.42, compared with 0.50 to 0.60 for wrought iron, ingot iron, and steels containing less than 0.35 per cent carbon.

The modulus of elasticity of carbon steels is between 29 and 30 million lb. per sq. in. and is not greatly affected by composition and heat treatment. Some of the other physical constants, and most of the electric and magnetic properties, are affected, more or less, by changes in composition. Since these properties are not of great importance to most engineers, discussion of them is omitted here.

98. **Cold-worked Carbon Steels as Engineering Materials—** Cold working has two advantages. First, sections of certain sizes, shapes, or surface finishes can be produced more readily and more economically by this method than by any other. Some important industrial products, in fact, cannot be produced at all except by cold working: it would be economically impracticable to produce by any other method wire small enough to be woven into screens or in quantities large enough for modern telegraph and telephone systems. In addition, cold working is the most effective and the cheapest method of securing a smooth surface and accurate size. Second, certain combinations of properties characteristic of cold-worked material cannot be secured by any other process; for example a tensile strength of 300,000 to 400,000 lb. per sq. in., combined with considerable ductility, can be attained readily.

The economic value of cold-worked carbon steel is attested by the fact that in an average year about 3 million tons of wire, 3 million tons of sheet and strip, and 1 million tons of bars and other cold-worked products are made in the United States. Sheet, strip, tubes, and bars are cold worked primarily to obtain certain sizes, shapes, and surface finishes economically. High strength is usually of secondary importance. Furthermore, most cold-rolled sheet and strip, and some cold-drawn wire, especially the low-carbon grades which are used for screens, fences, barbed wire, nails, screws and nuts, telegraph and telephone lines, and for many other common applications, are annealed before use. Because annealing completely destroys the effect of cold work, the properties of such material need not be considered further here.

Carbon steels which are cold worked to secure high strength as well as to produce special shapes and sizes, and which are not subsequently annealed, comprise an important class of engineering materials. The properties of these steels and how cold working affects them are, therefore, worthy of considerable attention. This class of material includes some low-carbon sheet, strip, and wire, but the most important is wire containing about 0.25 to 1.00

per cent carbon used for needles, surgical and dental instruments, music (piano) wire, springs, rope and cable wire, and for numerous other purposes where high quality and reliability combined with high tensile strength and considerable ductility are required.

99. The Important Properties of Cold-worked Steel—The static properties ordinarily determined on cold-worked steels are tensile strength and elongation, usually with a gage length of 10

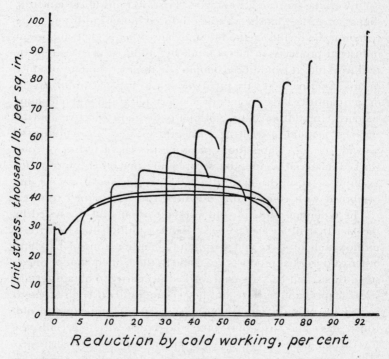

Fig. 59—Stress-strain curves of cold-worked low-carbon steel (Kenyon and Burns).

in. for wire and of 2 or 8 in. for sheet and strip. Owing to the small cross-section of most cold-worked materials, reduction of area, which is a valuable measure of ductility, cannot be determined accurately. Yield strength is rarely determined on cold-worked wire and sheet or strip; but for cold-rolled bars of large enough cross-section so that accurate measurements are possible, yield strength and reduction of area are frequently reported. Cold working increases the yield strength; with reductions in cross-section of 30 to 70 per cent it is at least 90 per cent of the tensile strength, and with higher reductions it may for practical purposes be the same as the tensile strength. As shown by Fig. 59,[6] the stress-strain curve of severely cold-worked steel is curved from the origin; the elastic limit is, therefore, very low and may be zero.

Several unstandardized tests are used to determine the ductility of cold-worked wire and sheet. Some of these are crude, but in experienced hands they give reliable indications of excessive brittleness or local irregularities. The most common of these is the bend test in which a specimen of definite size, clamped in a vise and bent 180 deg. over a definite radius, must not crack. In the other test, a specimen is bent back and forth 90 deg. over a mandrel until failure occurs. The number of 90-deg. bends before failure is a measure of the ductility.

Another test of the ductility of wire is the twist. A specimen of suitable length is twisted in a machine, which has one revolving head, until it fails by shear. The number of 360-deg. revolutions of the movable head of the machine is the number of twists. Some metallurgists consider that the twist is a good measure of ductility; others believe that its principal value is to detect local irregularities or flaws in the wire.

100. General Effects of Cold Working on Strength and Ductility—The primary effect of cold working is a rapid increase in tensile strength and an even more rapid decrease in elongation. This is shown in Figs. 60 and 61.[7] As Fig. 60 indicates, cold working increases the tensile strength of high-carbon steel wire more rapidly and to a greater degree than it increases the strength of low-carbon material. A reduction of area[8] of 70 per cent increases the tensile strength of high-carbon steel from about 130,000 lb. per sq. in. (see Fig. 60) to about 210,000 lb. per sq. in.; the same reduction increases the tensile strength of low-carbon steel from approximately 60,000 lb. per sq. in. to about 110,000 lb. per sq. in.

[6] R. L. Kenyon and R. S. Burns, *Trans. Am. Soc. Metals*, v. 21, 1933, p. 595.

[7] Prepared by E. E. Legge for Sisco, *The Alloys of Iron and Carbon*, Vol. II, *Properties*, McGraw-Hill Book Company, Inc., New York, 1937, pp. 113 and 114.

[8] The term reduction of area is used in cold working to signify the amount that the cross-section has been reduced by the cold-working operation. It should not be confused with the same term used in tensile testing.

In contrast to its effect on the tensile strength, which varies with the carbon content (and the amount of cold work), cold

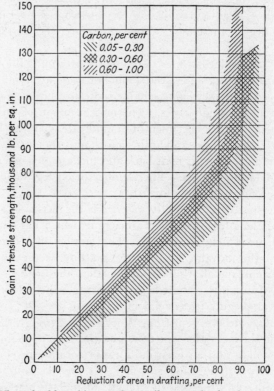

Fig. 60—Effect of cold working on the tensile strength of carbon steel (Legge).

working with reductions in cross-section as low as 10 per cent decreases the elongation of steels containing 0.05 to 1.00 per cent carbon to a small value (Fig. 61). Further reductions lower the elongation still more, but the effect is much less marked.

It should be emphasized that Figs. 60 and 61 indicate only approximately the properties resulting from various amounts of cold work. Although the total amount of cold working is the variable which has the greatest effect on strength and ductility, it is not the only one. The composition, as Fig. 60 indicates, is important, and the structure of the steel before cold working also has a large effect, especially for medium- and high-carbon steels.

The effect of cold working on the properties is not so pronounced for heavy sections, where complete distortion of the grains does not occur at the center of the piece, as it is in the case

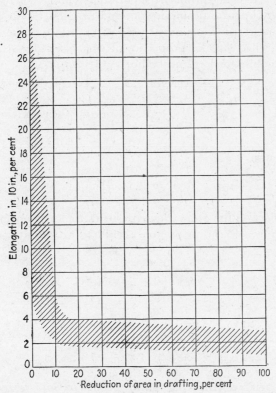

Fig. 61—Effect of cold working on the elongation of carbon steel (Legge).

of wire and thin sheet. This is shown in Table 6 which gives the static properties of a 1-in. round cold-rolled bar.

TABLE 6.   EFFECT OF COLD ROLLING ON THE TENSILE PROPERTIES OF A STEEL CONTAINING 0.14 PER CENT CARBON

Property	Annealed	Reduced 30 per cent by cold rolling	Reduced 60 per cent by cold rolling
Tensile strength, lb. per sq. in......	58,800	80,600	98,100
Yield strength, lb. per sq. in........	34,400	75,300	96,700
Proportional limit, lb. per sq. in.....	27,500	15,600	10,100
Elongation in 4 in., per cent........	41.7	22	10.5
Reduction of area, per cent........	65.8	58	43

Cold working has the same general effect on the properties of sheet and strip as it has on wire. The final tensile strength and elongation depend primarily upon the amount of reduction, secondarily upon the composition, and to a less extent on other variables. A reduction of 50 per cent by cold rolling has the following effect on the properties of 0.05 per cent carbon steel for automobile fenders and bodies:

Condition	Tensile strength, lb. per sq. in.	Yield strength, lb. per sq. in.	Elongation in 2 in., per cent
Hot-rolled strip.....................	55,000	40,000	28
Cold rolled 50 per cent...............	96,000	96,000	2
Annealed...........................	44,000	33,000	38

The effect on the properties varies with the carbon content. A reduction by cold rolling of 60 per cent has the following effect on strip:

Carbon, per cent	Increase in tensile strength, per cent	Decrease in elongation, per cent
0.10	65	70
0.20	63	70
0.30	61	68
0.50	57	67

101. Variables Affecting the Properties of Cold-worked Wire —There are so many variables, in addition to the amount of reduction, which affect the properties of cold-worked carbon-steel wire that only a brief summary can be given here. About 85 per cent of all wire is drawn from acid Bessemer or basic open-hearth low-carbon steel. Of the two kinds of steel used, hard-drawn Bessemer wire is stronger than hard-drawn basic open-hearth steel wire: depending on size, the tensile strength of the former varies from 90,000 to 150,000 lb. per sq. in. and of the latter from 80,000 to 125,000 lb. per sq. in. for comparable sizes. Basic open-hearth steel wire is, however, more ductile than Bessemer wire, has slightly higher elongation and withstands considerably more twisting than the Bessemer product.

Galvanizing low-carbon cold-drawn wire by passing it through a bath of molten zinc reduces the tensile strength and increases the elongation but induces brittleness as shown by the twist test. This brittleness is probably caused by the formation of a brittle iron-zinc compound at the interface between coating and steel where failure starts readily under torsional stress.

High-strength wire for cables, ropes, and springs and for music wire is usually made from high-grade deoxidized medium- and high-carbon steel. The steel is rolled to rods which are patented. The best combination of strength and ductility results from drawing a lead-patented rod. Air patenting is cheaper, but the properties of the wire are not so good. Wire drawn from either lead- or air-patented rod is, however, much superior to that drawn from a hot-rolled rod. Hard-drawn music and cable wire drawn from lead-patented rod has a strength of 160,000 to 220,000 lb. per sq. in. in sizes of 0.2 to 0.3 in. and of 280,000 to 400,000 lb. per sq. in. in sizes smaller than 0.1 in. in diameter. Despite the high strength and low elongation (0.5 to 1.5 per cent in 10 in.), the wire is very ductile and withstands many 90-deg. bends and can be wrapped around itself or coiled into long springs of small diameter without cracking.

The wire used for the cables of large suspension bridges is an acid open-hearth steel containing about 0.80 per cent carbon, 0.50 per cent manganese, and low sulphur and phosphorus. The wire is drawn from patented rods, and the usual size is 6 gage (0.192 in. in diameter). It has an average tensile strength of 215,000 to 225,000 lb. per sq. in., a yield strength for a permanent set of 0.75 in. in 10 in. of 160,000 to 175,000 lb. per sq. in., an elongation of 3 to 7 per cent in 10 in., and a reduction of area of 25 to 30 per cent. Rope or cable formed from high-strength wire has, owing to its construction, a breaking strength which is never more than 90 per cent, and usually only 70 to 80 per cent, of the sum of the breaking strength of the individual wires.

102. Effect of Cold Working on Dynamic Properties—Although cold working increases the endurance limit by about the same percentage as it increases the tensile strength, this means relatively little because most cold-worked material has such a small cross-section that standard highly polished specimens usually cannot be tested. For specimens of wire tested with the surface produced by the die, the endurance ratio varies from about 0.50, for material containing 0.05 per cent carbon, to 0.25

to 0.35, for high-carbon wire having a tensile strength of 275,000 to 350,000 lb. per sq. in. The low value for hard-drawn high-carbon wire is largely due to high internal stresses as reheating the wire to effect a partial or complete recrystallization of the grains raises the ratio.

Cold working also decreases the resistance of carbon steel to impact. The magnitude of this decrease depends primarily upon the amount of cold work and the carbon content—high-carbon steels are embrittled to a greater degree than low-carbon materials —and upon other variables. The actual Izod impact value may be as low as 5 to 10 ft-lb. In general, however, notched bar impact resistance is not an important property of cold-worked material.

103. **Heat-treated Carbon Steels as Engineering Materials—** With the exception of carburizing (see section 61) and the annealing of cold-worked material, low-carbon steels are seldom heat treated. Quenching generally improves the properties but hardly enough to justify the cost. Medium-carbon steels are frequently heat treated; the general improvement in strength and ductility, in machinability, or in some other property due to thermal treatment is usually well worth while. Since high-carbon steels are used primarily for tools where high hardness is the chief requirement, these materials are always quenched and tempered. Frequently they are also annealed or normalized to improve machinability or the structural condition prior to quenching.

The purpose of normalizing and annealing, and of quenching and tempering, and the effect of these operations on the structure should be apparent from the discussion in Chapter 7. The effect of heat treatment on the properties of cast carbon steels is dealt with earlier in this chapter. The characteristics of quenched and tempered high-carbon tool steels are discussed more appropriately in the chapter on tool steels (Chapter 15). It remains, therefore, to summarize briefly the properties of the medium-carbon grades after various thermal treatments.

Annealing and normalizing can be dismissed with a few words. Annealing is a softening operation, and with medium-carbon steels it is used chiefly to improve machinability. Compared with hot-rolled steel containing 0.30 to 0.60 per cent carbon, the tensile and the yield strength of annealed material are 6000 to 10,000 lb. per sq. in. lower and the elongation and reduction of area are slightly higher. Impact resistance is usually improved slightly by annealing. The endurance ratio, however, is not appreciably affected.

The tensile properties of hot-rolled and of normalized medium-carbon steels are nearly the same. This is to be expected as most carbon steels are air cooled after hot working, from temperatures which approximate the normalizing temperature. The primary purpose of normalizing is to homogenize the structure. It is, therefore, economically justified for large sections which may be heterogeneous in structure after forging or rolling, or for high-carbon tool steels, to produce an evenly distributed finely divided carbide which dissolves quickly when the steel is heated to the hardening temperature.

104. Properties of Quenched and Tempered Medium-carbon Steels—Owing to the internal stresses introduced by quenching (see section 58) medium-carbon steels are seldom used in the quenched and untempered condition. The properties of such materials are, therefore, of little interest. If, however, the internal stresses are relieved by tempering, quenched medium-carbon steels become valuable structural materials worthy of a brief survey here.

If quenched steel is tempered at a temperature high enough so that the particle size of the carbide changes, strength and hardness decrease and ductility increases almost uniformly as the tempering temperature increases. This is shown in Fig. 62 which gives the ranges of properties (included within the hatched bands) that result 95 per cent of the time from tempering water- and oil-quenched 0.40 to 0.50 per cent carbon steels at increasing temperatures.

Charts showing the effect of tempering on the tensile properties of quenched carbon and alloy steels of varying carbon content have been prepared by several technical societies. It is sufficient, therefore, to note here that, while they are undoubtedly of value in indicating the properties to be expected most of the time, they should never be used for specification purposes as individual specimens occasionally vary considerably from the average value shown on the chart.

As indicated in section 52, the properties determined on a 1-in. heat-treated bar may not be representative of the average properties of a 6-in. bar similarly treated. The effect of mass on properties is important. Since in many industrial applications large sections are used, it may be more essential for the engineer to know the average properties or, in some cases, the minimum properties than to know the properties at the surface. It is not always practicable to test full-sized I-beams or locomotive axles, hence

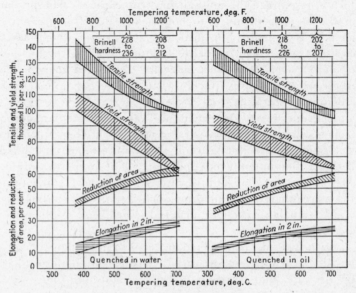

Fig. 62—Effect of tempering on the tensile properties and hardness of water- and oil-quenched 0.40 to 0.50 per cent carbon steel (S.A.E. 1045) (Sisco, *The Alloys of Iron and Carbon*, Vol. II, *Properties*, McGraw-Hill Book Company, Inc., New York, 1937, p. 200).

data which indicate the effect of increasing size of section are of considerable value.

In most large sections the cooling rate upon quenching decreases as the distance from the surface increases and, if other variables do not enter importantly, hardness and strength decrease and ductility increases slightly. Data for medium-carbon steel are given in Figs. 63 and 64. Average values from Fig. 62 for the tempering temperatures used are inserted as points in Figs. 63 and 64. The data given in these graphs indicate that the effect of mass is more pronounced in water-quenched than in oil-quenched material, and that for the same quenching treatment

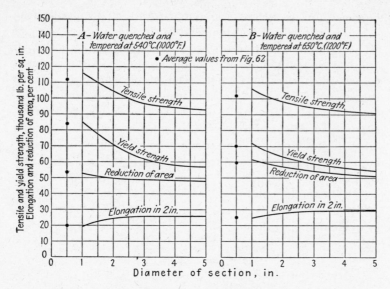

Fig. 63—Effect of section size on the tensile properties of water-quenched and tempered 0.40 to 0.50 per cent carbon steel (Sisco, *op. cit.*, p. 223).

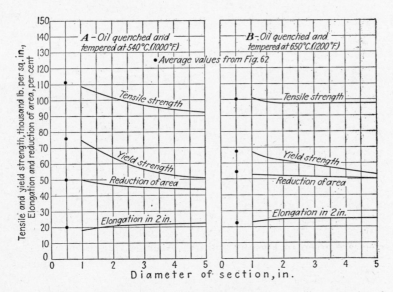

Fig. 64—Effect of section size on the tensile properties of oil-quenched and tempered 0.40 to 0.50 per cent carbon steel (Sisco, *op. cit.*, p. 224).

the effect of mass is less pronounced with high tempering temperatures than with lower temperatures.

The endurance ratio of quenched and tempered carbon steels is 0.50 ± 0.05 unless the quenching treatment has introduced stresses which were not wholly relieved by tempering. When such stresses are present the ratio may be as low as 0.30 or 0.40. Quenching and tempering usually have a favorable effect on impact resistance, which, in general, is much higher than that of a rolled steel of corresponding composition. Tempering increases the impact resistance of a quenched steel: if the Izod value of a water-quenched 0.30 per cent carbon steel is 10 ft-lb., it will be 20 to 25 ft-lb. after tempering at 700° F. (400° C.) and 45 to 65 ft-lb. after tempering at 1100 to 1200° F. (595 to 650° C.). The modulus of elasticity is, of course, unaffected by thermal treatment.

Chapter 12

GRAY CAST IRON AND MALLEABLE CAST IRON

IF iron ore and charcoal are mixed and heated to a dull red heat, the iron oxide is reduced to spongy metal which can be forged into wrought iron. At this temperature iron is ferritic and dissolves very little carbon; the reduced metal, therefore, contains less than 0.10 per cent of this element. If, however, iron ore and charcoal are mixed and heated to a higher temperature, for example 2000 to 2200° F. (1095 to 1205° C.), the reduced iron is in the gamma form and readily dissolves carbon. Carbon lowers the melting point of iron. If the reduction is carried out at a sufficiently high temperature and if the reduced iron is in contact with charcoal for a sufficiently long time, the result is molten iron containing 2.5 to 4.5 per cent carbon.

Because the high temperatures necessary to produce molten high-carbon iron from the ore could not be attained readily in primitive furnaces, cast iron appeared comparatively late in Western civilization. Early in the fourteenth century molten iron was accidentally made in a German *Hochofen*. The design of this early blast furnace was such that, given a fortuitous combination of enough charcoal and blast, molten metal instead of the customary chunk of red-hot low-carbon iron appeared at the bottom of the furnace. For many years such molten metal was considered spoiled or "burned," and when solid it was charged into the furnace to be refined again. No one knows when this high-carbon iron was found to be useful; it did not take man long, however, because, with his characteristic peace-on-earth-good-will-toward-men temperament, he was casting it into cannon late in the fourteenth century.

Cast iron is unique in the history of ferrous metals in that it was common in China at least 1000 years before it was known in Europe. This is remarkable in view of the fact that there was considerable trade between China and the West early in the Christian Era. Historians have never explained why other Chinese processes and products spread to the West during the time of the Roman Empire, but cast iron did not.

The ferrous material known as malleable cast iron is frequently miscalled malleable iron. Strictly speaking, malleable iron is a material, such as wrought or other low-carbon iron, that is readily worked, and the term should not be used instead of malleable cast iron which describes a material produced by annealing a special cast iron. The descriptive adjective malleable was applied to this variety of cast iron at least a hundred years ago because the original brittleness of the high-carbon metal is largely eliminated by annealing. Malleable cast iron is much more ductile than any other form of cast iron, comparing favorably with low-carbon steel in properties. Moreover, it combines these properties with the cheapness of melting cast iron and pouring it directly into a mold.

Malleable cast iron is much younger than ordinary cast iron. A process of annealing hard, white cast iron was first described in 1722 by the French physicist Réaumur, but the process now used in the United States and to a large extent elsewhere was not discovered until 1826, as the result of experiments conducted by Seth Boyden in a small foundry in Newark, New Jersey.

105. Gray, Mottled, and White Cast Iron—Cast iron is an alloy of iron and carbon containing about 2.0 to about 4.0 per cent carbon, 0.5 to approximately 3.0 per cent silicon, usually less than 1.0 per cent manganese, less than 1.0 per cent phosphorus, and less than 0.2 per cent sulphur. The iron carbide in these high-carbon alloys, while thermodynamically unstable, can under certain conditions be all retained as such; in a few cast irons, especially if the silicon is very low, all the carbon is present as Fe_3C. Silicon increases the instability of iron carbide; in most cast irons, which contain considerable silicon, some of the iron carbide dissociates into iron and carbon (graphite). By regulating the silicon content and other variables, such as the size of the section and the cooling rate, the amount of dissociation of the carbide can be controlled.

Most cast iron contains two forms of carbon, both of which can be varied as desired: combined carbon or cementite (Fe_3C), and free carbon or graphite (Fig. 65). Structure and properties, which are closely related, depend primarily on the relative amounts of these two forms of carbon and on their distribution.

Cast iron containing all or nearly all the carbon in the combined form has a silvery white fracture and is known as white cast iron. Very hard and brittle and practically unmachinable, it is important chiefly (1) as an intermediate product in the production of malleable iron castings and (2) when it is produced, by regulating the composition and by cooling rapidly, as a thin, hard layer on the surface of a softer iron casting. The latter

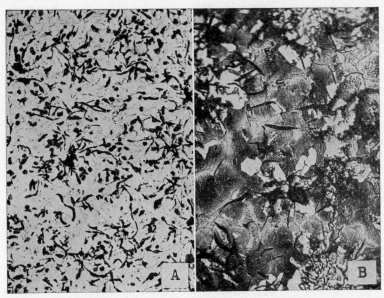

Fig. 65—Structure of gray cast iron (A), unetched, showing graphite particles and plates and (B), etched, showing graphite (black), ferrite (white), and pearlite; 100×.

product is known as chilled iron and is used for rolls, dies, and in other applications where high surface hardness and wear resistance are important.

Cast iron in which most of the iron carbide has dissociated into iron and graphite is usually soft and readily machinable. It has a gray, almost black, fracture and is thus known as gray iron. More than 95 per cent of all the iron castings produced are of gray iron. Cast iron in which about half of the carbide has dissociated into iron and graphite has properties which are median between soft gray iron and hard white iron. Owing to the relatively small amount of graphite, the fracture has a mottled appearance; the iron, therefore, is known as mottled iron. Like white cast iron, this material is hard, brittle, and practically unmachinable. White and mottled cast iron are of little industrial importance and are not discussed further in this book.

Gray cast iron is considered by most metallurgists as a ternary alloy of 92 to 95 per cent iron, 2 to 4 per cent carbon, and 0.5 to 3.0 per cent silicon with manganese, sulphur, and phosphorus also present. As an engineering material it is frequently considered as a steel containing 0.10 to 0.90 per cent carbon as iron carbide (cementite) plus 1.5 to 3.5 per cent graphite.

106. **General Characteristics of Gray Cast Iron**—Gray cast iron is a low-cost material which is easily melted and cast, and is cheaply machined. These are the primary reasons for its wide use. Of the hundreds of engineering applications for gray cast iron, some of the most important ones, together with the usual compositions, are given in Table 7.[1]

In contrast to steel manufacture in which impure raw materials are melted and refined by chemical reactions grouped metallurgically under the terms oxidation and deoxidation, chemistry plays a very minor role in the manufacture of gray-iron castings. The desired composition, structure, and properties are obtained primarily by selecting the proper raw materials in the right proportion and melting them. The proportions of pig iron—of which several grades differing chiefly in silicon content are available—scrap cast iron, and scrap steel used to produce cast iron of various compositions are given in Table 7.

The properties of gray cast iron which determine its suitability for engineering uses are the result of controlling four variables: (1) chemical composition, (2) rate of cooling from the solidification temperature, (3) special methods of melting, including superheating and ladle additions, and (4) heat treatment.

With the exception of a small tonnage melted on a reverberatory hearth known as the air furnace, all gray cast iron is melted in a cupola. This is a shaft furnace (Fig. 66)[2] into which the metallic materials, plus coke for fuel, and a flux are charged at the top; air is blown into the furnace near the bottom. The

[1] *Trans. Am. Foundrymen's Assoc.*, v. 39, 1932, pp. 59-64.

[2] B. Stoughton, *The Metallurgy of Iron and Steel*, McGraw-Hill Book Company, Inc., New York, 1934, Chap. 10, Fig. 13.

combustion of the coke supplies the heat to melt the metal which collects on the hearth from which it is drained into a ladle and then poured into sand or cast-iron molds. The slight chemical

TABLE 7. RECOMMENDED ANALYSES OF PLAIN CAST IRONS FOR COMMON ENGINEERING APPLICATIONS

Composition, per cent					Typical charge, per cent			Use
Total C	Si	Mn	P	S	Pig	Cast iron scrap	Steel scrap	
3.25	2.25	0.65	0.15	0.10	40	40	20	Automobile cylinders
3.35	2.25	0.65	0.15	0.10	40	40	20	Automobile pistons
3.40	2.60	0.65	0.30	0.10	50	45	5	Automobile castings, general
3.50	2.90	0.65	0.50	0.06	60	40	...	Automobile piston rings—individually cast
3.40	2.10	0.60	0.50	0.10	35	55	10	Agricultural implements—medium sections
3.50	2.20	0.55	0.70	0.10	40	60	...	Agricultural implements—light sections
3.25	2.25	0.50	0.50	0.09	50	50	...	Machinery—sections not over 1 in.
3.25	1.75	0.50	0.50	0.10	50	40	10	Machinery—1.5-in. sections
3.25	1.25	0.50	0.50	0.10	50	25	25	Machinery—2-in. sections
3.25	1.25	0.65	0.20	0.10	50	25	25	Pressure castings—air cylinders
3.40	1.75	0.80	0.35	0.09	55	20	25	Gas-engine cylinders—light
3.40	1.50	0.80	0.35	0.09	55	20	25	Gas-engine cylinders—medium
3.40	1.25	0.80	0.35	0.09	55	20	25	Gas-engine cylinders—heavy
3.30	2.00	0.50	0.60	0.10	50	40	10	Valves and fittings
3.50	1.15	0.80	0.10	0.07	70	30	...	Firepots and kettles
3.50	1.00	0.90	0.20	0.07	90	...	10	Ingot molds
3.60	1.00	0.75	0.20	0.07	60	40	...	Pots for caustic soda
3.60	1.75	0.50	0.80	0.08	70	25	5	Light and medium sand-cast water pipe
3.40	1.40	0.50	0.80	0.08	60	25	15	Heavy sand-cast water pipe
3.40	1.40	0.50	0.80	0.08	70	30	...	Soil pipe
3.35	0.65	0.60	0.35	0.12	12.5	80	7.5	Car wheels (0.90 per cent combined C)
3.60	1.25	0.55	0.40	0.10	45	40	15	Chilled plow iron
3.75	0.85	0.50	0.40	0.10	45	40	15	Plow mold boards

changes which usually take place during melting are taken into consideration in making up the charge.

In addition to low cost and easy machinability, gray cast iron has a number of properties—notably notch insensitivity, high damping capacity, and high compressive strength—which make it especially valuable in some applications. In tensile strength, ductility, and toughness, however, it is much inferior to steel. In addition, the absence of a well-defined yield point and modulus

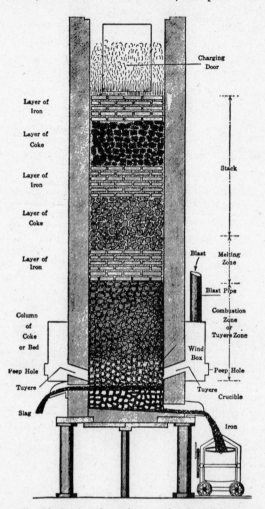

Fig. 66—Section through a cupola (Stoughton).

of elasticity makes it unsuitable for many engineering structures. Despite its disadvantages, however, the production of gray-iron castings is around 5 or 6 million tons a year in the United States alone.

107. **Structure of Gray Cast Iron**—Considering gray cast iron as a carbon steel containing graphite, the three primary metallographic constituents present at normal temperatures are alpha iron (ferrite), iron carbide (cementite), and free carbon (graphite). The cementite is always associated with ferrite as pearlite —the same constituent found in carbon steel—and the graphite is distributed through the ground mass as irregularly shaped plates or flakes of varying sizes (see Fig. 65). The ferrite of gray cast iron, unlike the ferrite of low-carbon steel which is relatively pure, contains all the silicon and a little of the phosphorus in solid solution.

Of the elements in gray cast iron, carbon has the strongest effect on structure and properties. This effect depends on the amount of total carbon as well as on the relative amounts of combined carbon and of graphite present. This in turn depends on the silicon which decreases the stability of the iron carbide, thus promoting graphitization. Next in importance is phosphorus, which combines with the iron to form iron phosphide, Fe_3P. A small amount of this compound dissolves in the ferrite, the rest forms a eutectic ($Fe-Fe_3P$) with iron. When the phosphorus is 0.1 per cent or above, the eutectic (known as *steadite*) is visible as a distinct constituent in the microstructure (Fig. 67). The eutectic melts at a temperature of 1750 to 1800° F. (955 to 980° C.), much below the melting point of gray cast iron. If about 0.5 per cent· phosphorus or more is present, there is enough eutectic to make the iron more fluid. High-phosphorus iron is, therefore, used for ornamental castings and other thin, intricate sections. Owing to the hardness of the phosphide eutectic, cast irons containing considerable phosphorus may be harder to machine than low-phosphorus material. In the amounts usual for American gray cast irons (Table 7) phosphorus has little effect on the strength, but it may increase the brittleness. For cylinders and various kinds of pressure castings 0.5 per cent is, therefore, usually the maximum permitted (Table 7). The effect of phosphorus on graphitization is negligible.

Commercial gray cast iron always contains enough manganese to insure that the sulphur is present as manganese sulphide. Owing to the notch insensitivity of gray cast iron, more sulphur is tolerated than in steel because manganese sulphide inclusions are not so likely to be loci of weakness where failure will start under repeated stress. Manganese in excess of the amount necessary to combine with the sulphur forms iron-manganese carbide. This compound is more stable than iron carbide; hence manganese inhibits graphitization. In the amount usually present (less than 1 per cent) the stabilizing effect of manganese is much less important than the strong graphitizing effect of silicon.

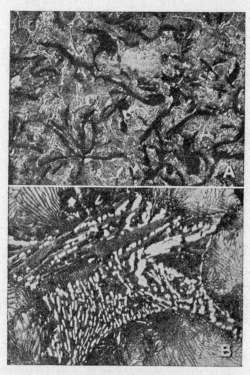

Fig. 67—Phosphide eutectic in gray cast iron (A) 100×, (B) 1000×. The eutectic is the irregular shaped light-colored constituent shown in A. At high magnification its duplex character is apparent (Künkele, *Giesserei*, v. 18, 1931, p. 73).

108. Relation between Properties and Structure of Gray Cast Iron—There is a close relation between properties and structure of gray cast iron. The properties are primarily dependent upon the characteristics of the "steel" matrix and upon the amount and distribution of the graphite. These in turn are dependent upon the variables already mentioned, namely, chemical composition, rate of cooling from the solidification temperature, special methods of melting, and heat treatment. In this section the effect of chemical composition and cooling rate are discussed briefly.

The amount of iron carbide to be decomposed into iron and graphite or to be left undecomposed depends (if the effect of cooling rate is ignored) upon the amounts of total carbon and silicon. For small specimens cast in sand molds the relation between total carbon, silicon, and structure is shown in Fig. 68.[3] The line HH'

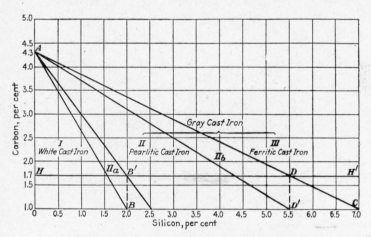

Fig. 68—The Maurer cast iron diagram.

is the boundary between cast iron and steel. Cast iron whose composition falls within area I solidifies and cools with no dissociation of the iron carbide into iron and graphite; the structure consists of pearlite plus excess cementite; the fracture is white, and the iron is hard and brittle. In cast iron whose composition falls in area IIa some of the iron carbide dissociates into iron and graphite in cooling; the structure consists of pearlite plus excess cementite and some graphite; the fracture is mottled, and the iron is also hard and brittle. If the composition falls within area II, most of the iron carbide dissociates into iron and graphite; the undissociated cementite is sufficient to form a matrix which is almost entirely pearlitic. In irons whose composition falls in area IIb most of the cementite dissociates; such irons have

[3] E. Maurer, *Kruppsche Monatshefte*, v. 5, 1924, pp. 115-122.

a matrix corresponding to a carbon steel containing 0.20 to 0.50 per cent carbon. In cast irons whose composition falls above line *AD* (area III) practically all the cementite dissociates; the matrix is carbonless, and there is a large amount of graphite present.

Cast irons whose composition falls within areas II, II*b,* and III have a gray fracture and are usually machinable. Some of them (area III) are relatively weak, others (area II) are strong. A modification of the Maurer diagram by Coyle [4] is shown in Fig.

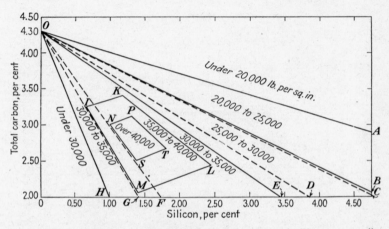

Fig. 69—Cast iron diagram showing effect of carbon and silicon on tensile strength (Coyle).

69, in which approximate tensile strengths are plotted against composition. This diagram shows that for small specimens cooled in sand molds the highest strengths are attained if the total carbon is 2.00 to 3.25 per cent and if the silicon is 1.00 to 2.25 per cent.

109. Effect of Cooling Rate—The relation among properties, structure, and composition is affected greatly by varying the rate of cooling from the solidification temperature to the gamma-alpha transformation temperature. As the mass is increased, the cooling rate is decreased, and the dissociation of the iron carbide is increased. Thus if a 1-in. sand-cast bar has a matrix corresponding to a 0.50 per cent carbon steel, the same iron if cast as a 6-in. bar in sand will ordinarily have a matrix which corre-

4 F. B. Coyle, *Trans. Am. Soc. Steel Treat.,* v. 12, 1927, pp. 446-465.

sponds to a 0.10 per cent carbon steel.   On the other hand an iron
of such composition that, when poured into a sand mold it will
have a matrix of pearlite, will, if poured into a cast iron mold,
form white iron on the surface next to the cold mold but will be
pearlitic in the interior of the casting.

Thus the lines of the Maurer diagram (Fig. 68) are moved
to the right if the cooling rate is increased, and to the left if the
cooling rate is decreased.   The approximate relation among
structure, cooling rate, and properties is shown in Fig. 70.[5]

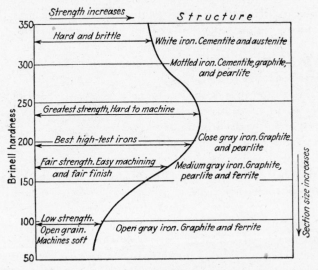

Fig. 70—Relation of hardness and strength of gray cast iron to structure
and section size (American Society for Testing Materials and American
Foundrymen's Association).

It is evident from the foregoing that the relation among the
composition, cooling rate, structure, and properties of gray cast
iron is not simple.   Another important factor which adds to the
complexity is the size and form of the graphite flakes.

110. Effect of Graphite Size and Effect of Heat Treatment
on Structure and Properties—The strength of slowly cooled
carbon-steel castings increases as the carbon (cementite) increases.
The strength of slowly cooled gray cast iron would also increase

[5] American Society for Testing Materials and American Foundrymen's
Association, *Symposium on Cast Iron*, June 1933, p. 30.

as the cementite increases if no graphite were present. Graphite destroys the continuity of the grains of the "steel" matrix and makes it weak and brittle. As the size of the graphite particles increases and as they become more flaky and plate-like, the iron becomes progressively weaker and more brittle. This is evident if malleable cast iron containing all the carbon as nodules (see Fig. 71) is compared with gray cast iron of approximately the same composition containing all the carbon as coarse graphite flakes. The tensile strength of the former is 50,000 lb. per sq. in., of the latter only 20,000 lb. per sq. in. It has been known for many years that the tensile strength is greatly influenced by the size of the graphite flakes, but only in the past 20 years has it been possible to control this and thus produce cast iron which can be used economically where considerable strength is required. Twenty years ago gray cast iron had an average tensile strength of about 25,000 lb. per sq. in., today a tensile strength of 50,000 lb. per sq. in. is readily attained.

High-strength cast iron must have a "steel" matrix containing considerable pearlite, and the graphite flakes should be small; there must, however, be 2.0 to 2.5 per cent graphite present if easy machinability is required. The control of the graphite size is accomplished by five methods. The first consists of melting an iron of such composition that it would normally solidify with a white fracture and then treating it by adding a special graphitizer, such as powdered silicon or calcium silicide, just before the castings are poured. The second consists of melting an iron which would normally solidify with a white fracture, and mixing with this a definite amount of a soft gray iron melted in another cupola. The third method consists of melting gray cast iron and superheating it considerably above the usual casting temperature. This decreases the size of the graphite flakes and increases the amount of pearlite in the casting. The fourth, used considerably in Europe, consists of pouring a low-silicon iron into a preheated mold. The fifth method consists of adding alloying elements. To produce high-strength iron by any of these methods the several variables, including the percentages of carbon and silicon, must be controlled carefully.

The structure and properties of gray cast iron can be altered by heat treatment. Annealing is commonly used to relieve strains introduced during solidification and cooling, and to soften edges, corners, or other parts of a casting which cool so rapidly that un-dissociated cementite prevents economical machining. High-strength cast iron containing a pearlitic matrix and fine graphite is occasionally quenched and tempered, but the increase in tensile strength is usually not enough to justify the cost or taking the chance that the casting may crack in quenching.

III. Evaluation of Gray Cast Iron for Engineering Applications—The suitability of gray cast iron for engineering structures and machines is judged chiefly by tensile, transverse, and compressive strengths. Hardness, endurance limit, wear resistance, and other properties may be valuable criteria of its value for specific applications. Most metallurgists experienced with cast iron consider the transverse test as the best single source of information on the quality of cast iron.

The transverse test is made by applying a load at the center of a cast (unmachined) round bar, supported at each end, until fracture occurs. The size of the bar depends upon the size of the casting and has been standardized [6] at 0.875, 1.20, or 2 in. in diameter with a span of 12, 18, or 24 in. between supports. The load necessary to fracture the bar and the amount of deflection at the center at the moment of fracture are noted. In the United States transverse strength is reported as the load in pounds; in Europe the load is converted by the formula

$$MR = \frac{Plc}{4I}$$

to a value called modulus of rupture. In this formula P is the breaking load, l the distance between supports, c the distance from the neutral axis of the bar to the extreme fiber, and I the moment of inertia.

The relation of modulus of rupture to tensile strength varies with the quality of the iron from 2.5 times the tensile strength for low-strength irons to approximately the same as the tensile strength for high-strength irons. Transverse strength or modulus of rupture is of value in design if cast iron is used as a beam and especially in pipe subjected to heavy earth loads.

Gray cast irons are graded by (minimum) tensile strength [7] (in thousand lb. per sq. in.) into seven classes: 20, 25, 30, 35, 40,

[6] American Society for Testing Materials, *Standards*, 1936, Spec. A48-36.
[7] See preceding footnote.

50, and 60. As discussed in section 67, since the stress-strain curves of gray cast iron are curved from the origin, this material has no proportional limit nor modulus of elasticity. The secant modulus, representing a point on the stress-strain curve of 25 per cent of the tensile strength, varies between 12 and 20 million lb. per sq. in.

In many engineering applications, for example machine beds, columns, pipes used as structural members and various other supports, cast iron is used for its strength in compression. This is determined by subjecting sand-cast bars 0.75 to 0.80 in. in diameter and 1 to 3 in. long to a compressive load until failure occurs. The stress-strain curve in compression is also curved from the origin. Compressive strength is higher than tensile strength: it varies from about 4 times the tensile strength for low-strength irons to about 3 times the tensile strength for strong irons.

112. **Properties of Gray Cast Iron**—The properties of common American gray cast iron are given in Table 8.[8] Unlike carbon steel, which has a fairly uniform ratio of 500 for tensile strength to Brinell hardness, the ratio for gray cast iron varies from 70 to 240. High-strength cast iron has a high ratio and low-strength material a low ratio. Size and distribution of the graphite are the most important factors in the strength-hardness ratio. The values in the lower half of Table 8 were determined by members of a subcommittee (XV) of Committee A-3 (A.S.T.M.) and co-operators with this committee and represent the range of properties obtained on 25 gray cast irons of various commercial analyses. The irons contained 2.50 to 3.95 per cent total carbon, 0.50 to 1.33 per cent carbon as Fe_3C, and 0.53 to 3.26 per cent silicon. All test bars were uniform and were machined before testing.

The other properties of gray cast iron can be summarized in a series of short sentences. Endurance limits are given in Table 8. The endurance ratio, determined on highly polished specimens, is more erratic than for steel. Values between 0.30 and 0.60 have been reported. A very important characteristic of gray cast iron is the almost negligible effect of surface on the endur-

[8] American Society for Testing Materials, *Proc.*, v. 33, 1933, I, pp. 87 to 137; *Standards* 1936, Spec. A48-36; and American Society for Testing Materials and American Foundrymen's Assoc., *Symposium on Cast Iron*, 1933, pp. 55-62.

TABLE 8. MINIMUM AND AVERAGE PROPERTIES OF AMERICAN GRAY
CAST IRON AND RANGE OF PROPERTIES ATTAINED ON
25 COMMERCIAL CAST IRONS

Class No.	Minimum tensile strength, lb. per sq. in.	Minimum transverse strength, lb.			Average modulus of rupture, lb. per sq. in.	Average compressive strength, lb. per sq. in.	Secant modulus, million lb. per sq. in.
		0.875-in. specimen, 12-in. span	1.20-in. specimen, 18-in. span	2.0-in. specimen, 24-in. span			
20	20,000	900	1800	6,000	42,000	80,000	14.2
25	25,000	1025	2000	6,800	46,000	92,000	14.5
30	30,000	1150	2200	7,600	54,000	108,000	16.0
35	35,000	1275	2400	8,300	60,000	118,000	18.0
40	40,000	1400	2600	9,100	64,000	120,000	19.0
50	50,000	1675	3000	10,300	68,000	140,000	20.0
60	60,000	1925	3400	....	70,000	150,000	

Tensile strength, lb. per sq. in.	Modulus of rupture,* lb. per sq. in.	Compressive strength, lb. per sq. in.	Shear strength, lb. per sq. in.	Endurance limit, lb. per sq. in.	Secant modulus, million lb. per sq. in.	Brinell hardness number
18,000 to 55,000	33,000 to 112,000	65,000 to 160,000	27,000 to 61,000	8,000 to 25,000	10 to 23	120 to 270

* 1.2-in. diameter bar, 18-in. span

ance limit; the same notch which reduces the endurance limit of steel as much as 75 per cent reduces the endurance of soft cast iron less than 15 per cent. The impact resistance of cast iron is low and is usually unimportant. Notched bar tests are meaningless, and drop tests are frequently erratic. The damping capacity of gray cast iron is higher than for any other ferrous material. Gray cast iron is readily machinable unless the surface is chilled; conversely, if the surface is chilled, cast iron is very wear resistant and is machined with great difficulty.

113. **Alloy Cast Irons**—Alloy cast irons are gray cast irons to which nickel, chromium, molybdenum, copper, and occasionally other elements have been added to improve the mechanical properties or to produce an iron with some special property such as high wear resistance, corrosion resistance, or heat resistance. For the latter purpose large amounts of alloying elements are usually

used; for a general improvement of properties 0.15 to 3.00 or occasionally 4.00 per cent nickel, 0.10 to 1.75 per cent chromium, 0.20 to 1.20 per cent molybdenum, or 0.10 to 1.00 per cent copper, either singly or more commonly in various combinations, are added. The effect of the alloying elements on cast iron is more complex, and even more difficult to predict, than in the case of steel (discussed in the next chapter), owing to the complicating influence of graphite. Suitable compositions have, however, been worked out which have resulted in improved strength, hardness, and wear resistance with no sacrifice in machinability.

The low alloys are, naturally, considerably more costly on a per-pound basis than the unalloyed cast irons but this cost per pound is not so important as the cost of the casting when completely finished and ready for use in a specific application. The use of a low-alloy cast iron frequently permits enough reduction in weight or increases the life of a part so much that the overall cost is less than the overall cost of a plain cast iron. The primary reason for the higher cost per pound is the cost of the alloying metals. Some added precautions are necessary in molding, core making, melting, and pouring the casting, but these do not usually add greatly to the cost.

The field of alloy cast irons is relatively new, but it is already broad. The recent (1939) handbook published by the American Foundrymen's Association contains a bibliography of 450 papers, most of which have been published in the last 10 years. Alloy cast iron is used by the automotive industry especially for cylinders, crankshafts and camshafts, pistons and rings, brake drums, clutch parts and crankcases, and to a lesser extent in chemical and oil-refining equipment, for pumps and compressors, and by the railroads for compressors, pistons, and steam cylinders. It is also used for crushing and grinding machinery and for heavy machine tools and dies.

Most alloy cast irons contain nickel and chromium in the proportion of 2 to 3 parts of nickel to 1 part of chromium. Molybdenum and copper are used alone, or with either nickel or chromium or with both. Small amounts of titanium or vanadium are occasionally added to produce small graphite flakes or a small grain size in the matrix. The improvement in properties resulting from the addition of alloying elements is attained primarily by control of the graphitization, i.e., by altering the number, size, shape, and distribution of the graphite flakes. The general effect of the four common alloying metals on the structure, which is reflected in the properties, is as follows: (1) Nickel dissolves in the iron and decreases the stability of the carbide thus promoting graphitization; it reduces slightly the size of the graphite flakes, reduces the grain size, and strengthens the matrix; most important, however, it prevents the formation of hard white iron at corners, edges, and in other thin sections, thus increasing machinability in gray irons which have a pearlitic matrix. (2) Chromium stabilizes the cementite and prevents graphitization; it reduces slightly the size of the graphite flakes and refines and strengthens the matrix. (3) Molybdenum has little effect on the stability of the iron carbide but reduces the size of the graphite flakes and also strengthens the matrix. (4) Copper has little effect on the graphite but hardens and strengthens the matrix.

If the carbon in gray cast iron is in its usual range, namely 3.00 to 3.50 per cent, the strength, as shown in Fig. 69, is increased by lowering the silicon. If, however, the silicon is lowered enough to produce considerable strengthening, there is danger that hard white iron will form in thin sections or at corners or edges that cool rapidly. If this occurs, these portions are practically unmachinable. As just mentioned, the addition of 2 per cent or even less nickel will prevent this. By adding nickel and by adjusting the silicon content the hardness and strength may be increased without sacrificing machinability, or the machinability may be increased without lowering strength or hardness.

Chromium, in stabilizing iron carbide, decreases graphitization in cooling and thus increases the strength and hardness by increasing the amount of pearlite and by decreasing the size of the graphite flakes. The amount used depends upon the composition of the iron, whether nickel is present, and the size of the section; enough is added (usually about 0.5 per cent) so that the combined carbon will be approximately 0.7 per cent.

Although molybdenum is an excellent strengthener, dissolving in the ferrite and strengthening it, its most marked effect is in reducing the size of the graphite flakes. When added to an iron of properly balanced composition, 0.50 to 1.00 per cent molybdenum increases the strength 10 to 50 per cent. Copper is also a strengthener of the matrix. Because it has little effect on the size or distribution of the graphite, it is not so commonly used as molybdenum.

By the use of properly balanced compositions machinable alloy cast irons with a tensile strength of 60,000 lb. per sq. in. or higher are readily made. Although the production and use of this material is not at present great enough to warrant more discussion in this chapter, applications are expanding rapidly. A few high-alloy cast irons are used industrially. The most important of these is an austenitic gray iron containing about 14 per cent nickel, 5.5 per cent copper, and 2 to 6 per cent chromium. This material is corrosion resistant and is practically free from scaling at temperatures up to 1500° F. (815° C.). It is used for containers and fittings where resistance to a number of acids and alkalis is important and where high temperatures are encountered.

114. Malleable Cast Iron as an Engineering Material—Malleable cast iron is a valuable engineering material and is widely used for machinery, railroad equipment and automobiles, agricultural machinery, pipe fittings, hardware, household appliances, and in many other applications. Intricate castings are more readily melted and poured with white cast iron than with carbon steel and, despite the cost of malleablizing, are cheaper than carbon-steel castings. Malleable cast iron compares favorably with gray cast iron in machinability and with low-carbon steel in properties. The annual production of malleable castings in the United States is 700,000 to 1,000,000 tons, of which about 70 per cent is used by the railroads and the automotive industry. Each modern automobile and truck contains 125 to 150 lb. of malleable cast iron.

To produce malleable castings, cast iron solidifying with a white fracture is poured into a sand mold; the hard, brittle casting is then annealed (malleablized) to dissociate the cementite. Malleable cast iron contains 2.0 to 2.5 per cent carbon, practically all of which is graphite (usually called temper carbon), 0.7 to 1.2 per cent silicon, 0.40 to 0.60 per cent manganese, less than 0.20 per cent sulphur, and less than 0.10 per cent phosphorus. The structure consists of a matrix of ferrite interspersed with nodules or "nests" of graphite (Fig. 71).

There are two processes of malleablizing. In one, used to a considerable extent in Europe, the castings are packed in an oxidizing material; in the other, used throughout the United States, the packing material is inert. When white cast iron is annealed in an oxidizing atmosphere, the carbon is oxidized and eliminated and the final structure consists mostly of ferrite. The castings, known as *white heart,* are more brittle, with a lower elongation and reduction of area, than *black heart* castings, which are annealed in a non-oxidizing atmosphere and which have a structure of ferrite and graphite (Fig. 71).

The malleablizing treatment consists of packing the white-iron castings and ferrous silicate scale or slag in pots and heating

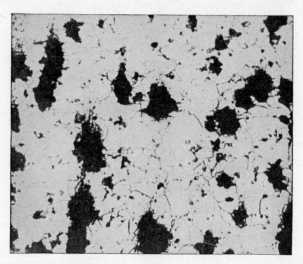

Fig. 71—Structure of malleable cast iron: ferrite (white) and graphite nodules (black); etched, 500×.

slowly to about 1600° F. (870° C.), holding at this temperature for 40 to 60 hr., and cooling at 10° F. (5° C.) per hr. to room temperature. To produce malleable cast iron with satisfactory properties strict attention must be paid to controlling the percentages of total carbon and silicon in the white iron in relation to the size of the casting, and to other variables. Long experience in this, plus considerable research work in the past 15 years, has resulted in marked improvement: since 1920 the average tensile strength has increased from 53,000 lb. per sq. in. to about 58,000 lb. per sq. in. and the average elongation in 2 in. from 16 to 23 per cent.

115. **Engineering Properties of Malleable Cast Iron**—White cast iron for malleablizing is melted chiefly in an air furnace; some, however, is melted in a cupola. The tensile strength and elongation (as measured on a test bar) of cupola malleable iron is lower than that of air-furnace malleable, but the bursting strength of castings is usually considerably higher. Cupola malleable, therefore, is widely used for pipe fittings. Most malleable iron is purchased under specifications issued by the railroads or by the valve- and pipe-fittings industry. Most of these specifications give the following as minimum properties:

Kind of malleable iron	Tensile strength, lb. per sq. in.	Yield strength, lb. per sq. in.	Elongation in 2 in., per cent
Air furnace......	50,000	32,000	10
Cupola..........	40,000	30,000	5

Reduction of area is usually about 20 per cent and is seldom determined.

Malleable cast iron is unique among ferrous materials in that the elongation increases as the tensile strength increases. This is shown by the data for air-furnace malleable given in Table 9.[9] Malleable cast iron, with a notched-bar impact resistance of 7 to 9 ft-lb., as compared with 1 ft-lb. or less for gray cast iron, is much tougher than gray cast iron. The modulus of elasticity is 25,000,-000 lb. per sq. in., i.e., slightly lower than that of carbon steel. Malleable cast iron has an endurance ratio of about 0.5, i.e., the same as carbon steel. It is considerably more sensitive to notches than gray cast iron.

TABLE 9. TENSILE PROPERTIES OF AIR-FURNACE MALLEABLE CAST IRON

Tensile strength, lb. per sq. in.	Elongation in 2 in., per cent	Tensile strength, lb. per sq. in.	Elongation in 2 in., per cent
51,000	16.5	55,000	19.0
52,000	17.0	56,000	19.6
53,000	17.6	57,000	20.3
54,000	18.3	58,000	21.0

In malleable iron, as in carbon steel, the tensile strength decreases with increasing size of section; a typical change is from

[9] *Proc. Am. Soc. Test. Mat.*, v. 31, part II, 1931, p. 317.

55,000 lb. per sq. in. for sections 0.25 to 0.50 in. in thickness to 45,000 lb. per sq. in. for sections of 1.25 to 1.50 in. The yield strength, however, is practically unaffected by section size. In contrast to steel, in which elongation usually increases with mass, the elongation of malleable iron decreases; at the center of a 2- or 3-in. section, for example, the elongation may be only about half what it is at the surface.

Malleable cast iron has poor wear resistance, but in machinability it ranks about the same as gray cast iron. It is easier to plane, drill, or mill than carbon or alloy steels including those containing lead or high sulphur.

Recently, for a few special applications, the graphitizing operation in the production of black-heart malleable has been modified, or alloying elements have been added and a special treatment used so that the annealed material contains some pearlite. The properties of pearlitic malleable cast iron depend upon the amount and distribution of the iron carbide; usually this is stronger and less ductile than fully graphitized material.

CHAPTER 13

LOW-ALLOY STEELS AS ENGINEERING
MATERIALS

ALLOY steels are about 60 years old. The pioneer investigations of the effect of the various alloying elements on carbon steel were made between 1875 and 1890 in England, Germany, France, and, to a lesser extent, the United States. Owing to the high price of alloying metals, the only use for these materials on a relatively large scale was in armor plate. By 1910, alloying metals were much cheaper, and from then on industrial applications multiplied rapidly, especially between 1915 and 1920 when there was an abnormal demand for high-quality alloy steel for war materials. This demand, together with the approximately simultaneous development of the first "stainless" steel, stimulated metallurgists all over the world to investigate the effect on carbon steel of all possible combinations of many alloying elements. The result has been alloy steels by the hundreds—steels containing one alloying element in addition to carbon, and steels containing half a dozen.

Much of the research work on alloy steels has been of the hit-or-miss type or has been carried out to develop a steel which would duplicate the properties of a patented composition without actual infringement. One result of this frenzied research over the past 25 years has been a phenomenal growth of metallurgical literature; another has been the development of many unnecessary alloy steels which, with slightly different compositions, duplicate the characteristics of some of the older and better known steels. However, some remarkable developments have resulted from this mass of hit-or-miss research, including several new steels and special ferrous alloys with splendid properties and of much value to industry. It has also shown to engineers that alloy steels make possible the design of certain structures that would be impossible with unalloyed carbon steels and cast irons. Without alloy steels the modern airplane, the streamlined railroad train, and the modern automobile would never have been developed to their present efficiency.

The most characteristic indication of the increasing value of alloy steels to the engineering professions is that their production has increased at a greater rate than total steel production. The output in 1910 was 600,000 tons, or 2 per cent of the total; in 1939 it was more than 3,000,000 tons, or about 6 per cent of the total output of the steel industry. Of this alloy-steel production the automotive and aircraft industries now use about 75 per cent.

The amount of published data on alloy steels and cast irons is so large that it is now impossible for a metallurgist to know everything that is going on in this field; it is even a hard job to keep up with developments in a single branch.[1] To summarize adequately in a small book the present status of knowledge of alloy steels is a difficult task, and it is, of course, quite impossible to give many details of their properties in a chapter or two. Consequently, the discussion in this and the next chapter is restricted to a brief description of the characteristics of these materials and to a concise outline of the metallurgical fundamentals in the relation of the common alloying elements to carbon steels.

116. **Balanced Compositions in Low-alloy Steels**—A workable definition of alloy steels and a general classification of these materials into low- and high-alloy steels, including common compositions for the low-alloy grades, are given in Chapter 4. Many low-alloy steels, especially the S.A.E. grades, are purchased under specifications which give desired ranges for the various alloying elements and for carbon and manganese, and usually maximum percentages for sulphur and phosphorus. Frequently, these specifications are accompanied by charts of average, typical, or minimum mechanical properties of the various steels after definite heat treatments. Such specifications and properties are the re-

[1] Alloys of Iron Research, founded in 1930 by The Engineering Foundation of New York, is reviewing this literature and correlating and summarizing the most important of the world's research on alloy steels and cast irons. Results are published in a series of 14 monographs. The expansion of research work is shown by the fact that, whereas it was estimated in 1930 that a book of 500 pages would summarize everything important known on nickel as an alloying element in steel, by 1940 two volumes containing a total of 1400 pages were necessary. Information on other alloy steels has expanded in the same proportion.

sult of long experience and are of unquestioned value to engineers. In the past few years, however, there has been a trend to make use of steels of "balanced compositions" rather than to attach too much importance to rigidly specified compositions and the necessity of accepting the properties accompanying such analyses.

The effect of the common elements on carbon steel is generally, though not always, known with some exactness. But, although the effect of any one of them may be known, the effect of two or more, when added to the same carbon steel, can rarely be predicted from the known behavior of the elements when used singly. To paraphrase Gillett,[2] if the effect of adding alloy A to carbon steel is 3, and the effect of adding alloy B is 2, the sum is not necessarily 5; it may be anything from 0 to 8. In other words, the effects of two or more alloying elements on carbon steel may be additive, subtractive, or they may intensify or cancel each other. Moreover, as carbon is the most important element present, it is necessary also to take into consideration whether the alloying metal will intensify, diminish, or neutralize the effect of carbon.

Steels of "balanced composition" are those in which the percentages of carbon and alloying elements, and the heat treatment (if any), are varied to produce a desired combination of properties for a particular application. Assume, for example, that for a structural application a steel must have a minimum yield strength of 50,000 lb. per sq. in. as rolled, must weld readily, and must not air harden after welding. A steel containing 0.30 per cent carbon, 1 per cent of alloy metal A, and 0.5 per cent of alloy metal B has the required strength and welds readily, but it air hardens after welding. Because this is not a balanced composition for this particular application, the carbon is reduced to 0.15 per cent, and the amounts of the alloying metals are increased to 1.5 and 0.75 per cent respectively. The yield strength is still well above the required minimum, the material still welds readily, but by a better balance of the carbon and metals A and B the steel does not air harden after welding. It is the job of the metallurgist to provide the engineer with properly balanced alloy steels for all his requirements, insofar as this is possible

[2] H. W. Gillett, Editorial, *Metals and Alloys*, vol. 1, 1929, pp. 259, 260.

with present-day metallurgical knowledge. A well-known and important use for low-alloy steels of balanced composition is in ordnance and armor plate.

The final criterion in the selection of an alloy steel for a specific application is economy. Any alloy steel is more costly than plain steel of corresponding carbon content and should not be used for a structure or a machine just because it contains one or more special metals, or because the steel maker says it is better than some other steel. It should be used only if considerable weight can be saved, or if the design can be materially simplified, and only if its total cost—meaning the cost of the steel, of its treatment (if any), and of fabrication—is less, when spread over the expected life, than the total cost of any competing material.

117. General Effects of the Alloying Elements on Carbon Steel—The general effects of the common alloying elements on the structure and, incidentally, on the properties of carbon steel are discussed in Chapters 5 and 6. It is the purpose of the discussion in this chapter to expand this and to show how these alloying elements are used to produce steels which are more satisfactory for certain applications than the unalloyed carbon steels.

Hot-rolled carbon steel is low in cost and has excellent properties, and with certain carbon percentages these properties can still be improved by heat treatment. Carbon steel also has several disadvantages as an engineering material. An important one is the rapid decrease of ductility as the carbon (and the strength) increases. Another is that optimum combinations of properties in heat-treated material can usually be attained only in small sections. A third is that carbon steels, whether hot-rolled or heat-treated, suffer marked deterioration of properties when used at temperatures considerably below or above normal. Alloying elements are added to carbon steels to overcome, partly at least, these disadvantages.

The principal effect of the alloying elements in low-alloy steels is to harden and strengthen the ferrite and to increase hardenability by heat treatment. All the common alloying elements dissolve in the ferrite and strengthen it to some extent. Five of these elements also form carbides (see Table 3) but of these only molybdenum, vanadium, and tungsten have a strong carbide-forming tendency. Changing the properties of carbon steel materially by the formation of such carbides is important chiefly in the high-alloy steels, which are discussed in the next chapter.

The ferrite-hardening (and strengthening) potency of the elements forming solid solutions with iron varies (increasing from chromium to phosphorus) as shown in Fig. 72.[3] None of these, with the possible exception of phosphorus, is so potent as carbon. In fact, the strengthening effect is small, provided the carbon

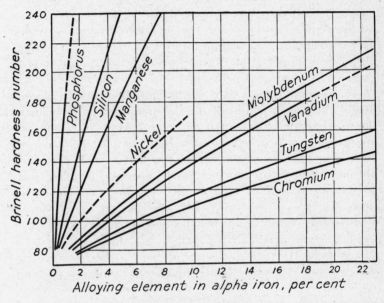

Fig. 72—Effect of the common alloying elements, when dissolved in iron, on its hardness (Bain).

content and the *structure* are held constant. This is shown by the curves for the furnace-cooled specimens plotted in Fig. 73.[4] If, however, the structure is altered by changing the treatment, small amounts of an alloying element may, as shown in Fig. 73, have a great effect.

118. Effects of Phosphorus, Manganese, and Silicon—Of the alloying elements which dissolve in the ferrite, phosphorus, as just

[3] E. C. Bain, *Functions of the Alloying Elements in Steel*, American Society for Metals, Cleveland, 1939, p. 66.

[4] Plotted from data by E. C. Wright and P. F. Mumma, *Trans. Am. Inst. Min. Met. Eng.*, v. 105, 1933, pp. 77-87.

noted, is the most potent in its strengthening action (Fig. 72). The addition of 0.01 per cent increases the tensile and the yield strength approximately 1000 lb. per sq. in., i.e., about as much as these properties are increased by carbon. This strengthening

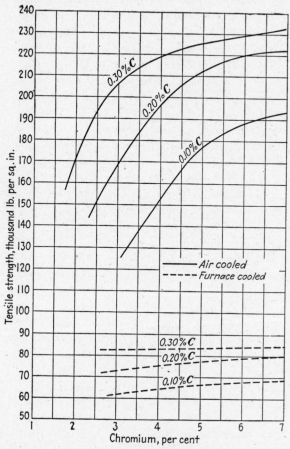

Fig. 73—Effect of carbon, chromium, and cooling rate on the tensile strength of carbon steels (Wright and Mumma).

is, however, attained with less sacrifice of elongation and reduction of area than in the case of carbon addition. Another advantage is that phosphorus, either alone or more intensely if copper is present, increases the resistance of the steel to atmospheric corrosion.

Because phosphorus, under certain conditions, is likely to cause brittleness under shock, it is not used as an alloying element in those S.A.E. steels which are usually heat treated. When it is added to hot-rolled low-alloy structural steels, the carbon should be preferably below 0.15 per cent, and a toughening element such as chromium or nickel (or both) should also be present.

Owing to their generally high oxygen content and to the uncertain quality of acid Bessemer steels, these materials, which contain 0.065 to 0.120 per cent phosphorus as an impurity, are, at present, not used for structural purposes. Nearly all the steels in which phosphorus is an alloying element are made by the basic open-hearth process.

Manganese, added to steel in amounts in excess of that necessary to combine with the sulphur and to deoxidize the metal—0.10 to 0.25 per cent for most steels—partly dissolves in the ferrite and partly replaces iron in iron carbide (Fe_3C) to form a carbide which may be represented by $(Fe,Mn)_3C$. If the manganese is below 2 per cent, the amount of this carbide formed is small. Moreover, this substance is so much like iron carbide that it has in itself no appreciable effect on structure and properties. The effect of manganese in solid solution is less than that of phosphorus: the amount by which 0.01 per cent manganese increases the tensile strength varies with the carbon content from about 100 to 500 lb. per sq. in.; it increases the yield strength somewhat more than this. A yield strength of at least 50,000 lb. per sq. in., together with good ductility, can be readily attained in hot-rolled structural shapes of 0.20 to 0.30 per cent carbon steel by adding 1.00 to 1.75 per cent manganese.

Manganese has a strong effect on the hardenability of carbon steel. In steels that are heat treated this is an advantage, as it permits the use of less drastic quenching media, which means less distortion or cracking. In hot-rolled structural steel increased hardenability may be a disadvantage, unless the carbon is very low, as air hardening may occur in cooling from the rolling temperature or after welding, with serious loss of ductility. In general, manganese reduces the ductility of untreated carbon steel, but this is not serious if the carbon is low.

Silicon in the amounts present in low-alloy steels (see p. 60) dissolves in the ferrite. Its effect on tensile strength is somewhat greater than that of manganese (Fig. 72); it raises the yield strength and yield ratio and does not appreciably reduce ductility. Its effect on hardenability is strong but not so strong as that of manganese. It has no appreciable effect on corrosion resistance when present in small amounts. In other than the low-alloy structural steels discussed later in this chapter, silicon is used as an alloying element in one important group of spring steels which contain about 2 per cent silicon, 0.60 to 0.90 per cent

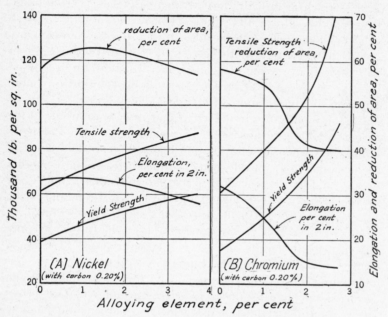

Fig. 74—Effect of (*A*) nickel and (*B*) chromium on the tensile properties of rolled carbon steels (Bain and Llewellyn).

manganese, and 0.50 to 0.65 per cent carbon (the S.A.E. 9200 series) and in certain steels for electric apparatus.

119. Effects of Nickel and Chromium—Nickel dissolves in the ferrite of carbon steel and exerts a strengthening effect which is somewhat less than that due to phosphorus, silicon, or manganese (Fig. 72). The effect of nickel on the tensile properties of a 0.20 per cent carbon steel is plotted in Fig. 74*A*,[5] which shows that nickel does not greatly lower elongation and reduction-of-area

[5] Figures 74*A* and 74*B* are based on data quoted by E. C. Bain and F. T. Llewellyn, *Trans. Am. Soc. Civil Eng.*, v. 102, 1937, p. 1249.

values. The toughening effect of nickel is especially evident if a carbon steel and a nickel steel are heat treated to the same tensile strength (see p. 83). Nickel also increases the endurance ratio and the impact resistance of carbon steels, which is especially marked if the steels are heat treated. This toughening effect is nickel's greatest virtue and is the chief reason why this metal is used so extensively in the low-alloy steels, especially in the S.A.E. grades, which are usually heat treated before use. Of approximately 70 low-alloy S.A.E. steels, 40 contain nickel.

Nickel does not form a carbide. It increases the hardenability of carbon steels mildly, being less effective in producing deep hardening than silicon, manganese, or chromium. It greatly increases the resistance of carbon steel to some forms of corrosion, especially in combination with copper.

Chromium dissolves in the ferrite and also forms carbides if the carbon is high. As shown by Figs. 72 and 73, its ferrite-strengthening effect when in solid solution is weaker than that of any of the common alloying elements, but it increases hardenability greatly, and it alters the structure, as shown by the curves for the air-cooled specimens in Fig. 73. The effect of chromium on the tensile properties of small air-cooled (hot-rolled) sections of a 0.20 per cent carbon steel is plotted in Fig. 74B. In such sections, the increase in tensile and yield strength and the decrease in elongation and reduction of area are much greater than the corresponding effects of nickel. Although chromium is a toughening element and increases the impact resistance of very low carbon steels, its primary function is to increase hardenability and to decrease the magnitude of the mass effect. For this reason, it is a common addition to the S.A.E. nickel steels in the proportion of about half as much chromium as nickel (Table 10).

Chromium is used widely as an alloy in high-carbon steels, in which it forms a carbide and also dissolves in the ferrite. When these materials are quenched and tempered at a low temperature, they are very hard and have good wear resistance. They contain about 1.0 per cent carbon and 0.75 to 1.50 per cent chromium and are used for tools, dies, and ball bearings.

120. Effects of the Other Common Alloying Elements—The other alloying elements used in low-alloy steels are copper, molybdenum, vanadium, and, to a limited extent, tungsten. Copper, in the small amounts added to carbon and low-alloy steels, dis-

solves in the ferrite, but its effect on tensile and impact properties is small. If more than 0.6 per cent is present, the steels, as noted in another chapter, may be precipitation hardened. Copper is most useful as an alloying element for its effect on atmospheric corrosion. The addition of 0.10 to 0.40 per cent reduces this variety of corrosion so much that a large proportion of low-carbon sheets, especially when very thin, and many of the new high-strength structural steels now contain copper.

Molybdenum, vanadium, and tungsten are strong carbide formers. In the amounts present in low-alloy steels a portion of these three elements dissolves in the ferrite and strengthens it moderately (Fig. 72). Molybdenum and vanadium are valuable chiefly for their effect on austenite grain size. Steels containing 0.10 to 0.25 or 0.30 per cent of either are usually fine-grained and are not so readily coarsened by overheating as some of the other low-alloy steels. Molybdenum, vanadium, and tungsten all contribute to deep hardening, but the effect is not very important. Molybdenum or vanadium is used in a number of low-alloy steels, especially the S.A.E. grades, usually together with another alloying element such as chromium, nickel, or manganese. The most important function of tungsten—and to a lesser extent of molybdenum—is to increase the hardness and stability of alloy steels at elevated temperature. For this purpose, relatively large amounts are required, usually in conjunction with chromium. This is discussed in the next chapter.

121. **Low-alloy Structural Steels as Engineering Materials**— As noted previously, there are two broad classes of low-alloy engineering steels: the structural steels and the S.A.E. steels. The structural steels have a higher yield strength than carbon steels. They are usually of carefully balanced composition and are used for structural purposes without heat treatment other than natural or controlled cooling after hot rolling. The S.A.E. steels are in general much more costly than the low-alloy structural steels and should be heat treated to secure optimum properties. In contrast to the structural steels, in which the function of the alloying elements is primarily to strengthen the ferrite and to produce a fine pearlite when the material is air cooled, in the S.A.E. steels the alloying elements also affect the response of the steel to thermal treatment and, in a few cases, harden it by forming carbides.

Low-alloy steels of high yield strength are 30 years old. One of the first contained about 0.25 per cent carbon and 1.50 per cent manganese and was used between 1900 and 1915 to reduce dead loads in long-span bridges and steamship construction in the United States and in England. A little later, a deoxidized carbon steel, misnamed silicon steel, was developed in the United States. This material contained 0.25 to 0.35 per cent carbon, 0.70 to 1.00 per cent manganese, and 0.20 to 0.40 per cent silicon. The yield strength of these two steels, in the hot-rolled condition, was 45,000 lb. per sq. in. or higher, and a considerable tonnage was used for bridges between 1915 and 1928. A steel of similar yield strength, containing 0.12 per cent carbon, 1 per cent silicon, and 0.70 per cent manganese, was developed in Germany in 1925 but, owing to its variable quality, it was not used long. This German steel is important as it was the first attempt to produce a steel of high yield strength, low enough in carbon to be welded readily without the troublesome brittleness in and around the weld which frequently results from welding a steel containing more than 0.20 per cent carbon and 0.75 per cent manganese.

About 10 years ago, the depression stimulated steel manufacturers to investigate the possibility of producing a low-cost, easily weldable, "tailor-made" steel which would have properties superior to those of ordinary structural steel. The depression also focused the attention of engineers upon the desirability of reducing cost in certain structures by the use of smaller sections of a steel of higher strength, and by welding instead of riveting. The result was that the steel makers produced the steels and the engineers used them for railway rolling stock, street cars, trucks, buses, cranes, steam shovels, and similar structures. One of the essential factors in this advance was the realization that tensile strength is not always the best criterion of the suitability of a steel for certain structural uses, and that resistance to buckling or crumpling, which is related to yield strength, is very important.

The low-alloy structural steels have, as rolled, approximately twice the yield strength of low-carbon steel, combined with high ductility, easy weldability, and a resistance to atmospheric corrosion which is much higher than that of carbon steel. In tonnage lots, they cost 15 to 50 per cent more than comparable sections of plain carbon steel. Owing primarily to their high yield strength, it is possible to reduce the size of a section 25 to 35 per cent and still design a structure that has ample stiffness. Despite somewhat higher fabricating and machining costs, it is frequently possible to save 10 to 15 per cent of the cost of a structure by the use of the properly selected low-alloy steel.

122. Composition and Properties of the Low-alloy Structural Steels—The first of the present crop of some 30 of these steels was made in 1929 and contained 0.30 per cent or less carbon, 1.05 to 1.40 per cent manganese, 0.60 to 0.90 per cent silicon, and 0.30 to 0.60 per cent chromium. Known under the trade name Cromansil, this steel attracted considerable attention, and a number of others followed it quickly under such trade names as Cor-Ten, Man-Ten, Hi-Steel, Jal-Ten, Konik, Yoloy, and others.

As a group, the low-alloy structural steels are characterized by low carbon (to improve ductility and weldability, and to prevent air hardening) and by the presence of at least two, and sometimes as many as five, of the following alloying elements: manganese, silicon, nickel, copper, chromium, molybdenum, phosphorus, and (rarely) vanadium. The percentage of alloying elements is usually low. Manganese is 1.70 per cent or less, with an average of about 1.25 per cent. Silicon is 1 per cent or less, the usual amount being between 0.20 and 0.70 per cent. Nickel varies from 0.3 to 2.0 per cent, and copper, owing to its favorable effect on resistance to atmospheric corrosion, is usually at least 0.10 per cent and may be as high as 1.50 per cent. Molybdenum, if present, is less than 0.40 per cent, and chromium is less than 1.5 per cent. Phosphorus, if used as an alloying element, is between 0.05 and 0.20 per cent; commonly it varies from 0.08 to 0.15 per cent.

In all the low-alloy structural steels the composition is balanced to ensure for hot-rolled sections a minimum yield strength of 50,000 lb. per sq. in., a tensile strength of 70,000 to 90,000 lb. per sq. in., and an elongation of 15 to 30 per cent in 8 in., depending upon composition. The impact resistance of most of these steels is satisfactory, usually it is higher than 25 ft-lb. Claims have been made that the endurance ratio is higher than for carbon steels, but not enough data have accumulated yet to accept this as generally true. As a group, the steels have a resistance to atmospheric corrosion considerably superior to that of carbon steels. These steels are outstanding in the relation of properties to cost. There are too many of them now; probably there will be many casualties in the next few years, but it seems certain that some will survive and that the survivors will be widely used as structural materials where a saving in weight is important.

123. The S.A.E. Low-alloy Steels—Of the alloying elements in low-alloy steels, nickel and chromium were the first used commercially. Steels containing about 3 per cent nickel were forged into armor plate between 1885 and 1890, causing a revolution in naval warfare. Chromium was used even earlier: steels containing 0.60 per cent were installed as main members of the Eads bridge over the Mississippi river at St. Louis in 1874. Extensive use of the steels included in the S.A.E. grades (Table 10) began about 1910. It has been claimed with considerable justification that the availability of these steels at a fairly reasonable cost was the chief factor in the development of the automotive and aircraft industries, and that without them the weight per horsepower of internal-combustion engines would be at least twice, and the efficiency less than half, of what it is today.

The principal classes of S.A.E. steels are given in Table 10.[6] As the series number of these steels is widely used in specifications

TABLE 10.   CLASSIFICATION OF S.A.E. LOW-ALLOY STEELS

S.A.E. series	Composition range, per cent				
	Manganese	Nickel	Chromium	Molybdenum	Vanadium
1300*	1.60 to 1.90				
2000	0.30 to 0.60	0.40 to 0.60			
2100	0.30 to 0.60	1.25 to 1.75			
2300	0.30 to 0.90	3.25 to 3.75			
2500	0.30 to 0.60	4.75 to 5.25			
3100	0.30 to 0.90	1.00 to 1.50	0.45 to 0.75		
3200	0.30 to 0.60	1.50 to 2.00	0.90 to 1.25		
3300	0.30 to 0.60	3.25 to 3.75	1.25 to 1.75		
3400	0.30 to 0.60	2.75 to 3.25	0.60 to 0.95		
4100	0.40 to 0.90	....	0.80 to 1.10	0.15 to 0.25	
4300	0.40 to 0.80	1.50 to 2.00	0.30 to 0.80	0.20 to 0.40	
4600	0.40 to 0.80	1.65 to 2.00	....	0.20 to 0.30	
4800	0.40 to 0.60	3.25 to 3.75	....	0.20 to 0.30	
5100	0.30 to 0.90	....	0.80 to 1.10		
6100	0.30 to 0.90	....	0.80 to 1.10	....	0.15 min.
9200	0.60 to 0.90	....	....	1.80 to 2.20†	

* There are two series of intermediate manganese steels, T1300, containing less than 0.05 per cent sulphur, and X1300, the free-machining grade containing 0.075 to 0.15 per cent sulphur. See footnote p. 225.
† Silicon content.

[6] *S.A.E. Handbook*, Society of Automotive Engineers, New York, 1940, p. 303.

and in the literature, its significance is worth a little attention. The first digit designates the type—thus, 2 is nickel steel, 3 is nickel-chromium steel, 4 is steel containing molybdenum (chromium-molybdenum, nickel-molybdenum, or nickel-chromium-molybdenum steel) and so on. The second digit gives the approximate amount of the principal alloying element—thus, 20 signifies 0.5 per cent nickel, 21 is 1.5 per cent nickel, and the 2300 steels contain 3.5 per cent nickel. The significance of the other series numbers is apparent from the compositions given in Table 10. The last two digits of the series number designate the median carbon content—thus, steel 2335 contains 3.5 per cent nickel and 0.30 to 0.40 per cent carbon, and steel 3325 contains 3.25 to 3.75 per cent nickel, 1.25 to 1.75 per cent chromium, and 0.20 to 0.30 per cent carbon. There are a few S.A.E. steels which differ from the rest of the series in the percentage of one alloying element. Such steels are given the prefix X before the series number.[7] An example of these steels is X3140 which contains 0.35 to 0.45 per cent carbon, 1.00 to 1.50 per cent nickel, and 0.60 to 0.90 instead of 0.45 to 0.75 per cent chromium. The manganese percentages of the S.A.E. 2000, 3000, 4000, 5000, and 6000 series vary, depending upon the carbon and alloy percentages, from 0.30 to 0.90 per cent. All these steels, whether carbon or alloy grades, are killed and have a specified silicon content of 0.15 to 0.30 per cent.

Some of the S.A.E. steels, especially the T1300, 2000, and 2300 series, are closely allied to some of the low-alloy structural steels discussed in the previous sections. Jal-Ten, for example, is T1325 containing a small amount of copper, and Hi-Steel is 2010 with 1 per cent copper and 0.12 per cent phosphorus.

124. **Properties of the S.A.E. Low-alloy Steels**—Composition, series number, and recommended heat treatment for all the S.A.E. steels are given in the *S.A.E. Handbook* and in many other readily accessible sources and need not be considered here. These steels are more expensive than the low-alloy structural steels, and furthermore, they must be heat treated to be of the greatest value. They

---

[7] In the unalloyed carbon steels, series 1xxx, the plain carbon steels are 10xx, the high-sulphur free-machining steels are 11xx, the high-sulphur free-machining steels containing 1.00 to 1.60 per cent manganese are X13xx, and the intermediate-manganese steels with 1.60 to 1.90 per cent manganese and less than 0.05 per cent sulphur are T13xx. See the *S.A.E. Handbook* for details on the modifications of the regular series.

are widely used in the construction of automobiles and aircraft—
especially engines—and for machine tools, particularly for highly
stressed parts such as crankshafts, camshafts, axle and other shafts,
gears, bolts, studs, steering knuckles, spindles, collets, valves, and
numerous others.

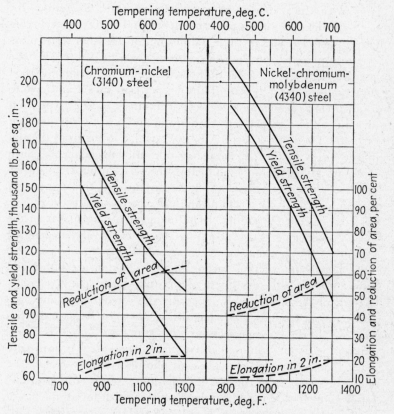

Fig. 75—Effect of tempering on the tensile properties of oil-quenched
(A) nickel-chromium (S.A.E. 3140) and (B) nickel-chromium-molybdenum
(S.A.E. 4340) steels (S.A.E. Handbook).

With the specifications for composition and heat treatment, the
S.A.E. Handbook also gives charts of minimum tensile properties
and hardness of the steels as quenched and as tempered at increasing temperatures. Fig. 75 is a combination of two such charts.
The data used for the construction of the S.A.E. charts of properties were obtained by dividing steels of the same alloy content

into two classes—according to the carbon percentage—and determining tensile properties. Tensile- and yield-strength values were plotted for the steels with the lower carbon, and elongation and reduction of area for the steels with the higher carbon. The curves such as are shown in Fig. 75 represent, therefore, conservative values which can be used safely in design.

The actual mechanical properties of a low-alloy steel—and a carbon steel as well—depend upon a large number of factors and

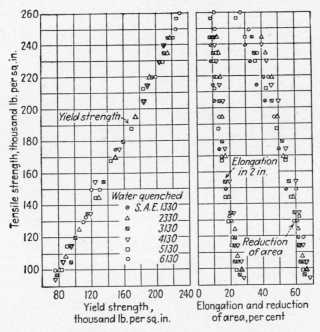

Fig. 76—Tensile properties of water-quenched and tempered S.A.E. low-alloy steels containing about 0.30 per cent carbon (Janitzky and Baeyertz).

may vary considerably if the composition, especially the carbon, varies in different parts of a lot of the same steel, or if the grain size varies, or if the heat treatment varies slightly owing to irregularities in heating, or in the furnace temperature, or in temperature-measuring equipment. For this reason it is safer to use minimum properties rather than average properties in design.

125. The S.A.E. Low-alloy Steels as Engineering Materials— The low-nickel steels, especially 2110, 2115, and 2120, are used regularly, in the rolled condition, for engine bolts and boiler plate and, to a lesser extent, in bridge and ship construction. Depending on the carbon content, the tensile strength is 65,000 to 90,000 lb. per sq. in., the yield strength is 45,000 to 55,000 lb. per sq. in., the elongation in 8 in. is 20 to 30 per cent, and the reduction of area is 45 to 70 per cent.

Most of the S.A.E. steels are used for applications involving high stresses, especially in moving parts. When properly heat

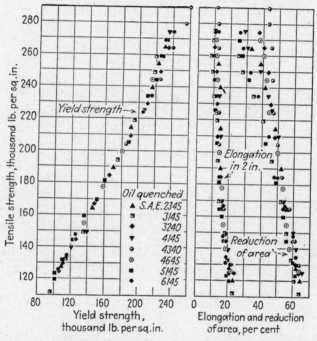

Fig. 77—Tensile properties of oil-quenched and tempered S.A.E. low-alloy steels containing about 0.40 to 0.45 per cent carbon (Janitzky and Baeyertz).

treated, they combine high ductility with high strength. Compared with carbon steels of the same tensile strength and hardness, heat-treated low-alloy steels have 30 to 40 per cent higher yield strength, 10 to 20 per cent higher elongation, and 35 to 40 per cent higher reduction of area. The impact resistance of the S.A.E. steels is frequently twice that of a carbon steel of the same tensile strength.

Another important characteristic of the S.A.E. low-alloy steels as a class is that they are deeper hardening than carbon steels, in other words, the mass effect is smaller. It is easier than with carbon steels to harden large sections throughout. Moreover, as the critical cooling rate is much lower, oil quenching can be used to attain high strength and hardness with less possibility of distortion or the introduction of high internal stresses.

The selection of a specific S.A.E. alloy steel for a certain application is sometimes difficult owing to the fact that in general the mechanical properties of the steels, when heat treated to the same tensile strength, do not differ greatly. This is shown in Figs. 76 and 77 from work reported by Janitzky and Baeyertz.[8] These investigators quenched 1-in. round bars of a number of S.A.E. alloy steels in water and in oil and tempered them at various temperatures in accord with S.A.E. recommendations. Yield strength, elongation, and reduction of area were plotted against tensile strength. For tensile strengths of 200,000 lb. per sq. in. or less, there is little difference in the steels. With higher strengths, more scatter is apparent in the ductility values. As most alloy steels are used in applications where a tensile strength of 200,000 lb. per sq. in. is sufficient, it is evident that the choice of a steel must be based upon cost or upon some factor other than tensile properties.

[8] E. J. Janitzky and M. Baeyertz, *Metals Handbook,* American Society for Metals, Cleveland, 1939, pp. 515-518.

Chapter 14

HIGH-ALLOY STEELS AS ENGINEERING MATERIALS

HIGH-ALLOY steels are a relatively recent development. Except for high-speed steel, austenitic manganese steel, and one or two others, most of the development work on these materials has been done in the past 20 or 25 years. Although a large amount of exploratory work on the alloys of iron with chromium and nickel was done in England, France, and Germany during the years 1885 to 1900, the remarkable corrosion-resisting properties of the iron-chromium alloys containing 11 to 30 per cent chromium and of the iron-chromium-nickel alloys containing 15 to 25 per cent chromium and 6 to 20 per cent nickel were overlooked. The now important so-called stainless steels were not discovered until the period between 1910 and 1915.

There are several hundred high-alloy steels which, as noted in section 34, can be divided into three general classes: (1) high-speed and other high-tungsten, high-chromium die and valve steels; (2) corrosion- and heat-resisting steels whose basic alloying element is chromium in amounts varying between 10 and 30 per cent, either alone or together with nickel or other alloying elements, and (3) special steels used in a few specific applications where unique magnetic and electric properties, or special expansion characteristics, or wear resistance, or some other properties are important. These steels vary widely in composition and are lumped together primarily for convenience.

High-speed steel contains about 75 per cent iron and 25 per cent alloying elements. Since it is used chiefly for tools and dies and only to a minor extent for other engineering purposes, it is included in the discussion on tool steels in the next chapter. Most of the discussion in this chapter on high-alloy steels as engineering materials deals broadly with the corrosion- and heat-resisting materials and to a lesser extent with the steels with special properties.

126. Classes of High-chromium Steels—The high-chromium and chromium-alloy steels may be divided into three classes: (1) special-purpose steels containing 3.5 to 10 per cent chromium with or without 0.5 to 4 per cent silicon, nickel, molybdenum, or tungsten as additional alloying elements; (2) corrosion- and heat-resisting steels containing more than 10 per cent chromium and not more than 2 per cent of another alloying element; and (3) corrosion- and heat-resisting steels containing more than 10 per cent chromium and more than 2 per cent of one or more other alloying metals.

Chromium steels containing 3.5 to 10 per cent chromium have better corrosion and heat resistance than the S.A.E. low-alloy steels containing chromium (see Fig. 80) and have excellent properties at elevated temperatures. Steel with about 0.10 per cent carbon, 4 to 6 per cent chromium, 0.40 to 0.75 per cent silicon, and about 0.50 per cent molybdenum is used widely in oil-refining equipment. Another steel in this class is silchrome, a material commonly used for automobile- and airplane-engine valves and containing about 0.50 per cent carbon, 7 to 10 per cent chromium, and 1.00 to 3.75 per cent silicon. Silchrome is resistant to attack by the exhaust gases of internal-combustion engines and has satisfactory strength and hardness at a dull red heat. Moreover, it costs considerably less than the highly alloyed valve materials containing nickel, chromium, and silicon.

The most important high-alloy steels in which chromium is the only alloying element in large amounts are those included in class 2. These may be divided into four groups:

2A—Low-carbon, high-chromium steel—usually called stainless iron—containing 12 to 18 per cent chromium and less than about 0.14 per cent carbon.

2B—Cutlery steels containing 12 to 16 per cent chromium and 0.20 to 0.60 per cent carbon.

2C—Tool and die steels containing 12 to 18 per cent chromium and 0.70 to 2 per cent carbon.

2D—Heat-resisting steels containing 20 to 30 per cent chromium, with less than 0.50 per cent carbon for hot-worked material, and with 0.50 to 2.5 per cent carbon for castings.

Small amounts—generally less than 2 per cent—of nickel or other metals are occasionally added to the plain chromium steels. With the exception, however, of 0.15 to 0.50 per cent sulphur to improve machinability, the addition of small percentages of a second alloying element is not common.

The principal corrosion- and heat-resisting steel of class 3 is the familiar low-carbon 18 per cent chromium, 8 per cent nickel alloy known to metallurgists and engineers as 18-8. This is a very important high-alloy engineering steel. Despite the cost, which varies between 25 and 60 cents a pound, depending upon the section and the carbon content, the amount of 18-8 used per year has increased from about 20,000 tons in 1929 to 78,000 tons in 1939.[1] Most of the 18-8 steels contain no other alloying element. A few which must have exceptional stability at elevated temperatures contain small percentages of molybdenum, titanium, or columbium, added to stabilize the carbon and prevent intergranular corrosion. This is discussed later.

127. Constitution of High-chromium Steels—Chromium in amounts less than 30 per cent dissolves completely in carbonless iron. It has marked effects on the temperature of the A_3 transformation, where alpha changes to gamma iron or vice versa, and on A_4, where gamma changes to the high-temperature modification of alpha (delta) iron or vice versa. These effects are important in commercial high-chromium steels and should receive some attention.

A portion of the iron-chromium diagram for alloys containing less than 50 per cent chromium is shown in Fig. 78.[2] From this diagram it is evident that adding 8 per cent chromium to carbonless iron lowers the A_3 point slightly and lowers the A_4 point nearly 275° F. (150° C.). Further additions of chromium raise A_3 and at the same time lower A_4 until, with the addition of about 12 per cent chromium, these two points merge. The result is what is known as the gamma loop and is a characteristic of several binary alloy systems of which iron is one component.

The significance of the gamma loop is plain. If an alloy containing 10 per cent chromium and 90 per cent iron is heated slowly, no change in structure occurs until a temperature of 1650° F. (900° C.) is reached. Here the alpha solid solution changes to gamma solid solution. If heating is continued, the

1 *The Iron Age*, May 23, 1940, p. 35.

2 A. B. Kinzel and Walter Crafts, *The Alloys of Iron and Chromium*, Vol. 1, *Low-chromium Alloys*, McGraw-Hill Book Company, Inc., New York, 1937, p. 43.

gamma remains unchanged until a temperature of 2350° F. (1200° C.) is reached, where it changes to alpha (delta) solid solution. In slow cooling, the reverse changes take place. If, now, an alloy containing 15 per cent chromium and 85 per cent iron is heated, no change (except grain growth) takes place between

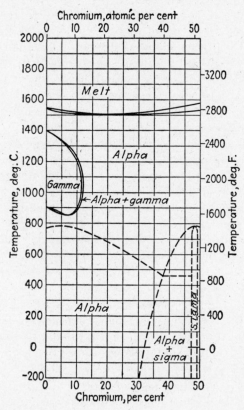

Fig. 78—Iron-rich portion of the iron-chromium phase diagram (Kinzel and Crafts).

room temperature and the melting point, and, conversely, no structural change occurs in cooling. Alloys containing more than 12 per cent (and less than 30 per cent) chromium and very little or no carbon have no allotropic transformations.

The concentration limits of the gamma loop are changed by carbon, which moves the extreme limit of the loop to the right and at the same time increases the width of the duplex alpha-plus-gamma field. Thus the loop, which with negligible carbon extends to 12 per cent chromium, extends to about 18 per cent chromium with 0.40 per cent carbon. These relationships are complicated further by the carbides which are formed by chromium and which together with iron carbide (Fe_3C) form $(Cr,Fe)_7C_3$ and $(Cr,Fe)_4C$ in the commercial high-chromium steels. The iron-chromium carbides are partly soluble in the gamma solid solution but not in the alpha solid solution and may be retained in supersaturated solid solution by quenching, in a manner analogous to the retention of iron carbide, Fe_3C, in the gamma iron of unalloyed high-carbon steel.

128. Relation of the Constitution of High-chromium Steels to Their Heat Treatment—From the foregoing discussion it is evident that we should know from the composition whether high-chromium steels will or will not respond to heat treatment. Thus, a steel containing 12 to 18 per cent chromium and less than 0.13 per cent carbon (class 2A, section 126) will or will not harden depending upon the relative amounts of chromium and carbon. If the steel contains 0.12 per cent carbon and 13 per cent chromium, some austenite is formed if the steel is heated to 1800° F. (980° C.), and this transforms to martensite upon quenching. If the steel contains 0.06 per cent carbon and 16 per cent chromium, no phase changes take place, and the steel does not harden when quenched from 1800° F. (980° C.). Low-carbon high-chromium steels in which no phase changes take place remain ferritic in structure at all temperatures. They are relatively soft and ductile, and the only change caused by heating is grain growth which reduces the ductility.

Cutlery steels containing 12 to 16 per cent chromium and 0.20 to 0.60 per cent carbon (class 2B, section 126) undergo a phase change: when they are heated to about 1800° F. (980° C.), the alpha solid solution changes to gamma and the carbide goes into solution. These steels respond to heat treatment very much like unalloyed high-carbon steels. In a steel containing 12 per cent chromium the structure is entirely pearlitic with only 0.3 per cent carbon when the steel is cooled slowly; it is, consequently, martensitic when the steel is cooled rapidly (Fig. 79A). These cutlery steels differ from unalloyed steel containing 0.80 to 0.85 per cent carbon chiefly in that the chromium lowers the critical cooling rate, i.e., they become as hard when quenched in oil, or even in air, as an unalloyed high-carbon steel when quenched in water.

Since steels containing 12 to 14 per cent chromium and 0.30 to 0.40 per cent carbon correspond to unalloyed "eutectoid" steels, it follows that high-chromium steels containing about 1 per cent carbon (class 2C, section 126) are hypereutectoid and, when quenched and tempered, have numerous excess carbide particles

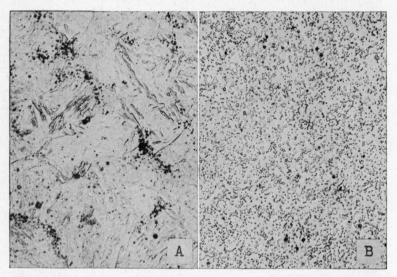

Fig. 79—Structure of (A) oil-quenched cutlery steel containing 0.30 per cent carbon and 12.7 per cent chromium, and (B) oil-quenched high-carbon chromium steel containing 0.70 per cent carbon and 17.5 per cent chromium; etched, 500× (Kinzel and Forgeng).

in the microstructure (Fig. 79B), which increase the wear resistance and make the steels useful for tools and dies.

The heat-resisting steels containing 20 to 30 per cent chromium (class 2D, section 126) may or may not respond to heat treatment, depending upon the carbon content. The carbon range for this class is 0.5 per cent or less for steels which are hot or cold worked, and from 0.5 to 2.5 per cent for those which are used in the form of castings. At room temperature the steels containing about 25 per cent chromium and less than 0.70 per cent carbon are ferritic; their structure consists of alpha solid solution and the carbide $(Cr,Fe)_4C$, and no phase changes take place in heating. These steels cannot be hardened; they can, of course, be annealed if cold worked.

The higher carbon grades respond to quenching, but this treatment is seldom used as no advantage results. High-carbon castings containing 20 to 30 per cent chromium are very hard as cast and must be annealed if machining is necessary.

The price of ferrochromium (70 per cent chromium) used in the manufacture of high-chromium steel varies inversely with the carbon percentage. Ferrochromium containing less than 0.5 per cent carbon, which must be used to produce high-chromium steels with low carbon percentages, is much more costly than ferrochromium containing 4 to 6 per cent carbon. The economic factor is, therefore, important in selecting a high-chromium steel for a certain application: the advantages resulting from the use of a steel containing less than 0.12 per cent carbon, instead of one containing 0.40 per cent, must be balanced against the higher cost of this material.

129. Mechanical Properties of High-chromium Steels—As remarked in the previous chapter (section 119), chromium has little solid-solution effect, i.e., when dissolved in alpha iron, it strengthens the iron relatively little. This is shown by the data in Table 11 [3] for annealed steels and in Fig. 73. If the composition is such that the steel undergoes a phase change, the principal effect of chromium is to increase the hardenability, thus producing marked changes in properties with relatively slow cooling rates (see Fig. 73).

TABLE 11.   EFFECT OF CHROMIUM ON THE TENSILE PROPERTIES OF ANNEALED STEELS CONTAINING 0.10 PER CENT CARBON

Chromium, per cent	Tensile strength, lb. per sq. in.	Yield strength, lb. per sq. in.	Elongation in 2 in., per cent	Brinell hardness
0	50,000	38,000	44	90
5	65,000	26,000	38	135
12	72,000	35,000	36	140
15.5	75,500	42,500	33	148
17	80,000	47,000	30	155
27	84,500	55,000	26	160

The tensile properties of high-chromium steels cooled in air or oil depend obviously upon how much carbon is present and

[3] Based on E. E. Thum, *Metal Progress*, v. 29, 1936, No. 6, pp. 49-57, 104.

upon what proportion of the carbides dissolves in the gamma solid solution at high temperatures. Some typical values for tensile properties of low-carbon 12 to 15 per cent chromium steel and for cutlery steel are given in Table 12.[4] The high-chromium steels are more resistant to tempering than carbon and low-alloy steels. Increasing the tempering temperature has little effect on the properties until a temperature of 950 to 1050° F. (510 to 565° C.) is reached when there is a sudden decrease in tensile strength, yield strength, and hardness and a moderate increase in ductility.

TABLE 12. TYPICAL TENSILE PROPERTIES OF HIGH-CHROMIUM STEELS

Composition, per cent		Quenched and tempered at		Tensile strength, lb. per sq. in.	Yield strength, lb. per sq. in.	Elonga-tion in 2 in., per cent	Reduc-tion of area, per cent	Brinell hard-ness
C	Cr	° F.	° C.					
0.09	12.2	400	205	146,000	135,000	15	38	290
		600	315	145,000	134,000	15	40	290
		800	425	143,000	134,000	16	46	290
		1000	540	135,000	120,000	20	52	250
		1200	650	95,000	79,000	29	60	200
0.09	15.3	400	205	170,000	160,000	8	18	363
		600	315	168,000	160,000	10	20	363
		800	425	166,000	160,000	15	45	363
		1000	540	160,000	148,000	18	46	363
		1200	650	90,000	83,000	21	50	200
0.30	13.0	600	315	240,000	208,000	3	5	470
		800	425	245,000	210,000	5	20	460
		1000	540	250,000	195,000	7	20	450
		1200	650	160,000	138,000	12	38	325
		1400	760	140,000	105,000	14	45	300

The impact resistance of the quenched and tempered low-carbon and medium-carbon (cutlery) steels is in general satisfactory, except when the steels are tempered at, or cooled slowly through, the temperature range 875 to 1000° F. (470 to 540° C.). For reasons yet unknown this treatment causes brittleness, which is manifested by very low notched-bar impact resistance. The endurance limit of both the hardenable and the unhardenable high-chromium steels is about one half of the tensile strength or approximately the same as for carbon and low-alloy steels. The

[4] Based on data by Giles, *The Book of Stainless Steels*, American Society for Metals, Cleveland, 1935, pp. 267-276; and Parmiter, *Trans. Am. Soc. Steel Treat.*, v. 6, 1924, pp. 315-340.

modulus of elasticity, however, seems to be somewhat higher; most available data indicate that it is between 31 and 32 million lb. per sq. in.

130. **Corrosion and Oxidation Resistance of High-chromium Steels**—Although high-chromium steels are more resistant to certain kinds of corrosion than any other ferrous material, they are not corrosion resistant in the broadest sense of the term. Neither are they always stainless. In fact, to some forms of attack, they are no more resistant than the unalloyed carbon steels.

Steels containing 10 per cent or more chromium are resistant to oxidizing media and to corrosion caused by fruit juices, food products, and beverages. The low-carbon 12 to 18 per cent chromium steels are resistant to a large number of organic acids and to all concentrations of nitric acid, except 65 per cent boiling nitric acid. They are also resistant to strong alkalis and to many salt solutions but are readily attacked by chlorides and other halides. Sulphuric acid, except when concentrated and cold or when containing nitric acid, and hydrochloric acid of all concentrations attack these steels readily.

In general, corrosion resistance is a function of the amount of chromium dissolved in the iron, but the relation is not direct. Corrosion resistance is not important with low percentages of chromium; it becomes more pronounced as the chromium increases from 4 to 10 per cent and increases very rapidly with slightly more than 10 per cent. The corrosion resistance is thought to be due to the formation of a thin, tight, adherent film of chromium-iron oxide which, if broken, is self-healing unless the corrosive agent (as, for example, hydrochloric acid or chlorides) dissolves the film as rapidly as it is formed. It is generally assumed that in order to produce a self-healing film there should be at least one atom of chromium to seven atoms of iron. Increasing the chromium from 10 to 30 per cent increases the corrosion resistance, but the increase is not proportional to that of the chromium.

Carbides, if not in solution, have a deleterious effect on corrosion resistance. For this reason, the cutlery steels should be heat treated if optimum corrosion and stain resistance is desired. The alloys containing carbon in excess of that which dissolves in the gamma solid solution at high temperatures are not so resistant to oxidizing media as the lower carbon steels.

The high-chromium steels rust slowly when exposed to the atmosphere, but the coating can readily be wiped off, leaving the surface underneath unaffected. Steels containing 12 to 14 per cent chromium and less than 0.12 per cent carbon are, therefore, widely used for automobile trim. In industrial atmospheres, especially those containing sulphur, the high-chromium steels may pit badly.

The resistance of the high-chromium steels to oxidation at elevated temperatures increases with the chromium but, as shown in

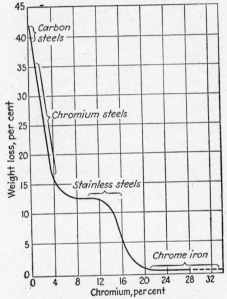

Fig. 80—Effect of chromium on the resistance of chromium steels to oxidation at 1830° F. (1000° C.) (MacQuigg).

Fig. 80, the increase is not important until more than 10 per cent chromium is present. With higher chromium percentages the increase in oxidation resistance is fairly uniform until about 20 per cent chromium is present, when the resistance is very high. The data shown in Fig. 80 were obtained [5] by heating 0.5-in. cubes with ground surfaces for 48 hr. at 1830° F. (1000° C.). With the exception of a few iron-nickel-chromium and iron-chromium-

[5] C. E. MacQuigg, *The Book of Stainless Steels*, American Society for Metals, Cleveland, 1935, pp. 351-368.

aluminum alloys, steel containing 20 to 35 per cent chromium is the most resistant of the ferrous alloys to high-temperature oxidation.

131. **The Constitution of 18-8**—Nickel (as well as chromium) is soluble in both alpha and gamma iron. When in solution it (1)

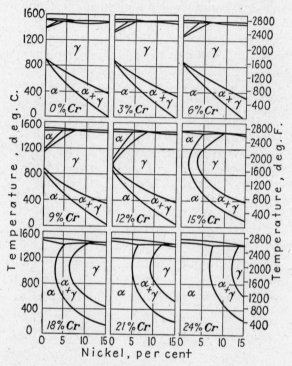

Fig. 81—Effect of chromium on phase changes in iron-nickel alloys (Bain and Aborn).

lowers the A_3 point, where alpha iron transforms to gamma on heating and where gamma transforms to alpha on cooling, and (2) makes these allotropic changes, especially the one on cooling, very sluggish. A small portion of the iron-nickel phase diagram is shown in the upper left corner in Fig. 81.[6] As noted on a previous page (p. 232), chromium restricts the temperature-concentration region where the gamma solid solution is stable, i.e.,

[6] E. C. Bain and R. H. Aborn, "The Iron-nickel-chromium System," *Metals Handbook*, American Society for Metals, Cleveland, 1939, pp. 418-422.

it produces a gamma loop; nickel, on the contrary, increases the limits of this area.

When chromium is added to the iron-nickel solid solution it dissolves. The first effect is a lowering of the delta- (alpha-)-gamma transformation temperature and a widening of the field where delta (alpha) is stable. This is apparent from the sections of Fig. 81 showing phase relations for alloys containing 3 and 6 per cent chromium. As the chromium is increased, the area of the delta (alpha) region is increased further, and with 9 per cent or more the low-temperature area where alpha is stable is also increased. Increasing the chromium thus moves the boundaries of the gamma and the alpha-plus-gamma phase regions to the right.

Consider now the small diagram at the lower left in Fig. 81 for 18 per cent chromium: if 3 per cent nickel is added and the alloy is heated, no phase changes take place at any temperature. If, however, 8 per cent nickel is present and the alloy is heated, a phase change occurs at about 660° F. (350° C.), and some of the alpha solid solution changes to gamma solid solution. If the alloy is heated still further, this allotropic change continues until at 1200° F. (650° C.) all the alpha has changed to gamma. There is no further change if the heating is continued almost to the melting point. Now, if the alloy is cooled, the reverse changes *should* take place, i.e., gamma should start to transform to alpha at 1200° F. and should be completely transformed at 660° F. Owing, however, to the sluggishness of the reactions, only a small amount of alpha is actually formed in slow cooling, and it is relatively easy to suppress by rapid cooling the formation of any and thus to obtain at room temperature an alloy that is entirely austenitic.

Austenitic steels are strong and ductile and are readily deformed cold into a variety of useful products. For a combination of maximum resistance to corrosion by certain media, austenitic structure at room temperature, and other useful properties the most economical composition is 18 per cent chromium and 8 per cent nickel, with carbon as low as is commercially possible. Even with this composition it is advisable to guard against the presence of any alpha by heating the material to 1830 to 2010° F. (1000 to 1100° C.) and quenching it in water or in an air blast. Increasing the nickel to 14 per cent increases the stability of the austenite but also increases the cost.

132. The Role of Carbon in 18-8—If 18-8 could be made free from carbon, most of the troubles of the manufacturers and users of this steel would be over. Unfortunately, however, this is impossible, and even if made by the best commercial practice, 18-8 contains 0.06 and frequently as much as 0.12 per cent of this element. Unfortunately also, only about 0.01 or 0.02 per cent carbon is soluble in the iron-chromium-nickel austenite at room temperature. This solubility increases with increasing temperature as shown in Fig. 82,[7] until at 1830° F. (1000° C.) 0.14 per

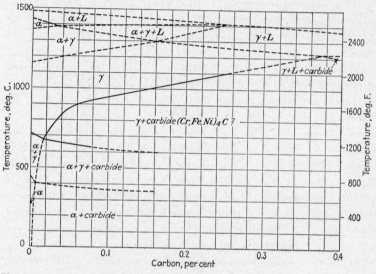

Fig. 82—Effect of temperature on the solubility of carbon in iron-chromium-nickel austenite (Kinzel and Franks).

cent, and at 2010° F. (1100° C.) 0.22 per cent is soluble. One advantage of quenching 18-8 is that the carbon is held in supersaturated solution at room temperature. This carbon, however, will precipitate if conditions are favorable. Severe cold working may cause some precipitation; in addition—and this is most important—on heating to a high temperature, as in welding or in service in superheaters or other equipment operating at elevated temperatures, some carbon precipitates from solution.

[7] A. B. Kinzel and R. Franks, *The Alloys of Iron and Chromium*, Vol. II, *High-chromium Alloys*, McGraw-Hill Book Company, Inc., New York, 1940, p. 275.

If this were the only thing that happened, it would not be serious. However, when the carbon precipitates, it is apparently thrown out of solution at the grain boundaries as a chromium carbide, thus impoverishing the austenite grains adjacent to the boundaries in chromium and making them susceptible to corrosion. The usual structure of quenched 18-8 showing the polyhedral grains of austenite is pictured in Fig. 83A [8]; the carbides

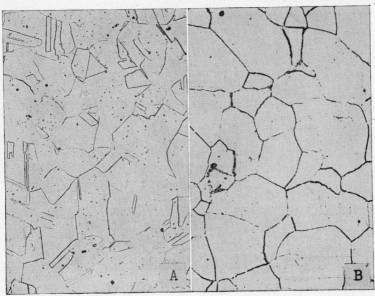

Fig. 83—Structure of (A) quenched 18-8 and (B) quenched and reheated 18-8 showing carbide precipitation at grain boundaries; etched, 250× (Kinzel and Forgeng).

which have precipitated at the grain boundaries are shown in Fig. 83B.

Carbide precipitation occurs frequently if 18-8 is heated in the range 570 to 1470° F. (300 to 800° C.), making the material very susceptible to a form of attack known as intergranular corrosion or intergranular disintegration. It is very hard to detect and was the cause of a number of disastrous failures before a cure was found.

Carbide precipitation can be prevented by reducing the carbon to 0.02 per cent or less, which is industrially impracticable, and

[8] Courtesy of A. B. Kinzel and W. D. Forgeng.

can be rendered innocuous by adding titanium equivalent to 5 times the carbon content, or columbium equivalent to 10 times the carbon content, to the steel when it is made. Both of these elements combine with the carbon to form a stable carbide and prevent the carbon from combining with the chromium. When 18-8 is "stabilized" with titanium or columbium it can be used at elevated temperatures or can be welded without danger of premature failure.

133. Properties of 18-8—The austenitic chromium-nickel steels can readily be cold rolled into sheet or strip or cold drawn into wire. They can also be riveted, soldered, or welded. Welding is now commonly used for fabricating 18-8. Because of its high electric resistivity and low thermal conductivity, spot welding has been especially successful. This method of joining is used in the construction of the stainless-steel streamlined trains which have attracted much attention recently.

Austenitic chromium-nickel steel has, as quenched, a fairly high tensile strength with high ductility and resistance to impact (Table 13). It hardens rapidly by cold work (Table 13). The increase in tensile and in yield strength is greater and the decrease in ductility is considerably less than that caused by comparable cold working of low-carbon steel. Carbon increases the strength (Table 13). The endurance ratio of quenched 18-8 is 0.40 to 0.45, i.e., somewhat lower than the usual ratio for carbon and low-alloy steels. Peculiarly, the endurance ratio is usually higher than the proportional limit.

TABLE 13. TYPICAL MECHANICAL PROPERTIES OF AUSTENITIC CHROMIUM-NICKEL STEEL

Composition, per cent			Condition of specimen	Tensile strength, lb. per sq. in.	Yield, strength, lb. per sq. in.	Elongation in 2 in., per cent	Reduction of area, per cent	Izod impact, ft-lb.
C	Cr	Ni						
0.06	18.0	8.0	Water-quenched bars	90,000	37,500	68	78	111
0.17	18.0	8.0	Water-quenched bars	96,500	40,000	65	75	103
0.07	17.9	8.5	Cold-rolled bars, 15%	142,700	117,800	30	61	88
0.07	17.9	8.5	Cold-rolled bars, 40%	227,600	201,000	11	43	17
0.07	18.0	9.5	Cold-drawn wire, 60%	263,000	......	4		
0.16	16.0	10.2	Cold-drawn wire, 85%	273,000	......	3		
0.07	18.0	8.0	Water-quenched sheet	86,400	33,500	63		
0.16	18.0	8.0	Water-quenched sheet	93,300	46,600	57		
0.06	18.0	14.0	Water-quenched bars	80,000	......	63	75	
0.14	18.0	14.0	Water-quenched bars	90,000		53	70	
0.14	25.0	20.0	Water-quenched bars	90,500	50,000	47	63	90

The coefficient of expansion of 18-8 is about 50 per cent higher than that of carbon steels, and the thermal conductivity at normal temperatures is about 0.04 cal. per sec. per sq. cm. as compared with 0.16 cal. per sec. per sq. cm. for low-carbon steel. The stress-strain curve of 18-8 is curved from the origin. This steel has, therefore, a low proportional limit, no yield point, and no true modulus of elasticity. The secant modulus varies from 26 to 28 million lb. per sq. in. The austenitic chromium-nickel steels have exceptionally high resistance to creep. This is discussed in a later chapter.

Nickel increases the resistance of low-carbon 18 per cent chromium steels to corrosion by non-oxidizing media, permitting these materials to be used economically in environments where the high-chromium steels containing no nickel would be attacked rapidly. These austenitic steels are resistant to many organic acids, organic solvents, and oils which attack the high-chromium steels. Their resistance to staining in the atmosphere is also higher than that of the plain chromium steels. Their oxidation resistance is high, especially at 1650° F. (900° C.), and if the chromium and nickel are both increased, they may be used at temperatures as high as 2010° F. (1100° C.). The corrosion and oxidation resistance and the strength and stability at high temperature can be increased by the addition of silicon, tungsten, or molybdenum.

134. High-nickel Steels and Special Iron-nickel Alloys— Nickel (see p. 240) dissolves in gamma and in alpha iron and has a strong effect on the position of A_3, not only lowering it to atmospheric temperature or below but, in addition, slowing greatly the rate of the phase change and producing some anomalies in properties which are of great value to industry. Alloys of iron with 20 to 30 per cent nickel may easily be made non-magnetic (despite the fact that both iron and nickel are magnetic). Alloys of iron with 30 to 60 per cent nickel have variable and controllable expansion characteristics which were discovered late in the 19th century in France. The fact that alloys of iron with 45 to 85 per cent nickel can be treated to produce high magnetic permeability and low hysteresis loss has led to wide use of some of them in telephone, telegraph, and radio equipment.

As shown in Fig. 84,[9] the coefficient of expansion between o and

[9] Based on data in J. S. Marsh, *The Alloys of Iron and Nickel,* Vol. I, *Special-purpose Alloys,* McGraw-Hill Book Company, Inc., New York, 1938, p. 160.

200° F. (−18 and 100° C.) decreases to nearly zero as nickel approaches 36 per cent. Increasing the nickel from 36 to 60 per cent makes it possible to have any desired coefficient of expansion between 1 and 12 × 10⁻⁶. As the result, a number of alloys have been developed for use in measuring tapes, watch parts, and parts of machines and instruments which must remain constant in dimension despite temperature changes. The use of invar struts in aluminum-alloy pistons is well known. Some of the commer-

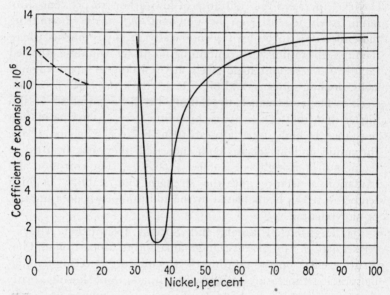

Fig. 84—Coefficient of expansion of iron-nickel alloys between 0 and 200° F. (Marsh).

cial alloys with controlled expansion characteristics are given in Table 14.

If chromium and tungsten are added to an alloy containing about 32 per cent nickel, the effect of temperature (in the vicinity of room temperature) on the modulus of elasticity is zero. This alloy is known as elinvar and is used for hairsprings of watches and for springs of other precision measuring instruments. The invars and other high-nickel alloys have the additional advantage that they have excellent corrosion resistance.

The alloys known as permalloy, hipernik, and perminvar are used in applications where their high or constant permeability

TABLE 14. COMMERCIAL HIGH-NICKEL ALLOYS

Name	Composition,* per cent						Characteristic properties
	Ni	Co	Cr	W	Al	Cu	
Invar	36	..	..	..	..	..	Low expansion from 0 to 200° F. (−18 to 100° C.)
Superinvar	31	5	..	..	..	..	Zero expansion near room temperature
Elinvar	32	..	5	2	..	..	Low thermoelastic coefficient
Dumet	42	..	..	..	..	..	For sealing in soft glass
Kovar	29	17	..	..	..	..	For sealing in hard glass
Platinite	46	..	..	..	..	..	Expansion same as platinum
Permalloy	78.5	..	..	..	..	..	High permeability at low field strengths
Hipernik	50	..	..	..	..	..	High permeability at higher field strengths
Perminvar	45	25	..	..	..	..	Constant permeability over a range of flux densities
Alnico I	20	5	..	..	12	..	Permanent magnet of high magnetic hardness
Alnico II	17	12.5	..	..	10	6	Same as above
Alnico III	25	..	..	..	12	..	Same as above
Alnico IV	28	5	..	..	12	..	Same as above

* Balance of composition is mostly iron.

produces marked economies or increased efficiencies in communication. Because under weak magnetizing forces permalloy has a permeability many times greater than that of all other ferrous materials except iron of the highest purity, permalloy is a commercially feasible high-permeability material. The development of this alloy has made modern long-distance telephony possible, and its use in the loading of submarine cables has speeded up the transmission of messages several hundred per cent. Hipernik has initial and maximum permeabilities much greater than those of commercial grades of high-purity iron and the advantage of relatively high maximum induction, which makes it valuable for use in radio transformers.

The efficiency of radio loud speakers and other apparatus requiring powerful permanent magnets has been greatly increased by the recent development of the iron-nickel-aluminum-cobalt permanent-magnet materials (see Table 14). In addition to alnico, two Japanese alloys are noteworthy: the M.K., containing 25 to 30 per cent nickel, 20 per cent cobalt, and 12 per cent aluminum; and the K.S., containing 10 to 25 per cent nickel, 15 to 36 per cent cobalt, and 8 to 25 per cent titanium.

135. **Austenitic Manganese Steel**—Of the large number of high-alloy steels which have not been discussed in this chapter, austenitic manganese steel is of sufficient industrial importance to deserve mention. This steel was discovered about 50 years ago by Hadfield in England during his pioneer researches on alloys of iron with manganese, silicon, nickel, chromium, and other elements. The annual tonnage of high-manganese steel used is small, but, as is the case with many ferrous materials, production is no criterion of its usefulness to industry. High-manganese steel contains 1.00 to 1.30 per cent carbon and 11 to 14 per cent manganese and is made by the basic open-hearth, Bessemer, or electric process. It may be poured into ingots and rolled into a variety of sections, or it may be cast in sand molds. Owing to its work-hardening capacity when cold, it cannot be machined readily; hence, if shaping is necessary, it usually must be ground. Economically this is a great disadvantage.

In amounts under 50 per cent, manganese dissolves in alpha and gamma iron. Like nickel it lowers the A_3 temperatures, where alpha transforms to gamma in heating and where the reverse change occurs in cooling, and slows the transformation rate. As noted in a previous chapter (p. 218), manganese also forms a carbide, $(Fe,Mn)_3C$, which is closely allied to Fe_3C in structure and properties. The phase relations for alloys of iron and 13 per cent manganese with 0 to 1.60 per cent carbon are shown in Fig. 85.[10] Alloys containing 1.00 to 1.30 per cent carbon and 13 per cent manganese, if cooled very slowly so that all phase changes take place, contain at room temperature alpha solid solution plus excess carbide. In the usual cooling after hot working, or in a mold in the case of a casting, these phase changes, owing to the low reaction rates, do not take place, and the structure consists of the gamma solid solution plus, possibly, a little alpha, plus excess carbide as massive particles or as a network around the grains. With this structure the steel is hard and brittle. If, however, the steel is heated to 1830 to 2010° F. (1000 to 1100° C.), the carbide goes into solution in the gamma (see Fig. 85), and if the steel is now quenched in water, a structure consisting wholly of austenite with no free carbide is obtained.

[10] C. Wells and F. M. Walters, Jr., *Trans. Am. Soc. Steel Treat.,* v. 21, 1933, pp. 830-864.

Unfortunately, tempering to relieve quenching stresses is impossible because, as Fig. 85 shows, reheating in the temperature range 930 to 1290° F. (500 to 700° C.) or even lower may cause precipitation of carbide or change of some gamma to alpha and thus may cause brittleness.

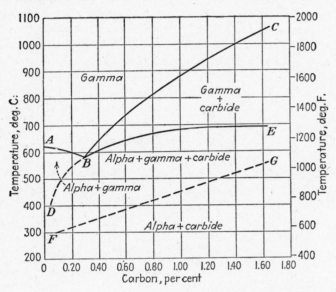

Fig. 85—Effect of carbon on the phase relations of an iron-manganese alloy containing 13 per cent manganese (Wells and Walters).

As water quenched, rolled austenitic manganese steel has the following properties:

Tensile strength, lb. per sq. in...... 130,000 to 160,000
Proportional limit, lb. per sq. in.... 40,000 to 60,000
Elongation in 2 in., per cent....... 60 to 70
Reduction of area, per cent........ 40 to 60
Brinell hardness................ 180 to 220

As is characteristic of austenitic alloys, the high-manganese steels have no well-defined yield point and are non-magnetic.

High-manganese steel is important industrially chiefly because of its high abrasion resistance. Although the Brinell hardness of the heat-treated steel is low, cold working causes a rapid increase to as much as 550 Brinell. As abrasion consists largely of cold working the surface, this capacity for work hardening has important ramifications. Thus, in steam-shovel buckets, in crushers, grinders, and other machines, and in rails, cross-overs, switches, frogs and such sections where pounding, pressure, and abrasion by rock and sand are encountered, high-manganese steel outwears high-carbon steel by several hundred per cent.

CHAPTER 15

TOOL AND DIE STEELS

THE group of carbon and alloy steels included under the generic term "tool steel" is one of the least important classes of ferrous materials in tonnage and is the most important in value to man. Without the aid of modern tools, steel in large tonnages could not be made or used cheaply, and probably could not be made or used at all; without the use of tools, not even the most primitive structure or machine could be built or used. Civilization is inconceivable without tools.

Weak in himself [says Carlyle] and of small stature, man stands on a basis . . . of some half square foot, insecurely enough; he has to straddle out his legs, lest the very wind supplant him. Feeblest of bipeds! Three quintals are a crushing load for him; the steer of the meadow tosses him aloft like a waste rag. Nevertheless he can use tools, can devise tools; with these the granite mountain melts into light dust before him; he kneads glowing iron as if it were soft paste; seas are his smooth highway, winds and fire his unvarying steeds. Nowhere do you find him without tools; without tools he is nothing; with tools he is all.

The steady, if slow, advance of civilization over the past ten or twelve thousand years has been largely the result of progress in the design of tools and in the material from which they are fashioned: from stone to copper, and then to bronze, and then to iron, and then after a long period to carburized iron (steel)—which was the most important step of all—and finally to high-speed and other alloy-steel tools which made possible great reductions in the cost of finished structures and machines.

A tool, as every one knows, is an implement or a mechanism used for working, moving, or changing the shape of material. Tool steel is not so easy to define. To the logical layman, tool steel should be any steel which is used for a tool; to the metallurgist, however, and to the engineer using tools, tool steel has a more restricted meaning. Metallurgically, tool steel is steel with special characteristics made with great care to ensure what **Gill** calls tool-steel quality.[1]   There are many cheap tools, including hammers, crowbars, axes, and others, which are made of basic open-hearth steel of ordinary quality.   These are tools, but the steel is not tool steel in the metallurgical sense.   Gill pertinently stated: "A steel rail can be cut apart and forged into a shear blade, satisfactory for certain purposes," but rail steel is certainly not of tool-steel quality.   There is, moreover, an important class of steel products, including valves, ball and roller bearings and races, magnets, and others, which are not tools, but which are fashioned of steel of tool-steel quality and which are, therefore, made and processed by the tool-steel makers.   Steel of tool-steel quality is nearly always made in the basic electric furnace.

136. Classification and Characteristics of Tool Steels—It is impossible to classify tool steels by their uses.   Many tools, such as drills, chisels, taps, dies, cutters, shear blades, and others, may be made of unalloyed high-carbon steel, of low-alloy steel, or of high-speed steel.   According to Gill, at least 95 per cent of all the thousand or more brands of tool steel is of 13 general types distinguished by chemical composition.   These types and their principal characteristics are given in Tables 15 and 16.

All tools can be divided broadly into two general classes: (1) cutting and shearing tools and (2) forming tools.   Requirements differ and should be considered before the proper steel is selected.   Thus, for cutting and shearing, high hardness, ability to withstand wear, stability of structure to withstand the heat generated by the friction of the cutting edge against the work, and a substantial amount of toughness to prevent chipping and breakage are important.   For shearing tools, a lack of deformation or warping in heat treatment is usually also important.   Forming tools consist chiefly of dies, which are used to transfer their impression to either hot or cold solid metal, or to molten metal.   In addition to possessing the qualities necessary in a cutting or shearing tool, forming tools must be resistant to distortion in heat treatment and to cracking caused by sudden changes in temperature during use.

[1] The classification and the general discussion of tool steels in this chapter are based largely upon a series of lectures to the American Society for Metals (New York Meeting, Oct. 1934) by J. P. Gill, and upon the sections on tool steel in the *Metals Handbook*, American Society for Metals, Cleveland, 1939, pp. 987-1029.

TABLE 15. CLASSIFICATION OF TOOL STEELS ACCORDING TO CHEMICAL COMPOSITION (GILL)

Type No.	Type	Chemical composition, per cent					
		Carbon	Silicon	Manganese	Tungsten	Chromium	Vanadium
1	High-carbon	0.60 to 1.40	0.15 to 0.50	0.10 to 0.35	....	....	0.10 to 0.40
2	Carbon-vanadium	0.60 to 1.40	0.15 to 0.50	0.10 to 0.35	....	....	0.00 to 0.20
3	Low-chromium	0.60 to 1.40	0.15 to 0.50	0.10 to 0.35	....	0.20 to 1.00	....
4	Oil-hardening manganese *	0.85 to 1.00	0.20 to 0.40	1.00 to 1.75	0.30 to 0.60	0.30 to 0.90	0.00 to 0.25
5	Silicon-manganese †	0.50 to 0.70	1.75 to 2.25	0.70 to 1.00	....	0.00 to 0.40	0.00 to 0.30
6	Low-tungsten	1.00 to 1.30	0.20 to 0.40	0.10 to 0.30	1.00 to 2.50	0.35 to 0.60	0.00 to 0.25
7	Tungsten chisel steel	0.45 to 0.60	0.20 to 1.50	....	0.75 to 2.50	0.75 to 2.00	0.00 to 0.30
8	Finishing tool steel	1.20 to 1.40	....	....	3.00 to 6.00	0.00 to 1.50	....
9	Chromium, for hot working †	0.70 to 1.00	....	....	....	3.00 to 4.25	....
10	Tungsten, for hot working	0.25 to 0.60	....	....	8.00 to 19.00	1.25 to 4.50	0.30 to 1.20
11	Chromium-tungsten, hot working †	0.30 to 0.50	0.20 to 1.00	....	0.75 to 7.50	1.00 to 7.50	....
12	High-carbon, high-chromium ‡	1.40 to 2.45	....	....	....	12.00 to 18.00	0.00 to 1.00
13	High-speed ‡	0.55 to 1.00	....	....	14.00 to 21.00	4.00 to 4.50	1.00 to 2.25

* If manganese is 1.50 to 1.75 per cent, may contain no other alloying elements.
† May contain molybdenum.
‡ May contain cobalt and/or molybdenum.

TABLE 16. CHARACTERISTICS OF PRINCIPAL TYPES OF TOOL STEEL (GILL)

Type No.	Usual working hardness Rockwell C	Resistance to wear	Toughness	Distortion in heat treatment	Resistance to softening at elevated temperature	Quenching medium	Depth of hardening
1	*	Low	*	High	Low	Water	Shallow
2	*	Low	*	High	Low	Water	Shallow
3	*	Low	*	High	Low	Water	Medium
4	58 to 62	Low	Medium	Low	Low	Oil	Medium
5	50 to 57	Medium	Medium	Medium	Medium	Water	Medium
6	62 to 65	Medium	Medium	Low	Low	Oil	Medium
7	50 to 55	Medium	High	Low	Medium	Oil	Medium
8	63 to 66	Medium	Low	High	Medium	Water	Deep
9	45 to 50	Medium	Medium	Low	Medium	Air or oil	Deep
10	45 to 55	Medium	Medium	Low	High	Air or oil	Deep
11	43 to 50	Medium	Medium	Low	High	Air or oil	Deep
12	58 to 66	High	Low	Low	High	Air or oil	Deep
13	62 to 66	High	Low	Low	High	Air or oil	Deep

* Depends upon carbon content and heat treatment.

Gill rates the important characteristics of most tool steels in the following order: hardness, wear resistance, toughness, distortion in heat treatment, resistance to deformation in use, resistance to softening at elevated temperatures, machinability, and cost. For all but the cheapest manually operated tools (crowbars, hammers, axes, etc.) the cost of the steel is of minor importance, as it is frequently only one or two per cent of the cost of machining and treating the finished tool.

The selection of the proper tool steel for a certain machining operation is difficult and is a problem in the solution of which the advice of the tool-steel metallurgist is very helpful. As Table 16 indicates, tool steels vary widely in characteristics. To select the proper steel means to balance undesirable against desirable properties and to take into account not only the cost of the steel and the cost of machining but also the cost of the finished tool over its expected life. Proper selection also depends upon the design of the tool: if the shape is such that the tool is likely to crack if quenched in water, a more costly oil-hardening steel rather than a cheaper water-hardening steel should be chosen.

137. Evaluation of Tool Steels—An accurate evaluation of a steel that is to be used for a specific tool in a specific machining operation is practically impossible, and as a result, large quantities of tool steel are, and always have been, purchased by brand name. A few users of large amounts of tool steel—for example some automotive manufacturers—purchase this material under specifications which include performance requirements, instead of by brand names, but in only a few cases has this proved entirely

satisfactory, owing to the large number of variables which must be controlled if acceptance tests are to mean anything.

Even if machining tests are made on a calibrated machine with carefully regulated feeds and speeds, the test is meaningless unless the design, machining and finishing of the tool, and the heat treatment are carefully standardized, and unless the material being cut is uniform in structure and hardness. According to Gill, "even under the best conditions tools made of the same steel will oftentimes show a variation of 200 per cent, and when results cannot be checked any closer than this, it is obviously unfair to compare tools made of different steels." Gill states that cutting or other machining tests may be of some value in comparing different types of steel, but there is considerable question of their usefulness in comparing steels of the same type and of about the same composition unless a very large number of tests can be run and a statistical analysis can be made of the results.

The only reliable performance test of a tool steel is to use it in actual production and to use enough similar tools of the same steel to make the results convincing. Large users of tool steel frequently distribute their yearly or half-yearly requirements among a number of tool-steel manufacturers and keep accurate records of the performance of each brand. At the end of this production test the company whose brand makes the best showing receives 50 per cent or more of the business for the next period.

138. Characteristics of High-carbon Tool Steels—The steels of types 1, 2, and 3 of Table 15 are the cheapest and, despite low wear resistance, high distortion in hardening, low resistance to softening at elevated temperature, and shallow hardening, the most widely used of the tool steels. There are four classes, graded according to carbon content as follows:

1—Carbon 0.60 to 0.75 per cent; used for machinery parts, hot-forging dies, rivet sets, battering tools, large chisels, and set screws.

2—Carbon 0.75 to 0.90 per cent; used for forging dies, boilermakers' tools, hammers, sledges, mining tools, and miscellaneous blacksmiths' tools.

3—Carbon 0.90 to 1.10 per cent; used for drills, saws, cutters, taps, small shear blades and dies, anvils, wood- and stone-working tools of various kinds, punches, and axes.

4—Carbon 1.10 to 1.40 per cent; used for small drills, taps and lathe tools, files, cutlery and small edge tools, jewelers' tools and dies, brass- and copper-working tools, wire-drawing dies, and razors.

As noted in Table 16, hardness and toughness vary with carbon content; they also vary with heat treatment, i.e., with tempering temperature. Since high hardness and considerable toughness are incompatible in an unalloyed high-carbon steel, it is necessary to sacrifice part of one or the other depending upon the use for which the tool is intended. Thus, for razors, which must be very hard and which are not ordinarily subjected to shock, a 1.20 per cent carbon steel, treated to give a hardness of 60 to 65 Rockwell C, is used; but for a hammer or a chisel, which

Fig. 86—Structure of water-quenched high-carbon tool steel: small carbide particles in martensitic matrix, etched, 500×.

must withstand battering, a steel containing 0.70 to 0.90 per cent carbon, treated to 50 to 55 Rockwell C, will be chosen.

Wear resistance, which usually is not so high in carbon steels as in some of the alloy steels (see Table 16), is secured by the use of a 1.20 to 1.40 per cent carbon steel, heat treated so that there will be numerous well-distributed excess carbide particles in a martensitic matrix. Such a structure (Fig. 86) is important for cutting tools and wire-drawing dies. Under the quenching conditions necessary to obtain high hardness, high-carbon steels warp considerably. In tools of simple section this may be minimized by quenching in special fixtures; for dies and some tools which must be finish machined before heat treatment and for which stability of dimensions is necessary, special non-deforming alloy steels, which harden in oil or air, are used.

It is emphasized elsewhere (p. 109) that drastically quenched high-carbon steel contains internal stresses which are sometimes so high that the tool may crack or even go to pieces with explosive violence if not immediately tempered to relieve the stresses. Tempering also reduces the hardness. Fortunately, however, most of the stresses can be relieved by low-temperature reheating, as shown in Fig. 87.[2] The hardness does not decrease materially

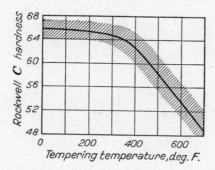

Fig. 87—Effect of tempering on the hardness of water-quenched high-carbon steel (*Metals Handbook*).

until the tool is reheated to 300° F. (150° C.) or above. It is evident from Fig. 87 that high-carbon steel possesses no stability at elevated temperatures. This is not necessary for wood working or for machining very soft metals at low speeds, but when using high speeds and heavy cuts, especially on cast iron and steel, when the point of the tool may be heated to 700° F. (370° C.) or above, a high-speed steel must be employed.

139. Hardenability of High-carbon Tool Steel—As discussed in a previous chapter (Chapter 6), high-carbon steels, even though of practically the same composition, differ in their response to quenching (hardenability). If the steel has an inherent tendency to become coarse-grained when heated considerably above the transformation temperature, it hardens relatively deeply and uniformly when quenched but is likely to crack. If it is fine-grained

[2] *Metals Handbook*, American Society for Metals, Cleveland, 1939, p. 992.

after such treatment, it is shallow hardening and may have soft spots on the surface, but it is not so likely to crack in quenching. Unalloyed high-carbon steels are all shallow hardening compared with tool steels containing considerable tungsten or chromium (Nos. 8 to 13, Table 15), but the hardenability can be controlled to some extent by controlling the grain-growth tendency during manufacture. The difference in hardenability between two lots of high-carbon steels of identical chemical composition is shown in Fig. 88.[3] Bars, ¾ in. in diameter, were quenched in brine from the temperatures noted and were not tempered. The fractures of

1450° F.   1500° F.   1550° F.   1600° F

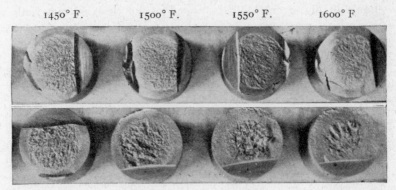

Fig. 88—Fracture of quenched and untempered high-carbon tool steel. Top, fine-grained, shallow hardening; bottom, coarse-grained, deep hardening; (Gill).

the "fine-grained" bars are shown at the top, and those of the "coarse-grained" bars at the bottom. The coarser grain and the greater depth of hardening for the latter are clearly evident.

Unalloyed high-carbon steels are apt to be erratic in their response to heat treatment. Even steels of the same composition, made by the same manufacturer, may differ in their tendency toward grain growth and in depth of hardening. Adding a small amount of vanadium to these steels (type 2, Table 15) produces a shallow-hardening material. Adding a small amount of chromium (type 3, Table 15) increases the depth of hardening and prevents soft spots. Thus, types 2 and 3 are modifications of type 1, made to control grain-growth tendencies and to render the response to heat treatment more certain.

[3] J. P. Gill, loc. cit.

140. The Manganese Tool and Die Steels—Advantage is taken of the effect of manganese when dissolved in alpha iron (ferrite) of decreasing the critical cooling rate and of increasing deep hardening to produce a valuable class of oil-hardening "non-deforming" tool and die steels (No. 4, Tables 15 and 16). These steels are moderately priced and are used when the design of the tool or die is such that distortion or cracking is likely to occur in water quenching. There are four steels in this group, containing 0.85 to 1.00 per cent carbon. As shown in Table 15, if the manganese is 1.50 to 1.75 per cent, the steel usually contains no other alloying element although the addition of 0.10 to 0.25 per cent vanadium to reduce grain growth is optional. To reduce the tendency toward grain growth and the possibility of cracking in quenching, and to avoid the use of expensive vanadium, the manganese may be lowered to 1.20 to 1.40 per cent, and about 0.5 per cent chromium plus 0.5 per cent tungsten may be added; or the manganese may be reduced to 1.00 per cent, and 0.75 per cent chromium may be added. These modified steels are not so likely to crack in quenching as the higher manganese steels, but, on the other hand, they do not become so hard. The steels of type 4 are quenched in oil from 1400 to 1500° F. (765 to 815° C.) and are tempered at 325 to 500° F. (160 to 260° C.). They are used as stamping dies, thread-rolling dies, dies for molding plastics, punches, broaches, blanking dies, and especially as master tools and gages.

As noted in Chapter 13, silicon-manganese steel (S.A.E. 9255 and 9260) containing 0.50 to 0.70 per cent carbon, 1.80 to 2.20 per cent silicon, and 0.60 to 0.90 per cent manganese is widely used for springs. Recently it has become popular as a tool steel, especially for punches, chisels, and shear blades, owing to its low cost and its fairly high wear resistance and toughness (steel 5, Table 16). Strictly speaking, silicon-manganese steel is a misnomer, as the amount of manganese is not greater than that present in many of the S.A.E. carbon and low-alloy steels. Since there is not enough manganese in the steel to affect the critical cooling rate materially, water quenching is imperative. Distortion in quenching is less than for plain high-carbon steels (Table 16), and wear resistance is higher. The steel hardens more deeply than high-carbon steel and is tougher. To increase deep hardening, 0.20 to 0.40 per cent chromium or 0.40 to 0.60 per cent molybdenum is occasionally added. Steels of type 5 are usually quenched in water from 1575 to 1625° F. (860 to 885° C.) and are tempered at 350 to 600° F. (175 to 315° C.).

141. Functions of Tungsten, Molybdenum, and Chromium in Tool and Die Steels—Tungsten, molybdenum, and chromium in the amounts found in tool and die steels (see Table 15) partly dissolve in gamma iron—and remain in solution when the gamma changes to alpha—and partly form hard and stable carbides. All

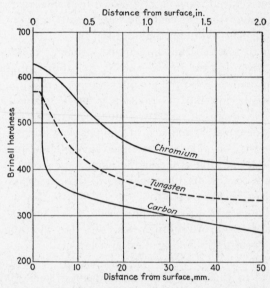

Fig. 89—Effect of 1.20 per cent chromium or tungsten on the deep hardening of 1.00 to 1.20 per cent carbon tool steels (Rapatz and Pollack).

three of these metals, when dissolved in gamma iron, decrease the reaction rate and make the steel deep hardening. This is shown by Fig. 89, based on work by Rapatz and Pollack,[4] for steels containing 1 to 1.20 per cent carbon and 1.20 per cent of chromium or tungsten. Larger amounts of dissolved chromium and tungsten have, of course, a more pronounced deep-hardening effect.

The carbides formed by these three metals dissolve to some extent (depending upon the amount of carbon and the temperature) in gamma iron and can be retained in supersaturated solution by quenching. This increases hardness and wear resistance.

[4] *Stahl u. Eisen,* v. 44, 1924, pp. 1698-1703.

In addition, the carbides in excess of those dissolved, if favorably distributed, increase wear resistance greatly, especially resistance to abrasion.

Tungsten, molybdenum, and chromium increase the resistance to tempering. This is shown by Fig. 90 [5] for steel with 0.35 per cent carbon and increasing chromium, by Fig. 91 [6] for steel with 0.35 per cent carbon and increasing molybdenum, and by Fig. 92 [7] for high-speed steel containing 0.70 per cent carbon, 18 per cent

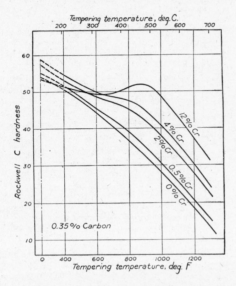

Fig. 90—Effect of chromium on the resistance of 0.35 per cent carbon steel to tempering (Bain).

tungsten, 4 per cent chromium, and 1 per cent vanadium. The increase in hardness of these steels when tempered between 900 and 1100° F. (480 and 595° C.) is due to the transformation to martensite of some austenite retained by the quenching treatment.

142. Low-chromium and Low-tungsten Tool and Die Steels —The low-chromium and low-tungsten tool and die steels (Nos. 6 to 9) are fairly or very deep hardening and, with the exception of No. 8, can be hardened with little distortion. They have higher

[5] E. C. Bain, *Functions of the Alloying Elements in Steel*, American Society for Metals, Cleveland, 1939.

[6] E. C. Bain, loc. cit.

[7] J. V. Emmons, *Trans. Am. Soc. Steel Treat.*, v. 19, 1932, pp. 289-332.

resistance to wear than unalloyed high-carbon steels and, with the exception of No. 8, are tougher. As Table 16 indicates, they are

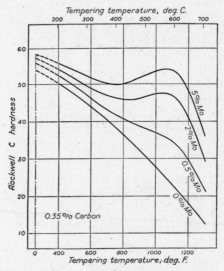

Fig. 91—Effect of molybdenum on the resistance of 0.35 per cent carbon steel to tempering (Bain).

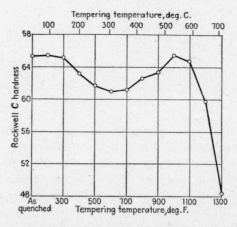

Fig. 92—Effect of tempering on the hardness of high-speed steel (Emmons).

not suitable for use at elevated temperatures as their resistance to softening is not high. They are, however, valuable tool steels, especially for finishing cuts.

Steels of type 6 (Table 15) are used chiefly as cutting tools—taps, reamers, broaches, and the like—for smooth finishing at slow speeds and feeds, especially of non-ferrous alloys. They are not resistant to tempering and thus cannot be used if the point of the tool becomes hotter than 300° F. (150° C.).

Steels of class 7, of low carbon content which is responsible for relatively high toughness, are used for chisels, punches, shear blades, and battering tools and occasionally for dies which can be water quenched. These steels do not have high resistance to tempering. According to Gill, chisels of steel No. 7 have three times the life of unalloyed chisel steel.

Steels of class 8 (Table 15) are widely used for fast finishing. As noted in Table 16, they become very hard when quenched in water but soften readily when heated. There are four steels in this group which are used for smooth finishing cuts and, at slow speeds, to machine hard materials. Owing to difficulties in heat treatment, these steels have been replaced for many purposes by steel No. 6 which is oil quenched but which is not so deep hardening.

There are four steels in group 9. These are used as dies that do not become heated above 600° F. (315° C.), for example, as hot-heading dies for bolts and rivets. They change little in dimensions when quenched and are deep hardening. Their toughness is satisfactory.

143. High-chromium and High-tungsten Tool and Die Steels —Steels of types 10, 11, and 12 are highly alloyed and are used primarily for dies operating at or exposed to fairly high temperatures. Seven steels are included in group 10 (Table 15), varying in tungsten and to a lesser extent in chromium. They are resistant to tempering and retain their hardness at temperatures as high as 1100° F. (595° C.). This is to be expected as some of them approach high-speed steel in composition and in many characteristics. Steels of group 10 are used as forging dies, as shears and punches for hot working metals, and to some extent as dies for die casting aluminum, brass, and bronze in permanent molds.

Steels of group 11 are resistant to temperatures as high as 800 to 900° F. (425 to 480° C.). The steels in this group, three of which contain also 0.80 to 1.00 per cent silicon, have good heat resistance and are used as dies for die casting aluminum alloys and in many types of forging dies, especially for hot working and where severe shock may be encountered.

There are nine varieties of the high-carbon, high-chromium die steel (No. 12, Table 15), four of which, with 2.10 to 2.45 per cent carbon, are oil hardening, and five of which, with 1.40 to 1.75 per cent carbon, are air hardening. Four of the oil-hardening steels contain 0.50 to 1.00 per cent molybdenum. The structure of the high-chromium die steels as forged and as quenched and tem-

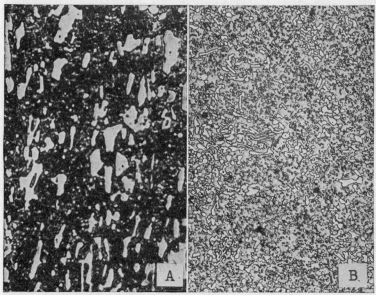

Fig. 93—Structure of high-chromium die steels (A) forged and annealed, 750×; and (B) oil quenched and tempered at 400° F. (200° C.), 500×; etched (Kinzel and Forgeng).

pered is shown in Fig. 93. Although, after annealing, the Brinell hardness of these steels is 200 to 230, they are difficult to machine. Steels of type 12 harden deeply with little distortion and do not soften appreciably when tempered below about 900° F. (480° C.). Their wear resistance is high. Despite high cost and difficulty of machining, these steels are among the best as dies for forming and trimming, blanking, thread rolling, and wire drawing, as shear blades, bushings, and rolls, and as small machine parts where resistance to abrasive wear is important. They are seldom used as cutting tools.

144. **Composition of High-speed Steel**—In 1868 Robert Mushet of England, while heat treating and testing some tool steels, discovered that one of them, containing about 2.2 per cent carbon, 2 per cent manganese, and 5 per cent tungsten, became very hard when cooled in air from a high temperature. Very soon thereafter this "self-hardening" steel was used widely for cutting tools. About 15 years later, it was found that the tool would cut better if chromium was added and the amount of manganese was reduced. By 1900, a large number of self-hardening steels were in use. Despite the fact that some of these contained as much as 12 per cent tungsten and 3 per cent chromium, and despite the fact that they were much better tools than the unalloyed high-carbon steels, they could not be used at the high speeds common today.

Engineers owe a large debt to two Americans, F. W. Taylor and Maunsel White, who, while working at Bethlehem Steel Company in October 1898, discovered the "weird and novel" heat treatment which gives high tungsten-chromium steel its property of red hardness. Taylor and White found that a steel containing 1.14 per cent carbon, 0.18 per cent manganese, 7.72 per cent tungsten, and 1.83 per cent chromium performed poorly in rapid machining when heat treated in the usual way. After considerable investigation the present-day treatment was developed. This consists of heating the tool slowly to 1500° F. (815° C.), then rapidly to a temperature slightly below the melting temperature—with modern high-speed steels this is 2200 to 2350° F. (1205 to 1285° C.), which would ruin carbon or low-alloy steel—and cooling it rapidly in oil or, sometimes, in air. The tool is then tempered immediately by reheating to 1000 to 1150° F. (540 to 620° C.). When heat treated in this way, high-speed steel machines at high speeds and with such heavy cuts that the point of the tool becomes red hot, without losing any hardness.

The general composition range of high-speed steel is given in Table 15 (type 13). High-speed steel compositions have undergone a slow evolution until, according to Gill, at the present time five principal compositions are used. These are shown in Table 17.

There are super-high-speed steels which are usually the 18-4-1 steel containing also 3.50 to 13 per cent cobalt. More than 85 per cent of the high-speed steel used is of the 18 tungsten, 4 chromium, 1 vanadium type. The carbon is 0.67 to 0.73 per cent, silicon is usually below 0.30 per cent, and manganese, which makes the steel sensitive to grain growth, is less than 0.35 per cent.

TABLE 17. COMPOSITION OF HIGH-SPEED STEELS

Type	Composition, per cent				
	C	W	Cr	V	Mo
18–4–1	0.55 to 0.75	17.00 to 19.00	3.50 to 4.50	0.75 to 1.25	
20–4–1	0.55 to 0.75	19.00 to 21.00	3.75 to 4.50	0.75 to 1.25	
14–4–2	0.55 to 0.75	13.00 to 15.00	3.50 to 4.50	1.75 to 2.25	
18–4–1 Mo	0.65 to 0.85	17.00 to 19.00	3.50 to 4.50	1.75 to 2.25	0.40 to 0.90
Molybdenum	0.55 to 0.75	2.00 to 4.00	3.50 to 4.50	0.75 to 1.25	6.00 to 9.00

145. Structure and Properties of High-speed Steel—Although considerable work has been done on the constitution of iron-tungsten-carbon alloys, little is known about the effect of 4 per cent chromium and 1 or 2 per cent vanadium on these alloys. Studies of microstructure indicate that high-speed steel when annealed consists of a relatively soft (probably ferritic) matrix and a large number of particles of a complex carbide. When the steel is heated to a high temperature, the matrix changes to austenite and some of the carbides go into solution. To produce red hardness and satisfactory cutting performance the temperature to which the steel is heated must be as high as possible without causing incipient melting. When the steel is quenched from this temperature, a structure such as is shown in Fig. 94A [8] results. It is thought that the polygonal grains of the matrix are composed of austenite plus untempered martensite. Tempering at 1050° F. (565° C.) probably changes the retained austenite to martensite and tempers the martensite slightly so that it etches rapidly (Fig. 94B).[9] The secondary hardening upon tempering is shown in Fig. 92.

The cause of red hardness, the most important property of high-speed steel, has not yet been explained satisfactorily. It is usually considered to be related to the high stability of the complex carbide particles and to the fact that the most favorable size

[8] J. L. Gregg, *The Alloys of Iron and Tungsten*, McGraw-Hill Book Company, Inc., New York, 1934, p. 294.
[9] J. L. Gregg, loc. cit., p. 295.

of the particles for stability of structure is not altered by temperatures as high as 1100° F. (595° C.).

High-speed steel is hard, strong, and brittle at room temperature and retains it hardness and strength at temperatures up to 1100 to 1200° F. (595 to 650° C.). Although there is a relation between elevated-temperature properties and cutting performance, the latter cannot be correlated accurately with the former. In general, tensile properties are not important.

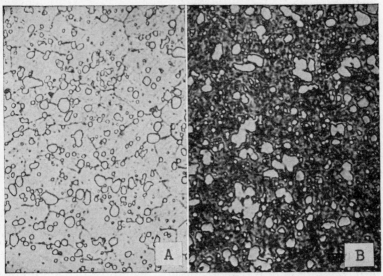

Fig. 94—Structure of high-speed steel (A) quenched and (B) quenched and tempered; etched, 750× (Gregg).

The cutting performance of high-speed steel, which is from three to fifty times that of unalloyed high-carbon steel of the same hardness, is largely dependent upon the heat treatment. The optimum quenching temperature depends upon composition, and a variation of ±50° F. (±30° C.) from the optimum will affect the performance of the tool. In general, cutting performance increases with tungsten up to about 22 per cent of this element. Vanadium is necessary for satisfactory performance, and approximately 1 per cent or more is always present. Chromium is held constant at about 4 per cent. For some applications, performance is improved enough by the addition of 3 to 13 per cent cobalt to warrant the additional cost of this expensive alloying element.

The most recent development in high-speed steels is the substitution of molybdenum for most of the tungsten (see Table 17). This was pioneered by Richie [10] at Watertown Arsenal and by Emmons,[11] who developed the steels commercially. Molybdenum has three advantages in high-speed steel: (1) since it is twice as effective as tungsten in producing red hardness, only 6 to 9 per cent is necessary, as Table 17 shows; (2) it is cheaper pound for pound than tungsten; and (3) it is not a strategic material as ample supplies of domestic ores are available. Molybdenum high-speed steel has, however, certain disadvantages which have retarded general adoption. It is more difficult to make and forge, and it is hard to heat treat. It is subject to grain growth at high temperatures and, most important, it seems to be definitely inferior to the standard 18-4-1 in some machining operations.

The testing of high-speed steel is subject to the limitations outlined for high-carbon tool steel in section 137. Hundreds of cutting tests have been made in an effort to compare steels of approximately the same composition but of different brands, or to compare steels of different compositions. In general, these tests have shown that slight variations in test conditions have more effect on results than differences in brands or even in steels. They have also shown that there is no simple nor universal test for evaluating the cutting performance, and that steels which fall into one order of merit in lathe tests with heavy cuts may fall into another order if the cut is light and into still another order for drilling or for milling. Unless tests are carefully carried out under controlled conditions for a long period of time, it is usually more satisfactory to purchase high-speed steel by brand name or according to results of experience with a certain brand.

[10] S. B. Richie, *Army Ordnance,* v. 11, July 1930.
[11] J. V. Emmons, *Trans. Am. Soc. Steel Treat.,* v. 21, 1933, pp. 193-232.

CHAPTER 16

PRECIPITATION HARDENING AND THE CON-STITUTION OF NON-FERROUS ALLOYS

THE hardening of steel is a process made possible because iron undergoes allotropic transformation in the solid state and because carbon is soluble in one of the allotropic forms of iron but not in the other. This phenomenon is a gift of Providence to mankind, and the metallurgist and the engineer, accepting it as such, are usually grateful that iron, the cheapest and most readily available of all metals, is the one in which an allotropic change takes place. Owing to this phenomenon, man can control the properties of his iron by alloying it with a little carbon, and by heating and cooling it at various rates he can make it hard or soft, brittle or tough, malleable or not, as he desires. With all the other industrially important metals and alloys no such control could be exercised until comparatively recently. The properties could be changed to a limited extent, it is true, by mechanical working and by heating the mechanically deformed material and cooling it again (annealing), but that was all.

Within the last 40 years, however, a new field has opened to the metallurgist and the engineer by the discovery of a new kind of treatment which can be applied to a large number of alloys and by which their properties can be changed radically. This new treatment, called precipitation hardening (or aging, or age hardening, and occasionally dispersion hardening) has been used most effectively with some of the light alloys of aluminum; recently it has been applied with success to a number of heavy alloys of copper, iron, nickel, and gold. Precipitation hardening, as discussed later, is a mechanism that depends upon temperature and time. It is because of the time factor that the terms *aging* and *age hardening* are so frequently used, despite the fact that they give no clue to the actual mechanism, namely the precipitation of a constituent from supersaturated solution. Many alloys which are hardened by holding or "aging" for hours, days, or weeks at room temperature will be hardened to the same extent by holding for minutes or hours at some higher temperature.

So many alloys the component metals of which do not undergo allotropic change can be precipitation hardened that nearly 10 years ago Merica [1] stated: "In fact, it is possibly not an exaggeration to say, quite contrary to our older conception, that hardenable alloys may be the rule rather than the exception among alloy systems." Since 1932 our knowledge of alloys capable of being precipitation hardened has been extended rapidly, and it is quite evident that the surface of this field has as yet only been scratched.

146. The Phenomenon of Precipitation Hardening—The treatment necessary to produce precipitation hardening was probably used first by Alfred Wilm in Germany about the year 1906, when he was experimenting with duralumin (94 to 95 per cent aluminum, 4 per cent copper, and about 0.50 per cent each of manganese and magnesium) for the construction of Zeppelin dirigibles. By the time of the first World War this treatment was known universally, and during the war precipitation-hardened aluminum-copper alloys were used increasingly for structures and machines, as they combine the advantages of light weight with high strength and ductility resulting from this treatment.

Although Wilm deserves much credit for his work on duralumin, it is likely that our knowledge of precipitation hardening would still be confined to a few light alloys if it had not been for the work of Merica, Waltenberg, and Scott who investigated the mechanism and who proposed a rational explanation of the phenomenon.[2] Their work demonstrated that precipitation hardening is not an isolated phenomenon, characteristic only of duralumin, but a principle applicable to all solid-solution type alloys containing a constituent whose solubility changes with temperature. Again quoting Merica:

Solid solutions and solid solubility are very common among alloy systems, and in them decreasing solubility with decreasing temperature is the rule. . . . But even more significant, [it is] reasonably within our power to render any alloy composition amenable to age hardening by the addition to it of a small amount of some suitably chosen hardening metal or metallic compound.

[1] P. D. Merica, *Trans. Am. Inst. Min. Met. Eng.*, v. 99, 1932, p. 13.

[2] P. D. Merica, R. G. Waltenberg, and Howard Scott, U. S. Bureau of Standards, Scientific Paper 347, 1919.

The silver-copper system is a simple example of alloys in which precipitation hardening occurs. The constitutional diagram of the system and a section picturing the behavior of the silver-rich alloys are shown in Figs. 95 and 96.[3] Sterling silver containing 92.5 per cent silver and 7.5 per cent copper is a typical precipitation-hardening alloy. As indicated by the solubility curve at the

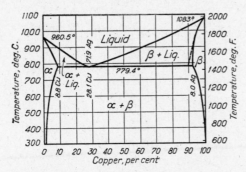

Fig. 95—The silver-copper phase diagram (Smith).

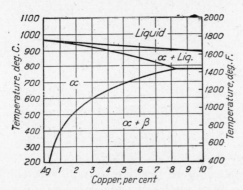

Fig. 96—The silver-rich portion of Fig. 95 showing variable solubility of copper in silver (Smith).

left side of the diagram, the solubility of copper in silver increases from less than 1 per cent at room temperature to about 8.4 per cent at 1435° F. (780° C.). If an alloy containing 92.5 per cent silver and 7.5 per cent copper is cooled slowly from 1435° F., copper begins to precipitate from the solid solution at 1400° F.

[3] C. S. Smith, "Constitution of Copper-silver Alloys," *Metals Handbook*, American Society for Metals, Cleveland, 1939, pp. 1360, 1361.

(760° C.) and continues to precipitate as the alloy cools to room temperature (Fig. 96). In slow heating, the reverse changes take place. If, on the other hand, the alloy is cooled rapidly from 1435° F. to room temperature, precipitation of the excess copper is prevented, and a supersaturated solution results. Reheating (aging) the quenched alloy at the proper temperature for the proper time causes precipitation of excess copper in the form of submicroscopic particles, effecting greatly increased hardness. As precipitation hardening of an alloy depends upon temperature as well as upon time, there may be several treatments which produce maximum hardness. Assume for example that an alloy containing a constituent in supersaturated solution at room temperature will attain maximum hardness if reheated to 300° F. and held for 3 hr. Maximum hardness may also be attained if the alloy is reheated at 400° F. for 2 hr. and at 500° F. for 20 min. If, however, the alloy is heated to 300° F. and held for 12 hr., to 400° F. for 4 hr., to 500° F. for 1 hr., or to 600° F. for a few minutes, the precipitated particles coalesce, and the hardness is lowered. The important effect of time is shown by data quoted later in this chapter. The effect of temperature on the precipitation hardening of sterling silver, as shown by data reported by Merica,[4] is as follows:

Treatment	Brinell hardness (500-kg. load, 10-mm. ball)
Cooled slowly...	70
Quenched...	55
Quenched and aged 30 min. at 570° F. (300° C.)...........	110
Quenched and aged 30 min. at 930° F. (500° C.)...........	75

147. The Mechanism of Precipitation Hardening—It is advisable at this point to refer back to sections 45 and 46 (Chapter 6) where it was stated that steel fails under stress by slipping or gliding along crystallographic planes of inherent weakness and that submicroscopic hard particles of iron carbide, Fe_3C, act as keys to prevent easy slip. High-carbon steel hardens in quenching because the change of the gamma iron (in which Fe_3C is soluble) to alpha iron (in which Fe_3C is almost completely insoluble) is not prevented and because the minute Fe_3C particles which are thrown out of solution are entrapped in enforced supersatu-

[4] P. D. Merica, *Metal Progress*, v. 27, No. 1, 1935, pp. 31-35.

rated solution in the alpha-iron crystal lattice, distorting the lattice and acting as keys to prevent slip. High-carbon steel is usually hardest when quenched. Reheating causes coalescence of the Fe_3C particles, and the higher the tempering temperature the farther coalescence proceeds and the fewer are the particles which act as slip-preventing keys.

In precipitation hardening, the mechanism differs from this in several important details. At elevated temperature, the hardening constituent is in solution and is retained in solution by rapid cooling. Usually the hardness of the quenched alloy is not greater, and may be less, than that of the annealed alloy. Owing, however, to a decreased solubility of the hardening constituent in the solid solution at low temperature, the latter is supersaturated and there is, of course, a tendency for the excess atoms to form aggregates or for the aggregates of the hardening constituent to coalesce into particles. But maximum hardening of the alloy will not occur until particles of a critical size are formed as is shown by Fig. 97 from Merica.[5] In some alloy systems, the formation of critically dispersed particles begins at room temperature immediately after quenching, but at this temperature the rigidity of the lattice is usually so great that the formation of the particles goes on very slowly. Heating the alloy accelerates particle formation, but it is relatively easy to carry the process too far and to produce particles larger than the critical size. This reduces the number of particles and, as Fig. 97 shows, is accompanied by decreased hardness (and strength).

For all age-hardening alloys not only is there a critical particle size which is responsible for maximum hardening, but also there are optimum treatments by which it is attained. These optimum treatments depend upon the composition of the alloy and to some extent upon its structural condition, that is, upon the amount of prior mechanical working. This will become evident from the discussion later in this chapter.

As a rule, maximum hardening and strengthening are attained with a particle size that is below the resolving power of the microscope. Owing to the fact that in many alloy systems changes upon aging in such properties as density, lattice constant, expansion, electric resistance, and others do not parallel exactly the

[5] See footnote 1, this chapter.

changes in hardness, it is thought by some that precipitation hardening is caused by the collection of atoms into knots which distort the lattice and which obstruct slip even before sizable collections of atoms are formed. This, however, is not of great moment. The important fact is that in many alloys it is possible to introduce small percentages of a "stranger" element that is more soluble at high than at low temperature, and that by a combination quenching (or "solution") treatment and subsequent aging at

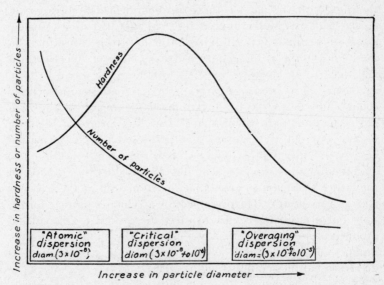

Fig. 97—Relation between number and size of particles and hardness (Merica).

atmospheric or at some higher temperature it is possible to control the engineering properties with a fair degree of precision.

148. Constitution and Heat Treatment of Aluminum-copper Alloys—The alloys of aluminum with 2 to about 12 per cent copper are important industrially and are, in addition, good examples of alloys that can be improved by a solution heat treatment followed by aging. The constitutional diagram of the aluminum-rich aluminum-copper alloys is shown in Fig. 98.[6] This is similar

[6] E. H. Dix, Jr. and H. H. Richardson, "Constitution of Aluminum-copper Alloys," *Metals Handbook*, American Society for Metals, Cleveland, 1939, p. 1222.

in its general outline to that of the silver-copper alloys (Fig. 95).
The essential difference is that copper and aluminum react to
form the intermetallic compound $CuAl_2$ (which probably dissolves a little aluminum), designated in Fig. 98 as theta (Θ). This
is the hardening constituent. If Fig. 98 is compared with Fig. 95,
it will be noted that the general shape of the line of solid solubility of $CuAl_2$ in aluminum is the same as of that of copper in
silver. At room temperature the solubility of copper is less than
0.50 per cent, at 840° F. (450° C.) it is 2.60 per cent (see inset

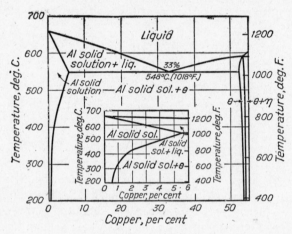

Fig. 98—The aluminum-copper phase diagram; inset, the aluminum-rich
portion (Dix and Richardson).

Fig. 98), and at 1005° F. (540° C.) it is about 5.6 per cent. This
means, of course, that up to 5.6 per cent copper can be retained in
supersaturated solution by quenching and can be precipitated (as
$CuAl_2$) in critical particle size by aging.

The structure of a cast and slowly cooled specimen containing
3.94 per cent copper is shown in Fig. 99A.[7] The appearance and
distribution of the theta constituent ($CuAl_2$) is clearly evident.
Upon heating this alloy to 1005° F. (540° C.) and holding at this
temperature for sufficient time, all the $CuAl_2$ goes into solution
and is retained in solution by quenching (Fig. 99B). Aging for
a day or two at room temperature, or for an hour or two in boiling
water, or for a shorter period at 300° F. (150° C.) precipitates the

[7] Courtesy of E. H. Dix, Jr., Aluminum Research Laboratories.

$CuAl_2$ in critical particle size. The effect of these treatments on the tensile properties and hardness is indicated in Table 18.

TABLE 18. EFFECT OF HEAT TREATMENT ON THE PROPERTIES OF AN ALUMINUM-COPPER ALLOY CONTAINING 4.5 PER CENT COPPER

Material	Treatment	Tensile strength, lb. per sq. in.	Yield strength, lb. per sq. in.	Elongation in 2 in., per cent	Brinell hardness*
High-purity aluminum	Wrought and annealed sheet	13,000	5,000	35	23
4.5% Cu	Sand cast and slowly cooled	20,100	8,800	7.5	46
4.5% Cu	Sand cast, heated 40 hr. at 1005° F. (540° C.) and water quenched	35,800	17,400	20.7	62
4.5% Cu	Sand cast, treated as above and aged 2 days at room temperature	42,300	24,000	19.0	83

* 500-kg. load, 10-mm. ball.

The solution heat treatment of aluminum-copper alloys and of duralumin—which, as mentioned, contains about 0.50 per cent each of manganese and magnesium in addition to about 4 per cent copper—requires some care owing to the fact that the temperature at which 4 per cent copper dissolves completely in aluminum—950 to 980° F. (510 to 530° C.)—is only a few degrees below the temperature (1018° F.) at which incipient melting occurs (see inset Fig. 98). Unless this temperature is controlled closely and measured accurately, reasonably complete solution of the $CuAl_2$ may not be attained, or the article being treated may be overheated and thus ruined.

None of the aluminum-copper alloys is actually a binary alloy as each contains some iron and silicon as impurities. Two of the alloys, containing 4 and 8 per cent copper, which are used for sand castings, are nominally binary alloys. The 4 per cent copper alloy is usually used in the heat-treated condition and combines relatively high strength with good resistance to shock. The 8 per cent copper alloy is used in the "as-cast" condition when an inexpensive material is required. Because it is somewhat difficult to cast, it is not used so widely as the more complex 8 per cent copper alloy containing a small amount of silicon or zinc (see Table 20).

149. The Complex Precipitation-hardening Aluminum-copper Alloys—The discussion in the previous section was confined to the alloys of aluminum and copper with no other intentionally added alloying element. There are several more complex alloys which are used as castings or as wrought sections after a solution heat treatment followed by aging. The most important of these are, of course, the wrought duralumin-type alloys. In addition to the common duralumin containing 4 per cent copper, 0.5 per cent

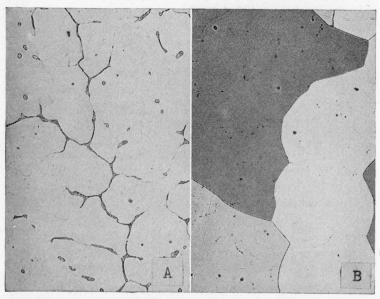

Fig. 99—Structure of an alloy containing 3.94 per cent copper, 0.02 per cent silicon, 0.02 per cent iron, and remainder aluminum. (*A*) as cast, 100×, and (*B*) quenched, 500×, etched (Aluminum Research Laboratories).

magnesium, and 0.5 per cent manganese, wrought alloys containing (*a*) 4.2 per cent copper, 1.5 per cent magnesium, and 0.6 per cent manganese, (*b*) 4.5 per cent copper, 0.8 per cent silicon, and 0.8 per cent manganese, and (*c*) 4.4 per cent copper, 0.8 per cent silicon, 0.8 per cent manganese, and 0.4 per cent magnesium are used in considerable quantities. After treatment, these alloys have a tensile strength of 60,000 to 70,000 lb. per sq. in., a yield strength of 37,000 to 50,000 lb. per sq. in., and an elongation of 10 to 24 per cent in 2 in

Also well known are the two alloys used for pistons of internal-combustion engines. These are usually cast in permanent molds and are used in the heat-treated condition. The composition is balanced to produce the most desirable expansion characteristics, easy machinability, and hardness at elevated temperature. The most common of the two alloys is the one formerly known as Y-alloy, containing 4 per cent copper, 2 per cent nickel, and 1.5 per cent magnesium. After a solution heat treatment and aging, the strength is about 45,000 lb. per sq. in. and the Brinell hardness (500-kg. load, 10-mm. ball) is 100 to 130. These properties are not affected by temperatures up to 300° F. (150° C.).

The other piston alloy contains about 10 per cent copper and 0.25 per cent magnesium. Its strength and hardness are about the same as of Y-alloy, and these properties are also retained up to 300° F. The piston alloys are brittle, with an average elongation of 0.5 per cent or less in 2 in.

150. The Heat-treatable Aluminum-magnesium and Aluminum-magnesium-silicon Alloys—The aluminum-magnesium and aluminum-magnesium-silicon alloys contain a constituent the solubility of which varies with temperature. Aluminum and magnesium form an intermetallic compound of uncertain composition, usually designated as $\alpha AlMg$. Magnesium is soluble in aluminum to the extent of 2.9 per cent at 390° F. (200° C.), 11.5 per cent at 750° F. (400° C.), and 14.9 per cent at 845° F. (450° C.), the eutectic temperature.

Silicon does not form an intermetallic compound with aluminum, but it does combine with magnesium to form Mg_2Si whose solubility in aluminum increases from 0.27 per cent at 390° F. (200° C.) to 1.05 per cent at 930° F. (500° C.) and 1.85 per cent at 1100° F. (595° C.), the eutectic temperature. Silicon in excess of the amount forming Mg_2Si does not affect the solubility of this compound in aluminum, but an excess of magnesium reduces its solubility. It is necessary, therefore, to be sure that only just enough magnesium is present if full advantage is to be taken of the improvement in strength resulting from precipitation hardening.

The only aluminum-magnesium alloy used in this country for heat-treated sand castings is the one containing 10 per cent magnesium. After heat treatment, its tensile properties are higher than those of any other aluminum-base alloy, and these properties are combined with high resistance to corrosion. It requires, however, special foundry practice and cannot be used for all types of castings. In Europe, alloys containing about 7 per cent magnesium are widely used for heat-treated castings. In the United States, however, alloys containing 4, 6, and 7 per cent magnesium are used only in the "as-cast" condition.

The only wrought aluminum-magnesium alloys used in this country contain less than 6 per cent magnesium and are used in the annealed or strain-hardened condition since, for all practical purposes, these alloys are not heat treatable. Two of these alloys, however, are rapidly attaining wide commercial acceptance. One contains 2.5 per cent magnesium and 0.25 per cent chromium and is characterized by good resistance to salt-water corrosion. The other contains slightly less than 6 per cent magnesium, with small additions of several other elements, and has proved especially useful for the production of fine wire. There are, however, several heat-treated aluminum-magnesium-silicon alloys which find extensive use for various wrought products. The oldest of these, containing 1 per cent silicon and 0.6 per cent magnesium, was used for many classes of products at one time but has largely been replaced by improved compositions. A modification of this alloy, containing 0.25 per cent chromium, is still used to some extent for forgings where a high degree of forgeability is desired. The other two alloys of this group contain, respectively, (a) 1.4 per cent magnesium, 0.7 per cent silicon, and 0.25 per cent chromium and (b) 0.95 per cent magnesium, 0.55 per cent silicon, and 0.25 per cent chromium. Both have high resistance to corrosion, strengths somewhat below those of the duralumin-type alloys, and a high degree of workability. The former has somewhat the higher strength and resistance to corrosion, while the latter excels in workability.

There are three common aluminum-magnesium-silicon alloys which are used in the form of heat-treated castings. One, containing 7 per cent silicon and 0.3 per cent magnesium, was developed to provide an alloy which would have the ease of casting of the 13 per cent silicon alloy but which could be heat treated to a higher strength. The other two are alloys developed for use in the automotive and aircraft industries. One contains 5 per cent silicon, 1.25 per cent copper, and 0.5 per cent magnesium and is used for liquid-cooled cylinder heads and other pressure-tight castings. The other is a low-expansion piston alloy containing 12 per cent silicon, 0.8 per cent copper, 1 per cent magnesium, and 1 to 2.5 per cent nickel. Typical properties of some of these alloys are given in the next chapter.

151. Constitution of the Common Copper-rich Alloys—None of the four series of important binary copper-rich alloys—namely, copper-zinc, copper-tin, copper-aluminum, and copper-nickel—can be heat treated in the sense that sterling silver or many of the aluminum-rich alloys can be heat treated. Sections of the copper-

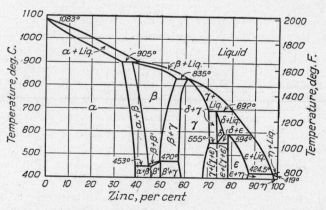

Fig. 100—The copper-zinc phase diagram (Phillips and Brick, *Metals Handbook*, p. 1367).

zinc and the copper-aluminum diagrams are given in Figs. 100 and 101.[8] Most of the useful alloys of copper with zinc (brass) and of copper with aluminum (aluminum bronze) contain less than 40 per cent zinc and less than 10 per cent aluminum respectively and are, consequently, ductile single-phase alloys consisting of a solid solution of zinc or of aluminum in copper. If the zinc in brass exceeds about 35 per cent, beta phase appears, reducing ductility and impact resistance. Only one such alloy, Muntz metal, containing 41 per cent zinc, is used widely, and in this the amount of beta phase is so small that ductility is not seriously affected.

Similar to conditions in the copper-zinc system, most of the commercial aluminum bronzes are single-phase alloys containing

[8] *Metals Handbook*, American Society for Metals, Cleveland, 1939, pp. 1342, 1367.

5 to 9 per cent aluminum (see Fig. 101). If the alloy contains more than 9.5 per cent aluminum, beta phase appears, reducing the ductility. Although the beta phase cannot be retained in solution by quenching, there is the possibility of securing transition structures by quenching a wrought alloy containing 10.5 to 11 per cent aluminum. The result is a tensile strength of 100,000 to 110,000 lb. per sq. in. and an elongation of 10 to 15 per cent, as compared with 65,000 to 85,000 lb. per sq. in. and 35 to 50 per

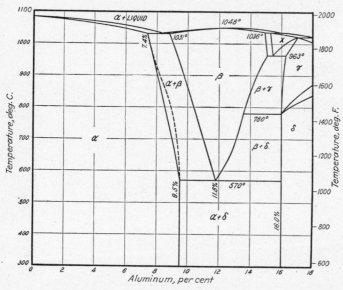

Fig. 101—The copper-rich portion of the copper-aluminum phase diagram (Jennison and Smith, *Metals Handbook*, p. 1342).

cent elongation for the alpha-phase alloy. No precipitation hardening is possible in the binary copper-rich copper-aluminum alloys.

The principal commercial copper-tin alloys are alpha-phase alloys and contain 1 to 10 per cent tin and usually also zinc, lead, or both. The only important binary alloy is phosphor bronze which contains 4 to 10 per cent tin and which is deoxidized in melting with a small amount (less than 0.5 per cent) of phosphorus. Tin increases the hardness and strength of copper. As shown in Chapter 18, a cold-rolled phosphor bronze used for springs has a tensile strength of about 100,000 lb. per sq. in. with 5 per cent tin; this increases to 120,000 lb. per sq. in. with 10 per cent tin. No heat treatment is possible with commercial copper-tin alloys as is indicated in Fig. 103A.

Copper and nickel form a continuous series of solid solutions free from any phase change. The strength of the solid solution of nickel in copper increases with the nickel from about 35,000 lb. per sq. in. for very low nickel to 80,000 for 60 per cent nickel; elongation decreases from 70 to 45 per cent in 2 in. There are

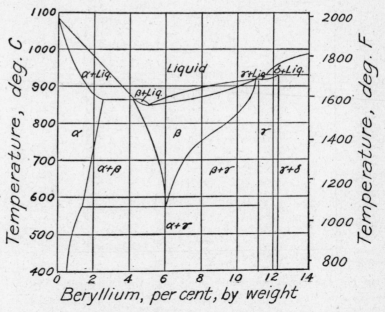

Fig. 102—Copper-rich portion of the copper-beryllium phase diagram (Jennison and Silliman, *Metals Handbook*, p. 1344).

a large number of important copper-nickel alloys which, owing to their controllable color, to their corrosion resistance, or to their thermoelectric properties, are used for coinage, ornamental metal work, ship construction (especially in parts exposed to salt water), thermocouples, and in other special applications. An alloy higher in nickel, Monel metal—containing 65 per cent nickel and 35 per cent copper—is widely used because of its high resistance to many corrosive media.

152. Precipitation-hardening Copper-rich Alloys—Recent developments in the age hardening of several heavy non-ferrous alloys are noteworthy. One of these alloys, silver-copper (sterling silver), is discussed in section 146 as an example of the phenomenon of precipitation hardening. The other two which deserve brief mention are the copper-beryllium and the copper-tin-nickel alloys.

The copper-beryllium diagram is shown in Fig. 102.[9] It will be noted that this figure resembles the silver-copper diagram (Fig. 95) and the aluminum-copper diagram in that the solubility of beryllium in copper increases with the temperature from about 0.5 per cent at room temperature to 2.4 per cent at 1475 to 1500° F. (800 to 815° C.). If an alloy containing 2 per cent beryllium is quenched from this temperature range, the alpha solid solution is retained; reheating to 480 to 750° F. (250 to 400° C.) causes precipitation of the gamma phase, accompanied by increased strength and hardness and greatly reduced ductility. For sheet containing 2.15 per cent beryllium the magnitude of the change is as follows: [10]

Property	Quenched from 1475° F. (800° C.)	Quenched and aged 2 hr. at 570° F. (300° C.)
Tensile strength, lb. per sq. in.	70,000	175,000
Yield strength, lb. per sq. in.	31,000	134,000
Elongation in 2 in., per cent	45	6.3
Brinell hardness	110	340

Beryllium is unique in that it causes precipitation hardening not only when alloyed with copper but also when alloyed with nickel, iron, and some austenitic steels. It is a costly element and has, therefore, not been used widely, although the high endurance limit of an alloy containing about 2 per cent beryllium and the remainder copper, reported by Gillett [11] to be about 100,000 lb. per sq. in., indicates that it may find considerable use as a spring material. The copper-beryllium alloys are discussed in Chapter 18.

An important development in cast copper-rich alloys was the discovery that the addition of 2 to 8 per cent nickel to a bronze containing 10 per cent tin results in an alloy that is age harden-

[9] *Metals Handbook,* American Society for Metals, Cleveland, 1939, p. 1344.
[10] *Metals Handbook,* loc. cit.
[11] Quoted by P. D. Merica, *Metal Progress,* March 1935, p. 46.

ing. The effect of 2 per cent nickel on the phase diagram of the copper-rich copper-tin alloys is shown in Figs. 103*A* and 103*B*.[12] As is evident in Fig. 103*A*, there is little change in the solubility curve of the delta constituent with increasing temperature. If nickel is added, however, the solubility curve at temperatures below 1020° F. (550° C.) is moved sharply to the left, from 16 to 4 per cent tin. If a cast alloy containing 8 per cent tin and 7.5 per cent nickel is heated to 1400° F. (760° C.) and quenched in

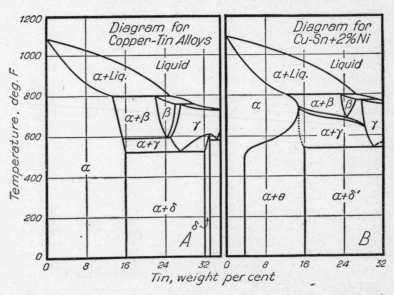

Fig. 103—Copper-rich portion of (*A*) the copper-tin phase diagram and (*B*) the copper-tin phase diagram with 2 per cent nickel (Merica).

water, the structure is wholly alpha. If, now, it is reheated to 600° F. (315° C.), the hardening constituent theta (Θ) precipitates. The effect on the properties as given by Merica is as follows:

Property	As cast	Quenched and aged
Tensile strength, lb. per sq. in.......	55,000	90,000
Yield strength, lb. per sq. in........	25,000	50,000
Elongation in 2 in., per cent........	18	15
Reduction of area, per cent.........	18	25

12 Merica, loc. cit.

153. Value of Precipitation Hardening in Non-ferrous Alloys —Naturally, precipitation hardening as a valuable industrial process cannot be compared with the heat treatment of steel. Precipitation hardening is a young art and, with the exception of the study of age-hardenable light alloys of aluminum upon which much work has been done and which have been used with great effectiveness by the airplane and automotive industries, research and development of this method of improving the properties of non-ferrous alloys are still in their infancy.

It is not likely that alloys hardenable by precipitation will ever be used in large tonnages. Most heavy non-ferrous alloys are used primarily for their color, their corrosion resistance, or their electric properties. In many applications mechanical properties are not of vital importance. Merica thinks that, with the exception of the aluminum alloys, the demand in the near future for alloys that can be age hardened will be "intensive rather than extensive." Many alloys in small lots will be needed rather than large quantities of a few. It is likely that precipitation-hardened heavy alloys will be "specialties" for many years. According to Smith,[13] precipitation-hardening copper alloys have great potential usefulness owing to the possibility of combining high strength with relatively high electric conductivity. High strength, when obtained by alloying and cold work, is accompanied by greatly lowered conductivity. This is not the case when the strength is obtained by precipitation hardening.

Important work has been done on the precipitation hardening of gold-base dental alloys, naturally a limited field, and some advances have been made in hardening of white metals that are used for bearings. For example, an alloy containing 97.5 per cent lead and 2.5 per cent antimony has a tensile strength of 4500 lb. per sq. in. as annealed; quenching from 455° F. (235° C.) results in a tensile strength of 5000 lb. per sq. in.; and aging for about 2 months at room temperature increases this to 10,000 lb. per sq. in.

154. Precipitation Hardening in Low-carbon Steels—In a previous chapter (section 35), where the fundamental structure of carbon steels is discussed, ferrite was defined as alpha iron holding in solution small amounts of silicon, phosphorus and possibly

[13] C. S. Smith, private communication, September 4, 1940.

other elements, and traces of carbon. Of the elements which may be in solution in very small quantities in alpha iron, three—carbon, oxygen, and nitrogen—can, under suitable conditions, precipitate and cause age-hardening effects. As the solubility of these in iron at various temperatures is not known with certainty, Fig. 104 [14] is an approximate picture. It will be noted that the slope of these curves resembles the slope of the solubility curves of the other alloy systems discussed in this chapter. The uncer-

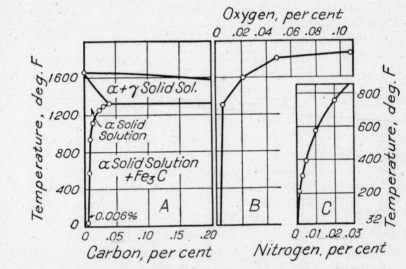

Fig. 104—Iron-rich portion of the (A) iron-carbon phase diagram, (B) iron-oxygen phase diagram, and (C) iron-nitrogen phase diagram, showing changes in solubility of carbon, oxygen, and nitrogen with temperature (Epstein and Miller).

tainty concerning oxygen is especially great. It is, for example, known that low-carbon steels which are thoroughly deoxidized are "non-aging"; but it is possible that oxygen decreases the solubility of carbon and of nitrogen in ferrite and thus promotes their precipitation, instead of precipitating itself.

Aging in carbon steel is a phenomenon that is common only in the low-carbon grades. Since these steels are used rarely in the quenched condition, precipitation hardening due to iron carbide

[14] S. Epstein and H. L. Miller, "Aging in Iron and Steel," *Metals Handbook*, American Society for Metals, Cleveland, 1939, p. 602.

or iron nitride retained in solution by quenching, followed by slow spontaneous precipitation at room temperature or more rapid precipitation at slightly elevated temperature—in a manner exactly analogous to precipitation hardening in duralumin—is seldom encountered. It is, however, possible, by quenching a steel containing 0.04 to 0.10 per cent carbon and by aging at 140° F. (60° C.) for 10 to 15 hr. to increase the Brinell hardness from 120 to 160.

There is another and more common variety of precipitation hardening in low-carbon steels, known as strain aging. If steels susceptible to aging are strained by cold working, a hardening constituent—probably iron carbide, iron oxide, or iron nitride—precipitates during straining and for some time afterward (at room temperature), and this is accompanied by increased hardness and strength and by decreased impact resistance. The effect of the precipitation can be detected readily by cold working a rimming steel and a deoxidized steel of the same analysis and by testing a sample of each immediately and at intervals of several weeks or months.

155. The Consequences of Aging in Low-carbon Steel—The embrittlement caused by strain aging is marked. For example, a low-carbon steel susceptible to aging, with a room-temperature impact resistance of 35 ft-lb., may have an impact value as low as 15 ft-lb. after cold working. This may be 5 or 6 ft-lb. if the material is tested after 3 months. A non-aging steel of the same carbon content, with a room-temperature impact value of 45 ft-lb., will have an impact value of about 40 ft-lb. when subjected to the same amount of straining, and of about 35 to 38 ft-lb. when tested after 3 months.

The quench aging of steel is an interesting phenomenon but is of little practical importance. Strain aging, however, frequently has unpleasant consequences. Low-carbon deep-drawing sheet for automobile bodies and fenders is given a light final cold working after hot rolling, which produces conditions ideal for precipitation of the hardening constituent. Unless the sheet is deep drawn immediately, the loss of ductility may be so great that the steel will not withstand the drawing operation successfully. Strain aging has been known also to be the cause of failures in boiler plate in strained areas around rivet holes. Considerable effort is being expended at present, by deoxidation and by other methods, to control grain size and aging characteristics which seem to be related to each other and to the method of melting the steel.

156. Age Hardening in Alloy Steels—Of the large number of common low-alloy steels, only those containing about 1 per cent copper are subject to precipitation hardening. The solubility of copper in alpha iron increases from about 0.4 per cent at room temperature to 1.4 per cent or more at 1525° F. (830° C.). Low-carbon steels containing 0.7 to 1.5 per cent copper can, therefore, be hardened by a treatment causing precipitation of the hardening constituent (in this case a solid solution of about 4 per cent iron in copper). This treatment consists of heating to 1650° F. (900° C.), cooling—quenching is not necessary—and reheating for 3 or 4 hr. at 930° F. (500° C.). Precipitation hardening increases tensile strength and yield strength about 20,000 lb. per sq. in. Ductility is decreased, but the age-hardened copper steels are not brittle.

A number of recent investigations have been concerned with the age hardening—produced by adding titanium—of highly alloyed iron-nickel, iron-nickel-manganese, and iron-nickel-cobalt alloys. Most of this work has been exploratory, and little industrial use, other than in radio tubes, has been made as yet of the alloys developed. It seems probable, however, that precipitation-hardened alloys containing 5 to 25 per cent iron, 25 to 40 per cent nickel, and the same amount of cobalt, to which 2 or 3 per cent titanium has been added, may in the near future be of considerable use for heating elements in electric appliances and for other purposes where high strength and ductility at elevated temperatures are valuable.

Alloys of iron with 8 to about 33 per cent tungsten can be age hardened owing to the variable solubility of an iron-tungsten intermetallic compound in alpha iron. As quenched, the alloys are soft enough to be machined. By reheating to 1290 to 1470° F. (700 to 800° C.) Brinell hardness values of 300 to 500 are attained. The work which has been done on this series [15] is also largely exploratory, and no wide commercial use of the iron-tungsten alloys seems in sight at present. Another series of alloys of equal or even more interest are the iron-cobalt-tungsten alloys,[16] espe-

[15] By W. P. Sykes of General Electric Co.
[16] Also investigated by W. P. Sykes.

cially those containing 50 per cent iron, 30 per cent cobalt, 20 per cent tungsten, and only a trace of carbon. Quenching from 2370° F. (1300° C.) produces a hardness of 40 Rockwell C, equivalent to a Brinell number of 385, and a tensile strength of 185,000 lb. per sq. in. Aging at 1130° F. (600° C.) increases the hardness to 65 to 69 Rockwell C, equivalent to a Brinell number of 700 to 800, i.e., to that of a very hard tool steel.

There are many interesting possibilities of improving the properties of high-alloy steels by precipitation hardening. The large amount of work now going on in this field should have important consequences in the future.

CHAPTER 17

LIGHT ALLOYS AS ENGINEERING MATERIALS

FOR about 30 years after aluminum metal was first produced (1825) it was a laboratory curiosity worth about $100 a pound. In 1857, Sainte-Clair Deville, as the result of research supported by Napoleon III, succeeded in bringing the price down to $25 and two years later to $17 a pound, still too high for anything but jewelry. Despite the fact that alumina (Al_2O_3) is a very abundant oxide in the earth's crust and can be produced economically in pure form, cheap aluminum was impossible, owing to the high cost of the sodium metal and the aluminum chloride necessary for successful reduction of the oxide, until the discovery of the electrolytic process. This process, which quickly brought the price down to less than $1.00 and later to $0.18 a pound, was discovered by Charles M. Hall in 1886. A patent was issued in 1889. Paul Héroult, inventor of the arc electric furnace which bears his name, discovered the electrolytic process about the same time and was granted a French patent in 1886 and a British patent in 1887, but his application in the United States was denied, the Patent Office recognizing the priority of Hall's invention. Héroult did not begin manufacture of aluminum metal in France until the success of Hall's process had been demonstrated in the United States.

Industry was slow to recognize the value of aluminum: in 1893 less than 100 tons was used in the United States; 10 years later domestic production was about 3000 tons. The discovery of duralumin and its heat treatment by Wilm in Germany (see p. 270) stimulated the use of aluminum. In 1915 world production was 85,000 metric tons; by 1939 this had increased to about 675,000 tons, of which the United States and Germany each produced between 165,000 and 200,000 tons.

The history of magnesium and its alloys parallels in many ways the history of aluminum. Isolated as a metal in 1830, it was a laboratory curiosity until 1852 when Bunsen produced considerable quantities by electrolysis of fused magnesium chloride. It was not until about 1895 that production was put on a commercial basis in Germany. For 20 years, Germany had a virtual monopoly in the manufacture of magnesium, until the first World War forced other countries to undertake production. The American industry began about 1915 and was firmly established a few years later. Since 1920, the price has dropped from about $1.75 a pound to $0.30 a pound, and yearly consumption in the United States has increased from 50 to about 2000 short tons. World consumption was estimated at 25,000 tons in 1939, of which Germany used two thirds.

157. **Manufacture of Aluminum Metal**—Aluminum metal is produced by electrolyzing alumina (Al_2O_3), which is prepared by purifying bauxite—a hydrated oxide of aluminum containing iron oxide and silica as the principal impurities. Bauxite deposits of satisfactory quality are distributed throughout the world, and alumina of high purity can be obtained cheaply from these deposits. Owing to the high melting point of alumina—3720° F. (2050° C.)—and to its high heat of formation, it cannot be reduced by methods commonly used for iron, zinc, lead, or copper. It can be reduced by carbon at 3250° F. (1790° C.) or above, a temperature at which aluminum is quickly volatilized. Since the deposition potential of aluminum is greater than that of hydrogen, and since aluminum reacts with water, electrolytic deposition of the metal from an aqueous solution of its salts is not possible. In order to electrolyze an aluminum compound it is necessary, therefore, to dissolve it in a substance which does not react with aluminum and which is more resistant than aluminum oxide to electrolytic decomposition. The discovery of such a substance—cryolite, a double fluoride of sodium and aluminum, Na_3AlF_6—and the method of using it are the basic features of Hall's patent. Cryolite melts at about 1830° F. (1000° C.) and, when molten, dissolves about 16 per cent of its weight of alumina. By electrolyzing a molten bath of cryolite and aluminum oxide with a current of low voltage and high amperage, Al_2O_3 is dissociated into aluminum and oxygen; the molten aluminum, being heavier at 1850° F. (1010° C.) than the molten cryolite, settles to the bottom of the bath. Powdered alumina is added from time to time to

replace that electrolyzed. The molten metal is removed by tapping or ladling and is poured into molds to solidify as pigs weighing about 50 lb. each. The efficiency of the process varies from 75 to 90 per cent, and the metal so produced has an average purity of 99.5 per cent. The aluminum pigs are generally re-melted in lots of 3000 to 30,000 lb. to eliminate entrapped electrolyte and dross and thus to improve the quality. This remelted metal is poured into ingots of various sizes, ranging from 1 lb. to as much as 3000 lb.

158. **Melting and Casting Aluminum Alloys**—Aluminum has several characteristics which make melting simple compared with steel or cast iron. The principal ones are its low melting point— 1220° F. (660° C.)—and the formation of a tenacious film of oxide when the metal is exposed to the air, which provides protection from further oxidation. In the manufacture of alloys, aluminum ingots are melted in a crucible, iron-pot, or barrel furnace, or in large lots in an open-hearth furnace. If the alloying element melts at a low temperature, as for example magnesium and zinc, it is added directly to the molten metal just before pouring. If the alloying element has a high melting point, as for example copper, manganese, and nickel, it is added as a hardener. This is a rich alloy of aluminum with the alloying metal and is made by melting aluminum, superheating it, and slowly adding the alloying metal. For the manufacture of aluminum-copper alloys the hardener usually contains about 50 per cent copper. Silicon, manganese, and nickel hardeners contain 15 per cent silicon, 10 per cent manganese, and 25 per cent nickel respectively. Hardeners melt readily when they are added to molten aluminum.

When melting is completed and the temperature of the metal is adjusted to that required for the particular alloy being made, the metal is poured, either into large ingot molds for fabrication into wrought sections, or into molds for castings. There are three methods of producing aluminum-alloy castings: (1) pouring into sand molds, (2) pouring into metal (permanent) molds, and (3) pouring into metal dies under pressure (die casting). Producing a sand- or permanent-mold casting of high quality is an art that demands specialized knowledge of patterns, sands, cores, and molding practice and is beyond the scope of this book. In general, sand molds are used for large or intricate castings or for the production of small quantities. Permanent-mold or die castings, owing to the high cost of molds or dies, are cheaper than sand castings only if large quantities of certain sizes and shapes are required. Because permanent-mold and die castings can be held to close tolerances, less machining is necessary than for sand castings.

159. Development of Wrought Alloys of Aluminum—Credit for the development of wrought high-strength aluminum alloys should be given chiefly to the aircraft industry. As mentioned previously, Wilm's early work was done in connection with Zeppelin's development of the rigid dirigible, and, according to Bossert,[1] prior to the first World War the Aluminum Company of America supplied the U. S. Navy with aluminum-alloy (duralumin) sheet (designated 17S-T [2]) for the Navy's rigid dirigible. In 1915, the minimum requirements for 17S-T (duralumin) sheet were 50,000 lb. per sq. in. tensile strength and 24,000 lb. per sq. in. yield strength. The composition of 17S is essentially the same now, but, owing to improvements in manufacture and heat treatment, the minimum tensile strength is now 55,000, and the minimum yield strength is 32,000 lb. per sq. in. Alloy 17S has been largely replaced in aircraft construction by a recently developed alloy (24S) containing more magnesium, which has a minimum tensile strength of 62,000 lb. per sq. in. and a minimum yield strength of 40,000 lb. per sq. in.

In its use of large quantities of high-strength aluminum alloys the aircraft industry was interested primarily in the strength-weight ratio; cost was of secondary importance. In other industries, however, first cost and total cost over the expected life of a structure are very important. It was only 10 or 15 years ago that these alloys were considered seriously for automobile, truck, and bus construction and for electric- and steam-railway rolling stock; their consideration for bridge and building construction is still more recent. For these fields, new alloys have been developed and new wrought sections have been made available so that, now, relatively large quantities of aluminum alloys are used in the transportation field.

There are two classes of wrought aluminum alloys: (1) alloys

---

[1] T. W. Bossert, *Metal Progress*, Jan. 1937, p. 42.

[2] In the specifications of the Aluminum Company of America "S" designates a wrought alloy. If this is followed by a "T," it designates a wrought and heat-treated material.

that are not heat treated and that owe their properties to strain hardening by cold work, and (2) alloys whose strength may be improved by heat treatment and whose properties may be altered still more by cold deformation. Untreated alloys are available in five "tempers": annealed, quarter hard, half hard, three-quarters hard, and hard. The annealed alloys have the lowest tensile and yield strengths and the highest ductility, and the hard alloys have the highest strength and lowest ductility of the five classes. This is shown by the data in Table 19.[3]

160. The Manufacture of Wrought Aluminum Alloys—Aluminum and its alloys can readily be hot and cold worked by rolling, forging, pressing, extruding, or drawing into a variety of sections, including such thin material as fine wire and foil. Although some alloys are not suited for certain types of wrought products, aluminum and its alloys can generally be secured in the form of sheet, plate, foil, wire, rod, bar, rolled and extruded shapes, tubing and pipe, rivets and forgings. Sheet, plate, and foil are well-known rolled products which have been available for many years. These products are made in thicknesses from about 0.0003 in. to 3 in. and in widths from less than 1 in. to as much as 10 ft. Rolled shapes are a development of the past 10 years, and at present I- and H-beams, tees, zees, angles, and channels as deep as 12 in. and as long as 85 ft. are produced. Forging is an important method of producing finished sections, especially for the automotive and aircraft industries, and large numbers of forged connecting rods, propellers, crankcases, and other engine parts are made each year.

Aluminum alloys are shaped readily by extruding (forcing a hot ingot, billet, or bar through a die), and intricate hollow and solid sections can be produced (Fig. 105) in this way, so intricate that it is virtually impossible to form them by any other process of working. Extrusion is also used for certain structural shapes, especially I- and H-beams, angles, and channels. All aluminum-

---

[3] Data in Tables 19 and 20 are based on Zay Jeffries, C. F. Nagel, and R. T. Wood, *Trans. Am. Soc. Civil Eng.*, v. 102, 1937, pp. 1267-1296; and E. H. Dix, Jr., and J. J. Bowman, "Alloys of Aluminum and Magnesium," in *Symposium on High-strength Constructional Metals*, American Society for Testing Materials, March, 1936, pp. 109-126; and revised September, 1940, by E. H. Dix, Jr., and his associates at the Aluminum Research Laboratories of Aluminum Company of America.

TABLE 19. TYPICAL COMPOSITIONS AND TENSILE AND ENDURANCE PROPERTIES OF WROUGHT ALUMINUM ALLOYS

Specification No.			Nominal composition, per cent					Condition	Tensile strength, lb. per sq. in.	Yield strength, lb. per sq. in.	Elongation in 2 in., per cent †	Endurance limit, lb. per sq. in.
S.A.E.	Alcoa *	A.S.T.M.	Cu	Si	Mn	Mg	Cr					
29	3S	B79-39T	....	....	1.25	....	....	Annealed..........	16,000	5,000	30	7,000
								Half hard.........	21,000	18,000	8	9,000
								Hard.............	29,000	25,000	4	10,000
20	4S	......	....	....	1.25	1.0	....	Annealed..........	26,000	10,000	20	14,000
								Half hard.........	34,000	27,000	9	15,000
								Hard.............	40,000	34,000	5	16,000
	14S	......	4.4	0.80	0.8	0.4	....	Heat treated and aged..	70,000	62,000	14 ‡	
26	17S	B78-39T	4.0	....	0.50	0.5	....	Annealed..........	26,000	10,000	20	
								Heat treated......	60,000	37,000	20	
	A17S	......	2.5	....	....	0.3	....	Annealed..........	22,000	8,000	24	
								Heat treated......	43,000	24,000	24	
24	24S	......	4.2	....	0.50	1.5	....	Annealed..........	26,000	10,000	20	12,000
								Heat treated......	68,000	44,000	20	18,000
27	25S	......	4.5	0.80	0.80	....	....	Heat treated and aged..	57,000	37,000	21 ‡	15,000
	27S	......	4.5	0.80	0.80	....	....	Heat treated and aged..	60,000	50,000	9	13,000
280	A51S	......	....	1.00	....	0.6	0.25	Heat treated and aged..	47,000	41,000	20 ‡	10,500
201	52S	B109-39T	....	....	....	2.5	0.25	Annealed..........	29,000	14,000	25	17,000
								Half hard.........	37,000	29,000	10	19,000
								Hard.............	41,000	36,000	7	20,500
	53S	......	....	0.7	....	1.3	0.25	Annealed..........	16,000	7,000	25	7,500
								Heat treated and aged..	39,000	33,000	14	11,000
	61S	......	0.25	0.6	....	0.9	0.25	Annealed..........	18,000	8,000	22	7,500
								Heat treated and aged..	45,000	39,000	12	12,500

* Aluminum Company of America.
† Elongation values are for specimens of 1/16-in. sheet except those marked ‡ which are for 0.505-in. round bars.

alloy tubing is seamless and is produced by extruding from hollow ingots followed by cold working to finished size. Many hollow sections are made by forming a round disc into a cup-shaped section on a press. Tubes vary from 0.025 to 10.5 in. inside diameter, or $\frac{7}{32}$ to $11\frac{1}{4}$ in. outside diameter.

Although aluminum and its alloys can be cold drawn into wires as small as 0.0025 in. in diameter, most of the drawn wire which is

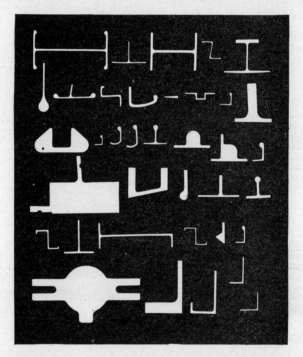

Fig. 105—Cross-sections of extruded shapes of aluminum alloys (Aluminum Company of America).

produced is of a larger size and is used for the fabrication of stranded electrical conductors. For this purpose, it is common practice to use composite cable, known as aluminum cable steel reinforced (A.C.S.R.), consisting of a central core of one or more galvanized high-strength steel wires surrounded by one or more layers of high-conductivity aluminum wire. This type of cable combines the high strength of the steel with the high conductivity and light weight of aluminum.

161. Fabrication of Aluminum Alloys—The aluminum alloys used for structural purposes can be fabricated with much the same equipment as that used for steel. The principal exception is that quenched and aged alloys cannot be welded or worked at temperatures above 400° F. (205° C.), as this would destroy the effect of the heat treatment. If such hot working is necessary, the piece must be heat treated again after forming. The high-strength alloys are relatively soft as quenched and can be subjected to considerable distortion before aging starts. The time available for such forming before the alloy becomes too hard varies between one and several hours, depending on composition. An alternate method of forming duralumin-type alloys consists of heating to 900 to 950° F. (480 to 510° C.) under close pyrometric control and forming the hot alloy in a cold die of sufficiently large cross-section to provide an effective quench. This process (patented) eliminates the necessity of a second quenching and aging treatment, which, because of possible warping, is not always practicable for fabricated sections.

Aluminum alloys can be riveted, sheared, drilled, or punched with the same equipment as that used for steel. While tools commonly used for machining steel will perform satisfactorily on aluminum, for the best grade of work more top and side rake are used on aluminum than on steel; the tools are kept very sharp, and the tool surfaces are kept smooth and bright. High-carbon steel tools are usually satisfactory, but high-speed steel and tungsten carbide are more frequently employed in production machining. For automatic screw machine work 17S-T and a special free-cutting alloy (11S) containing—in addition to copper, manganese, and magnesium—0.5 per cent each of lead and bismuth are commonly used. Aluminum and its alloys cannot be cut with a torch, but they can be joined by gas, metallic- or carbon-arc, atomic-hydrogen, or resistance welding. In any welding process, a refractory oxide forms which necessitates the use of a flux to produce a sound weld. In general, the welding of aluminum and its alloys is no more difficult than the welding of most of the other common metals. Owing, however, to some of the characteristics of aluminum, considerable training and experience are required to produce uniformly high quality welds.

162. Properties of the Wrought Alloys—The tensile and endurance properties of the principal wrought alloys are given in

Table 19. For some applications, the heat-treated alloys S.A.E. 26 and 24 (Alcoa 17S) and 24S are cold worked slightly before use. This increases the tensile strength over that shown in Table 19 by about 3000 lb. per sq. in. and the yield strength by about 10,000 lb. per sq. in. and reduces the elongation from 20 to 13 per cent in 2 in.

The specific gravity of the wrought alloys is about the same as of the casting alloys (see p. 306), namely, in the range of 2.66 to 2.92 depending upon composition. The electric conductivity of aluminum is lowered by alloying and is affected by heat treatment and by mechanical working. For wrought material, it varies from about 50 per cent of the international copper standard for annealed alloys to about 30 per cent for some of the heat-treated alloys. The coefficient of thermal expansion is about twice that of steel.

The Brinell hardness of the wrought alloys (500-kg. load, 10-mm. ball) varies from approximately 30 to 85 for untreated alloys (S.A.E. 29, 20, and 201), and from 30 to 120 for the heat-treated material, depending upon the temper. Endurance limits (based on 500 million cycles) are low; the endurance ratio is highest for the annealed alloys and is only about 0.25 for heat-treated high-strength sections. It is characteristic of the annealed alloys that the endurance limit is higher than the yield strength.

Both wrought and cast alloys are heat treated by heating between 910 to 980° F. (490 to 525° C.), depending on the alloy, followed by quenching in cold water. The precipitation hardening (aging) treatment depends upon the composition: for the duralumin-type alloys—S.A.E. 26 and 24—it is 3 to 4 days at room temperature; other alloys are aged from 1 to 18 hr. at temperatures ranging from that of boiling water to 325° F. (160° C.). In the case of the duralumin-type alloys, about 90 per cent of the aging occurs in the first 24 hr.

163. Characteristics and Applications of the Wrought Alloys —The principal characteristic of the wrought alloys, especially of those responding to heat treatment, is a high strength-weight ratio; in other words, the specific strength (strength divided by specific gravity) is high. This is discussed in section 168. It is sufficient to note here that this characteristic is the one which is primarily responsible for the wide use of these alloys in aircraft construction. For some applications the low modulus of elasticity, 10.3 million lb. per sq. in., may be a distinct disadvantage.

Alloys which are not heat treated—S.A.E. 29, 20, and 201 (Table 19)—are used chiefly in the form of sheet, plate, and extruded shapes and to a lesser extent as bars, rods, and tubing. They are low in price, are readily formed and easily welded, and have high resistance to corrosion. They are, consequently, widely used where their properties suffice: for example, bus and truck bodies, low-stressed parts of railway cars, airplanes and boats, cooking utensils, chemical equipment, shipping containers, and architectural trim.

The three duralumin-type alloys—S.A.E. 26, 24, and 27—are used extensively in aircraft, and also as structural shapes in other fields. Alloy 26, usually known as duralumin, is available as sheet, plate, tubing, bars, rods, wire, rivets, forgings and structural shapes and was, in the past, used widely in aircraft construction. In recent years, however, it has been superseded largely by alloy 24, the so-called superduralumin, which has 15 or 20 per cent higher strength. Alloys 24 and 26 are both available as "Alclad" sheet (discussed below) which is rapidly assuming a role of importance in aircraft construction. Alloy 27 is a forging alloy and is largely used for connecting rods and propeller blades (Fig. 106). Alloy Alcoa 14S is a high-strength forging alloy, used for aircraft fittings and for connecting rods and crankcases. Alloy Alcoa 27S is a special-purpose alloy used almost exclusively in the form of plate and structural shapes. Alloy S.A.E. 280, owing to the ease with which it may be hot worked, is used for crankcases and other difficult forgings.

The aluminum alloys, as a class, are highly resistant to corrosion in most atmospheres and in many common chemicals and solutions. In common with all other metals they are, of course, not corrosion resistant under all conditions of service and must be employed with full knowledge of their characteristics and limitations (see Chapter 20). In general, the strain-hardened wrought alloys are somewhat more resistant to corrosion than the heat-treated alloys and, in most cases, an artificially aged alloy is less resistant than one which ages at room temperature. Heat-treated alloys which have not received a rapid quench, or which may have been subsequently reheated, may be subject to intergranular corrosion. From the viewpoint of composition, alloys containing magnesium and silicon (alone or combined) generally are more resistant to corrosion than those containing copper as the principal alloying element. Various methods of coating the surface to increase corrosion resistance are used, such as paint, or an anodic or "Alclad" coating. In its most common form, Alclad sheet consists of a strong alloy core with a thin bonded surface

Fig. 106—Aluminum-alloy adjustable propeller blades (Aluminum Company of America).

layer of high-purity aluminum. In the form of $\frac{1}{16}$- to $\frac{1}{8}$-in. sheet the tensile and yield strengths of Alclad 17S-T are about 3000 lb. per sq. in. lower, and the elongation is about 2 per cent lower, than for the uncoated material. For design values, properties equivalent to those of uncoated sheet are secured by using slightly thicker material.

164. General Characteristics of Aluminum Casting Alloys— The aluminum alloys, in general, are readily cast in sand molds and permanent (metal) molds or by pressure die casting. Since the three processes vary to a marked extent, it is obvious that all alloys are not equally suitable for the three types of products, nor are the products of the three entirely comparable. Although it is not the purpose of the discussion in this chapter to describe the casting of aluminum alloys in detail, it is important that the engineer recognize the differences between the three processes in order to select intelligently the one best suited for the application at hand.

Sand castings of almost unlimited size and shape can be made from scores of aluminum alloys, each having unique properties or foundry characteristics. Where only a few castings are required, or if the casting is relatively large, sand castings are indicated. On the other hand, when large numbers of relatively small parts are required, or if a smooth surface and a minimum amount of machining are desired, permanent-mold or die castings are to be preferred. The method of casting, too, affects the properties to be expected from a given composition, permanent-mold and die castings usually having a somewhat higher strength than sand castings. In general, when the number and the size of the castings to be made would justify the use of any of the three methods, die castings are the cheapest and can be cast to the closest tolerances, while sand castings will cost the most and will require the broadest tolerances.

The alloys whose principal characteristics are given in Table 20 can be divided broadly into five classes. The first of these includes S.A.E. alloys 33, 36, and 31 (Alcoa 112, 212, and 645) which are low-cost general-purpose alloys of moderate strength as cast and are relatively easy to machine. These alloys are not so corrosion resistant as some of the others, but they are used widely for crankcases, transmission cases, housings, and many other automotive and aircraft castings in which light weight is more important than strength or resistance to corrosion. The second class includes S.A.E. alloys 38 and 324 (Alcoa 195 and 220). These are high-strength, heat-treated alloys used primarily for structural parts where the strength-weight ratio is important. The former is the original heat-treatable aluminum casting alloy and has somewhat better foundry characteristics, but a lower resistance to corrosion, than the latter. Where its strength is adequate, S.A.E. 38 alloy is preferred to S.A.E. 324 because of its lower cost and better foundry characteristics.

The third class, in which silicon is the chief alloying element, includes S.A.E. alloys 35, 37, 322, and 323 (Alcoa 43, 47, 355, and 356). These alloys are noted for their good foundry characteristics, permitting thin intricate castings to be poured readily, and have good resistance to salt-water corrosion. Their strength, even

Fig. 107—Cast aluminum-alloy piston (Aluminum Company of America).

when heat treated (Table 20), is less than that of S.A.E. 38 and 324 alloys, but they are more ductile and shock resistant than the alloys of aluminum and copper (S.A.E. 31, 33, and 36). They are leak-proof and are used for marine castings, water-cooled cylinder heads, and a large variety of small castings. The alloys of this class are cast in sand or, frequently, in permanent molds.

The fourth class includes Alcoa alloys 214 and 216, alloys which have good strength and ductility as cast and are corrosion resistant and leak-proof. They are difficult to cast into thin sections, but their specific gravity is low, their strength-weight ratio is high, and their resistance to most corrosive media is excellent.

The fifth class, mentioned in the previous section and in an earlier chapter (section 144), includes S.A.E. 39 and 34 (Alcoa 142 and 122). These alloys are used chiefly for pistons of automotive and aircraft engines (Fig. 107) and for air-cooled cylinder heads of aircraft engines (Fig. 108). As cast in permanent molds and subjected to a solution heat treatment and precipitation hard-

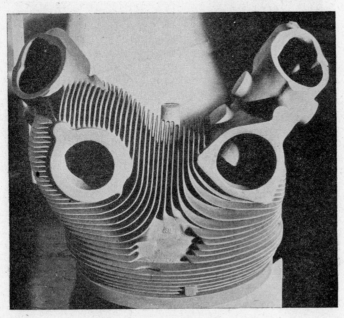

Fig. 108—Cast aluminum-alloy cylinder head for air-cooled airplane engine (Aluminum Company of America).

ening, they have high strength and a Brinell hardness (500-kg. load, 10-mm. ball) of 100 to 140; they retain their strength and hardness satisfactorily at operating temperatures of the engine.

165. Properties of Sand-cast Aluminum Alloys—Two general types of alloys are used for sand castings: (1) those whose properties depend upon composition, and (2) those whose properties depend primarily upon heat treatment. Typical compositions, tensile properties, and general characteristics of both classes are

given in Table 20.[4] The tensile properties are those determined on standard 0.5-in. test bars (Fig. 109) cast separately[5] and tested without machining. The test specimens of aluminum alloys (as of all other cast metals) should, of course, be cast under conditions which duplicate as closely as possible the solidification and cooling of the castings. The properties of specimens machined from castings depend upon the location of the specimen: if it is taken from a thin section, which cools rapidly, the strength will

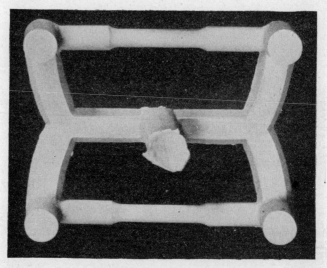

Fig. 109—Standard 0.5-in. test bars for aluminum alloys (Aluminum Research Laboratories).

be higher than if it is taken from a heavy section. The properties of separately cast bars are probably as representative of the average properties of a casting as it is possible to attain industrially. Such specimens serve, moreover, to control the quality of the metal and the effectiveness of the heat treatment.

As indicated by the data in Table 20, the "as-cast" alloys have a tensile strength of less than 30,000 lb. per sq. in. and an elongation of less than 10 per cent in 2 in. It is possible by solution heat treatment and age hardening to secure a tensile strength of 35,000 to 44,000 lb. per sq. in. The specific gravity of the alloys (both as

4 See footnote 3, this chapter.
5 U. S. general specification QQ-M 151, Figs. 11a and 11b.

TABLE 20. TYPICAL COMPOSITION, TENSILE PROPERTIES, AND USES OF ALUMINUM CASTING ALLOYS

S.A.E.	Specification No.		Nominal composition, per cent					Tensile strength, lb. per sq. in.	Yield strength, lb. per sq. in.	Elongation in 2 in., per cent	Principal characteristics
	Alcoa *	A.S.T.M.	Cu	Si	Mg	Ni	Fe				
				Sand castings							
35	43	B26-38T-J	....	5.0	....	....	....	19,000	9,000	6.0	Easily cast, corrosion resistant, leak-proof
37	47	B26-38T-K	....	12.5	....	....	....	26,000	11,000	8.0	Same as above, better properties, "Modified" †
33	112	B26-38T-C	7.5	....	....	2.0‡	1.2	23,000	14,000	1.5	Low-cost, general-purpose alloy
36	212	B26-38T-CC	8.0	1.2	....	....	1.0	22,000	14,000	2.0	Same as alloy 33
	214	B26-38T-L	....	....	3.8	....	....	25,000	12,000	9.0	Corrosion resistant
	216	....	....	....	6.0	....	....	27,000	16,000	6.0	Same as alloy 214
31	645	....	2.5	....	....	11.0‡	1.5	29,000	20,000	4.0	Good strength, low corrosion resistance
				Sand cast and heat treated							
38	195-T4	B26-38T-G	4.0	....	....	....	....	31,000	16,000	8.5	Good combination of properties
38	195-T6	B26-38T-G	4.0	....	....	....	....	36,000	22,000	5.0	Same as above, different treatment
324	220-T4	B26-38T-N	....	....	10.0	....	....	45,000	25,000	14.0	High tensile properties
322	355-T6	B26-38T-N	1.3	5.0	0.5	....	....	35,000	25,000	3.5	Corrosion resistant, leak-proof
323	356-T6	B26-38T-M	....	7.0	0.3	....	....	32,000	22,000	4.0	Easily cast, corrosion resistant
39	142-T61	B26-38T-H	4.0	....	1.5	2.0	....	37,000	32,000	0.5	Piston and cylinder-head alloy
34	122-T61	B26-38T-F	10.0	....	0.2	....	1.2	36,000	30,000	1.0	Piston and cylinder-head alloy
				Die castings							
305	13	B85-39T-5	....	12.0	....	....	....	33,000	18,000	1.8	Easily cast, corrosion resistant
307	85	B85-39T-7	4.0	5.0	....	....	....	35,000	19,000	2.7	General-purpose alloy
09	93	B85-39T-9	4.0	2.0	....	4.0	....	33,000	20,000	1.0	Takes high polish

* Aluminum Company of America. † Structure controlled in melting and casting. ‡ Percentage zinc.

cast and as wrought) varies with composition from about 2.66 to about 2.92 (0.095 to 0.105 lb. per cu. in.), i.e., they are either slightly lighter or slightly heavier than aluminum (specific gravity 2.71), depending upon whether the principal alloying element is magnesium or copper.

The modulus of elasticity of all aluminum alloys is approximately 10.3 million lb. per sq. in., i.e., about one third of that of steel. The Brinell hardness of "as-cast" alloys ranges from about 40 to 70 (500-kg. load, 10-mm. ball), while for the heat-treated alloys a hardness value of 75 to 100 is common. The endurance limits for the alloys listed in Table 20 range from 6000 to 9500 lb. per sq. in. This gives an endurance ratio of 0.25 to 0.38 for cast, and of 0.17 to 0.28 for heat-treated, alloys, based on a rotating-beam test of 500 million cycles. These ratios are one third to one half of those usual for carbon and low-alloy steels.

166. **Permanent-mold and Die Castings**—Casting aluminum alloys in permanent molds by gravity, or under pressure, is widely practiced, especially for pistons and other simple sections. The compositions of the alloys used for die and permanent-mold castings may be the same as for sand castings or they may be modified somewhat. Thus, alloy S.A.E. 33 (Alcoa 112) is used for both sand and metal-mold castings, and modifications of this alloy containing 1.5 and 4.0 per cent silicon have been specially developed for casting in permanent molds. Pistons for internal-combustion engines are cast in permanent molds with alloy S.A.E. 34 (Alcoa 122), but recently an alloy containing 0.8 per cent copper, 12 per cent silicon, 1 per cent magnesium, and 2.5 per cent nickel has been developed [6] which has lower thermal expansion and permits a closer fit of the piston in the cylinder. Alloy 39 (Alcoa 142) is used most frequently for air-cooled cylinder heads for aircraft engines. An alloy (not included in Table 20) containing 4 per cent copper and 3 per cent silicon (Alcoa 108) has excellent casting properties and is used for sand castings; with 4.5 per cent copper and 5.5 per cent silicon it is used in metal molds.

There are eight aluminum die-casting alloys with an A.S.T.M. specification number, three of which are included in Table 20. The properties of all eight alloys are very much alike: the tensile strength ranges from 29,000 to 33,000 lb. per sq. in. and the

---

[6] Aluminum Company of America, U. S. Patent 1,799,837.

elongation in 2 in. from 1 to 4 per cent. In general, the die-cast aluminum-silicon alloys (5 and 12 per cent silicon) are used where corrosion resistance is important. The alloys of aluminum with copper machine easily and have a bright color. An alloy containing both copper and silicon combines the advantages (and disadvantages) of both elements. In general, the design of a casting is much more important than the properties in determining the choice of an alloy.

167. **Magnesium Alloys**—Magnesium metal is produced industrially by electrolysis of molten anhydrous magnesium chloride, which is obtained from brine or sea water. Globules of molten magnesium, containing 99.9 per cent or more magnesium, rise to the top of the bath and collect in a large mass, which is removed at intervals and is cast into ingots. Magnesium metal is used in pyrotechnics, for incendiary bombs and flares, for flashlight powder, as a base for a large number of chemicals, as a deoxidizer for nickel, and as an important constituent of aluminum and zinc alloys.

Magnesium metal has a tensile strength of about 18,000 lb. per sq. in., a yield strength of about 2500 lb. per sq. in., and an elongation of 10 per cent in 2 in. By alloying with 2 to 13 per cent aluminum the tensile strength is doubled and the yield strength is increased 500 to 800 per cent. All the magnesium-aluminum alloys may be heat treated and age hardened. The magnesium alloys are cast in sand or in permanent molds, or into ingots which are extruded into a number of forms. After extrusion, the alloys are rolled or forged into bars, sheets, angles, I-beams, or other sections. Tubes as large as 6 or 7 in. in diameter can be extruded. Sheets are hot rolled at a temperature of 600 to 800° F. (315 to 425° C.) and are finished to exact size by cold rolling.

Magnesium alloys weigh one third less than the alloys of aluminum (specific gravity about 1.8), and in the form of castings and wrought sections they are used primarily by the aircraft industry for housings, pans, cases, and covers of various kinds and for a large number of lightly stressed fittings. In Europe considerable use has been made of these alloys for propellers, cowling, fuel tanks, and a few structural members; in this country they are rarely used for highly stressed parts. Magnesium alloys are machined readily and can be welded. Their greatest handicaps

TABLE 21. TYPICAL COMPOSITIONS AND TENSILE AND ENDURANCE PROPERTIES OF MAGNESIUM ALLOYS

Alloy designation			Nominal composition, per cent			Condition	Tensile strength, lb. per sq. in.	Yield strength, lb. per sq. in.	Elongation in 2 in., per cent	Endurance limit, lb. per sq. in.
A.S.T.M.	American Magnesium Corp.	Dow Chemical Co.	Al	Mn*	Zn					
						Sand cast				
B80-38T-2	241	A	8.0	0.2	....	Heat treated	33,000	11,000	9	7,500
	240	G	10.0	0.1	....	Heat treated	33,000	12,000	7	10,000
B80-38T-3	246	B	12.0	0.1	....	Heat treated	33,000	19,000	1	9,000
B80-38T-4	265	H	6.0	0.2	3.0	Heat treated	29,000	21,000	0.5	7,000
						Cast	28,000	11,000	6	9,000
						Heat treated	35,000	12,000	9	10,000
						Heat treated	38,000	20,000	4	9,500
						Die cast				
B94-39T	230	K	10.0	0.1	1.0†	Cast	28,000	22,000	0.5	
						Wrought				
B107-38T-11	3S	M	....	1.5	....	Heat treated ‡	32,000	15,000	16	8,000
B107-38T-6	53S	F	4.0	0.3	....	Annealed ‡	35,000	20,000	15	10,000
						Hard ‡	44,000	30,000	9	
B107-38T-8	57S	J	6.5	0.3	0.75	Extruded §	40,000	30,000	16	13,000
B107-38T-9	58S	O	8.5	0.2	0.5	Extruded §	43,000	32,000	16	16,000
	59S	..	10.0	0.1	....	Extruded §	46,000	35,000	13	17,000
						Extruded §	50,000	38,000	10	16,000
						Extruded ‖	56,000	40,000	3.5	16,000

* Minimum, except for B107-38T-11.   † Maximum silicon percentage.   ‡ Sheet.   § Extruded and stretched.   ‖ Extruded and heat treated.

are the low modulus of elasticity of 6.5 million lb. per sq. in. and their susceptibility to salt-air or salt-water corrosion which may be serious unless the surface is well protected. Typical compositions and tensile and endurance properties are given in Table 21.[7]

168. **Strength-weight Ratios of the Light Alloys**—There are many structures, of which the airplane and the streamlined railway train are outstanding examples, in which dead weight must be kept at a minimum. In such structures, two factors must be given special consideration. These are the strength-weight ratio and the relative stiffness. The strength-weight ratio, usually called specific tensile strength, specific yield strength, or specific endurance limit, is the quotient of the actual property, in pounds per square inch, divided by the specific gravity. The relative stiffness depends, of course, on the modulus of elasticity. There has been considerable interest in these factors lately.[8]

The specific-strength values of some ferrous and non-ferrous structural materials are given in Table 22.[9] On the basis of these data, an alloy steel, such as chromium-molybdenum, heat treated to a tensile strength of more than 150,000 lb. per sq. in. has the best specific properties and should, therefore, be the best structural material for saving dead weight. Magnesium alloys rank second and, on this basis, might be considered the best of the cast materials. Heat-treated cast and wrought aluminum-copper alloys have high specific tensile strength and yield strength, but their specific endurance limits are low. Although such data as are given in Table 22 are important, they should, of course, not be the sole criterion of the value of a metallic material for a specific use. There are other factors, such as ductility, impact resistance, notch sensitivity, damping capacity, corrosion resistance, and others, that have to be considered (in addition to cost) and that may be decisive. In many structural applications stiffness is very important. If a steel beam has a stiffness of 100, a beam of the same dimensions of a heat-treated aluminum alloy will have

---

[7] Same source as Tables 19 and 20.

[8] See for example, "Symposium on Structural Application of Steel and Light-weight Alloys," *Trans. Am. Soc. Civil Eng.*, Paper 1979, v. 102, 1937, pp. 1181-1483.

[9] Most of the data in Table 22 are taken from a paper by A. W. Winston, in "Symposium on Structural Application of Steel and Light-weight Alloys" (see previous footnote), pp. 1385-1396.

a stiffness of 33. The stiffness of a comparable beam of heat-treated magnesium alloy is only 22. By a small increase in the depth, however, an aluminum- or a magnesium-alloy beam can be made as stiff as the steel beam and still retain much of the weight advantage.

TABLE 22. SPECIFIC STRENGTHS OF COMMON FERROUS AND NON-FERROUS STRUCTURAL MATERIALS

Material	Tensile strength, lb. per sq. in.		Yield strength, lb. per sq. in.		Endurance limit, lb. per sq. in.	
	Actual	Specific	Actual	Specific	Actual	Specific
Cast						
Mg-Al, heat treated, A.S.T.M. B80-38T-4	36,000	19,700	13,000	7,100	10,000	5,500
Al-Cu, S.A.E. 36	22,000	7,800	14,000	5,000	7,500	2,700
Al-Cu, heat treated, S.A.E. 38	36,000	13,000	22,000	7,900	6,000	2,200
Gray cast iron	40,000	5,600	......	......	20,000	2,800
Cast steel, 0.30% carbon	76,000	9,700	42,000	5,300	33,000	4,200
Wrought						
Mg-Al, extruded, A.S.T.M. B107-38T-8	43,000	23,900	30,000	16,700	17,000	9,500
Duralumin, heat treated	60,000	21,500	36,000	12,900	15,000	5,400
Low-alloy structural steel	80,000	10,200	60,000	6,800	40,000	5,100
Cr-Mo steel, heat treated	125,000	15,900	90,000	11,500	70,000	8,900
Cr-Mo steel, heat treated	190,000	24,200	160,000	20,000	95,000	12,100

Chapter 18

COPPER AND COPPER-BASE ALLOYS AS
ENGINEERING MATERIALS

Emphasizing the importance of copper and its alloys as engineering materials is as unnecessary as pouring perfume on the rose. These metals are such an integral, but commonly unnoticed, part of our daily life that even the housewife in the kitchen and the clerk in the store would find it difficult to establish a new routine of existence if copper suddenly disappeared from the world. Judged solely from the standpoint of absolute value to mankind, copper and its common alloys, the brasses and the bronzes, cannot compete with carbon steels, but each is of vital importance to our civilization and could hardly be eliminated without destroying or at least seriously crippling most branches of industry.

It has been said with justification that electricity is the *elixir vitae* of machine civilization. It is difficult to conceive of an electrical industry if copper and its ores had never been known, unless nature had provided man with a substitute of equal conductivity, plasticity, and cost. Second only to high conductivity in importance is the resistance of copper and some of the copper-rich alloys to corrosion in certain environments, especially sea air and sea water.

The average automobile uses 45 lb. of copper and its alloys, the average steam locomotive 4500 lb., and the modern steamship more than 3,000,000 lb. as castings, in pipes and tubes, and in electrical equipment. No metal has proved so suitable for steamship propellers as manganese bronze; four of these, weighing 37 tons each, drove the "Queen Mary" across the Atlantic Ocean in four days.

With two or three exceptions, the copper and copper-rich alloys discussed in this chapter have been important engineering materials for years and, unlike some of the light alloys discussed in the previous chapter, are covered by specifications of the American Society for Testing Materials.[1] In addition, most of them also conform to specifications adopted by the Society of Automotive Engineers, the Association of American Railroads, the American Society of Mechanical Engineers (Boiler Construction Code), the American Standards Association, the U. S. Navy, and the U. S. Army, and to general Federal specifications. These standards—especially those issued by A.S.T.M.—should be consulted for exact chemical composition and for minimum mechanical-property and other requirements which must be met before the material can be considered to be of good commercial quality.

169. **Manufacture of High-purity Copper**—Although copper is present in the earth's crust to the extent of only 0.01 per cent, ore deposits of commercial importance are fairly widespread. Compared with iron ores, copper-ore deposits of commercial quality are lean. The ores of the United States contain on an average somewhat less than 2 per cent copper. In the important ores, copper occurs as the oxide, carbonate, silicate, and sulphide, of which the last named is the most abundant. In some parts of the world, notably in the vicinity of Lake Superior, long weathering of copper ores followed by reduction of the resulting oxide or the carbonate, or the deposition of copper from solution, has produced large deposits of relatively pure native metal, which was distributed far to the south by the glaciers. Native copper was the only metal (except small quantities of meteoric iron) used by the American Indians for tools and weapons until the white man arrived.

The production of high-purity copper from lean sulphide ores is a complex process, but copper exceeding 99.9 per cent purity can be produced cheaply. In brief, the process consists of concentrating and roasting the complex sulphide ore (copper, plus iron, plus other metals) to form oxides and to eliminate some of the sulphur and arsenic as the oxide. The roasted concentrate is smelted with coke and a flux in a reverberatory furnace to remove part of the iron. The copper and iron sulphides fuse into a matte containing about 40 per cent copper. This matte is charged into a Bessemer converter and is blown in a manner similar to the

---

[1] See *A.S.T.M. Standards*, Part I, Metals, 1939.

refining of pig iron to produce Bessemer steel. The copper and the remaining iron sulphides are oxidized, and the iron oxide combines with silica to form a silicate slag. The result of these reactions is "blister copper" containing 95 to 97 per cent copper and considerable copper oxide.

In addition to copper oxide, blister copper contains small amounts of sulphur, iron, lead, arsenic, antimony and possibly other elements, and frequently 25 to 50 cents worth of gold and silver per ton. The final step consists of casting the blister copper into blocks which are electrolyzed. Electrolytic copper contains 99.95 per cent or more copper, with sulphur as the principal impurity. About 25 per cent of the electrolytic copper produced is used for making copper-base alloys; the remainder is melted in a large reverberatory furnace, oxidized to remove sulphur, and then "poled." This consists of inserting green wood poles beneath the surface of the molten metal. In the reaction between the wood and the molten copper oxide enough oxygen is removed so that the remainder, 0.03 to 0.04 per cent, when evolved during solidification, exactly balances the normal shrinkage of the metal. Poled copper is known as "tough-pitch." Its density in the cast condition is approximately 8.5 g. per cu. cm., compared with 8.94 for the pure metal. Tough-pitch copper is used for wire for electric conductors, for sheets, and for many other purposes.

Lake (Superior) copper, which constitutes about 15 per cent of the commercial copper in the United States, is—as previously mentioned—a high-purity native copper and does not usually need electrolytic refining. It differs from electrolytic copper in that it may contain a small amount of silver (which does not affect conductivity) and from 0.002 to 0.04 per cent or even more arsenic which, in the higher amounts, may reduce relative conductivity from 100 to 40 per cent.

A recent development in copper refining is the production of oxygen-free copper. Oxygen in tough-pitch copper is present as cuprous oxide particles, which are almost completely insoluble in the solid metal. For most purposes this oxide is not harmful, but if extremely high ductility is essential, the copper should be practically free from oxygen. The oxide is also harmful if the copper is heated in an atmosphere containing hydrogen as this gas diffuses into the metal, reacts with the oxide, and causes brittleness. There are two types of oxygen-free copper. The more common one is produced by deoxidizing the molten metal with phosphorus or some other element having a high affinity for oxygen. The residual phosphorus, although only about 0.02 per cent is present, reduces the electric conductivity as much as 20 per cent. To produce high-conductivity oxygen-free copper (known as OFHC), very pure copper is melted and cast in an atmosphere free from oxidizing gases. A recent innovation consists of granulating brittle copper cathodes, which have been deposited electrolytically and which are free from oxygen, followed by "coalescing" these in a press at high temperatures, which welds the particles together and extrudes the metal as a solid bar.

Copper is malleable and is hot and cold worked into sheet, plates, tubes, and a variety of other shapes. As in the case of most other metals and alloys, cold working increases strength and reduces ductility.

170. **Properties and Uses of High-purity Copper**—Copper has the highest electric conductivity of all the common metals. On a strength basis, its conductivity is more than twice that of high-purity aluminum. About one half of the 800,000 tons of copper consumed in the United States in 1937 was used for electrical equipment and for wire in light and power lines. When annealed, high-purity copper has a conductivity of 100 per cent according to a standard set up in 1913 by an international commission. Recently improved methods of purification have resulted in conductivities as high as 102 per cent.

Copper is also the best heat conductor of any of the commercial metals, which makes it (and its alloys) useful as cooking utensils and as radiators and other heat-dissipating apparatus. In general, copper and the copper-rich alloys have excellent resistance to corrosion by the atmosphere and by water. Owing to this corrosion resistance and to a reasonable price, copper and some of its alloys are widely used by the building industry for roofing, downspouts, gutters, screens, drainage and water pipes, and for hardware and interior fixtures. When exposed to the atmosphere for long periods, copper oxidizes and forms a green patina which is ornamental in addition to being adherent and protecting the underlying metal from further attack. Approximately 10 per cent of the copper consumed annually is used by the building industry.

Copper and copper-rich alloys have a wide range of mechanical properties. Annealed high-purity copper has a tensile strength of approximately 30,000 lb. per sq. in., an elongation in 2 in. of about 60 per cent, and a reduction of area of as much as 90 per cent. It is, therefore, weaker and more ductile than high-purity iron. At the other extreme, precipitation-hardened copper-beryllium alloys may have a tensile strength of 190,000 lb. per sq. in. with accompanying low ductility.

The tensile strength of high-purity copper may be increased to 65,000 or 70,000 lb. per sq. in. by drastic cold working; elongation is lowered to about 5 per cent. According to Gillett,[2] the endurance limit of annealed tough-pitch copper is approximately 10,000 lb. per sq. in., and cold working increases it to as much as 20,000 lb. per sq. in. The modulus of elasticity is approximately 16 million lb. per sq. in.

For some applications the low strength of high-purity copper wire is a distinct disadvantage. Unfortunately, most alloying elements added to increase strength reduce conductivity to a fraction of the value for high-purity copper. A satisfactory compromise between increase in strength and decrease in conductivity results from the addition of small amounts of cadmium. The effect is shown in Table 23[3] which gives minimum tensile-strength and conductivity values of copper and copper-cadmium alloys in comparison with brass and bronze.

TABLE 23. TENSILE STRENGTH AND CONDUCTIVITY OF HIGH-PURITY COPPER AND COPPER-RICH ALLOY 10-GAGE (BROWN AND SHARPE) WIRES (0.102 IN. DIAMETER)

Material	Composition, per cent (balance copper)	Minimum tensile strength, lb. per sq. in.	Minimum conductivity, per cent
Copper, soft...................	....	37,000	98
Copper, medium hard.........	....	50,000	97.5
Copper, hard drawn..........	....	64,300	96
Copper-cadmium.............	0.8 Cd	79,200	85
Copper-cadmium.............	1.0 Cd	83,400	80
Copper-cadmium.............	0.8 Cd, 0.5 Sn	90,000	55
High-strength bronze.........	1.2 Sn	84,000	40
Silicon bronze................	2.0 Sn, 0.75 Si	123,900	12
Brass, cold drawn............	20.0 Zn	127,000	25

[2] Metals and Alloys, v. 3, 1932, p. 200.

[3] Based on data by C. H. Davis in Symposium on High-strength Constructional Metals, American Society for Testing Materials, March 1936, pp. 79-94.

171. Nomenclature of the Copper-rich Alloys—Although the copper industry is no worse than the steel industry in the use of trade names and in confused nomenclature, so many misnamed alloys are commonly used that some attention to this subject— to amplify the brief discussion in Chapter 1 (p. 13)—seemed advisable. The most common examples of confused nomenclature are calling a copper-zinc alloy "bronze" if it has a color resembling that of the copper-tin alloys, or calling a copper-zinc-nickel alloy "nickel silver" if it has a silvery white color. This confusion is regrettable, but in most cases nothing can be done about it as the names are firmly fixed by years of usage. The important fact to remember about the copper-rich alloys is that the name may be more descriptive of color than of composition, and that a "bronze" may contain no tin and may even be a brass; likewise, nickel silver contains no silver.

The usual name and the typical compositions of some common copper-rich alloys are given in Table 24. It is evident that manganese bronze (alloy 2), hardware bronze (alloy 10), and commercial bronze (alloys 11 and 12) are in reality brasses. The only true bronzes given in Table 24 are alloys 13 and 14, which are copper-tin alloys deoxidized by phosphorus. Nickel silver, formerly known as German silver, is the name of a group of brasses, containing 17 to 28 per cent zinc, in which a considerable part of the copper is replaced by nickel. The composition of two of these alloys is given in Table 24. Another example of confused nomenclature is the casting alloy containing 85 per cent copper and 5 per cent each of zinc, tin, and lead. As this alloy contains 5 per cent tin, it is as much of a bronze as it is a brass, but it is called red brass and is, consequently, sometimes confused with wrought red brass which contains 85 per cent copper and 15 per cent zinc (alloy 9, Table 24).

172. Characteristics and Uses of the High Brasses—As shown by the diagram in Fig. 100, 39 per cent zinc dissolves in copper at room temperature. Alloys containing less than this percentage of zinc—when in a state of equilibrium—are, therefore, single-phase solid solutions and are known as alpha brasses. As shown also by Fig. 100, alloys containing about 36 to 39 per cent zinc may have a duplex structure if heated to a high temperature but should be single phase at room temperature. Actually, however, owing to a phenomenon known as coring, cast alloys usually have a duplex structure if the zinc is higher than 31 or 32 per cent. A zinc content of 35 per cent is about the maximum for an alloy that is to be fabricated as a single-phase material.

Although there is a continuous series of alpha brasses containing from 5 to 39 per cent zinc, these alloys are commonly and arbitrarily divided into two classes: high brass, containing 30 per cent or more zinc, and low brass, containing approximately 25 per cent zinc or less (Table 24). Since zinc is cheaper than copper, it follows that high brass is used as widely as possible, and that the zinc content is usually close to the upper limit, which is about 35 per cent.

TABLE 24. TYPICAL COMPOSITIONS OF SOME COMMON WROUGHT COPPER-RICH ALLOYS

Alloy No.	Common name	Composition, per cent								
		Cu	Zn	Sn	Pb	Ni	Mn	Al	Fe	P
1	Muntz metal	60	40							
2	Manganese bronze	59	39	0.7	....	....	0.5		0.8	
3	Leaded brass	61	36	....	3					
4	High brass	65	35							
5	Cartridge brass	70	30							
6	Nickel silver	55	27	....	....	18				
7	Nickel silver	65	17	....	....	18				
8	Low brass	80	20							
9	Red brass	85	15							
10	Hardware bronze	85	13.3	....	1.7					
11	Commercial bronze	90	10							
12	Leaded commercial bronze	88.5	10	....	1.5					
13	Phosphor bronze	96	....	5	....	....	....	....	....	0.15
14	Phosphor bronze	92	....	8	....	....	....	....	....	0.15
15	Aluminum bronze	95	....	....	....	....	....	5		
16	Aluminum bronze	92	....	....	....	....	....	8		

Although the alpha brasses can be hot worked commercially if they are free from lead, they are not so plastic at elevated temperatures as the beta alloys. In common with most solid solutions they are, however, plastic at room temperature and can be readily drawn, rolled, or spun into a variety of shapes. In fact, these alloys combine a degree of plasticity, strength, ductility, corrosion resistance, pleasing color, and low cost unattainable in any other material of engineering importance. Alloys 3, 4, and 5 are used for a large variety of cast and wrought sections, especially hardware and pipe fittings, for tubes and pipe, for ornamental sections and building trim, for cartridge cases, radiator cores, grillwork, springs, and for many kinds of nails, screws, and rivets.

Muntz metal and its modification, manganese bronze (alloys 1 and 2, Table 24), usually contain beta phase at room temperature (see Fig. 100) which reduces plasticity when the alloys are cold. These materials are, however, characterized by extreme plasticity at a red heat and can readily be extruded or rolled. Owing to their resistance to atmospheric and water corrosion, these two alloys, especially manganese bronze, are used extensively for extruded or hot-rolled pipes and condenser tubes. Muntz metal is now being replaced, particularly for condenser tubes in marine equipment, by a brass known as admiralty metal. This contains not less than 70 per cent copper, 1 per cent tin, and the remainder zinc. Other than for condenser tubes, admiralty metal, so called because it was developed by the British Admiralty, is used for preheaters, evaporators, air-conditioning equipment, and in other applications where high resistance to salt water, fresh water, oil, or steam is required. Admiralty metal is an alpha-phase alloy and is not so easily hot worked as Muntz metal and manganese bronze, but it is readily worked when cold.

In general, the machinability of the annealed, non-leaded brasses is about the same as that of low-carbon steel, in other words, they are too soft and gummy to be cut readily. Cold working, however, improves machinability, which is also greatly improved by adding lead (see section 86). Alloy 3 (Table 24) can be machined readily in automatic machines. If this alloy is given a machinability rating of 100, the same brass containing only 1 per cent lead will have a rating of 70 (determined under the same conditions), and alloy 4—without lead—will have a rating of only 30. However, lead reduces ductility, i.e., it makes the brass more difficult to deform cold and makes it virtually impossible to work the alpha-phase alloys at elevated temperatures.

173. Characteristics and Uses of the Low Brasses and the Nickel Silvers—As the amount of zinc in brass is reduced, the yellow color changes to red. Alloys 8, 9, 10, 11, and 12 (the last two of which are called bronzes because of their color) are used for hardware, ornamental and architectural sections, wire for screens, and for costume jewelry, in addition to being used for

tubes, pipe, radiator valves, and other fittings for low-pressure water and steam. An advantage of the low brasses is that, when the copper exceeds 80 per cent, the alloy is not subject to "season cracking," a phenomenon prevalent in the high brasses when they are exposed to a combination of corrosion and stress. Season cracking is the spontaneous failure of the stressed material after a considerable time in a corrosive environment, especially in atmospheres containing ammonia. The time element depends upon the severity of the stress and the severity of the corrosion. Stress caused by cold working, or applied externally, is necessary for failure of this type.

The low brasses, like the high brasses, are readily deformed cold provided the lead content is low. Also like the high-zinc alpha brasses, they are difficult to hot work although commercial bronze (alloy 11, Table 24) can be rolled or pierced and, to a limited extent, pressed or extruded provided more than traces of lead are absent.

There are several nickel silvers in addition to alloys 6 and 7 of Table 24. Most nickel silvers have a copper content of 45 to 65 per cent. A fairly common alloy is the one containing 75 per cent copper, 20 per cent nickel, and 5 per cent zinc, usually sold under the trade name Ambrac. All the nickel silvers can be classed as low brasses containing nickel. If the copper plus nickel exceeds 63 per cent, the alloys contain only alpha phase. They can be hot worked readily only if the zinc is about 40 per cent or less than 10 per cent, but they can be cold worked easily.

Nickel silvers are valuable because of their white color, a corrosion resistance that is generally superior to that of the common brasses, good mechanical properties, and moderate cost. The effect of composition on color is shown by Fig. 110.[4] The nickel silvers are used chiefly for ornamental metal work, as a base for silver- and gold-plated ware, and for marine hardware and food-handling equipment.

174. **Properties of the Brasses**—Some typical tensile properties of brass and nickel silver are collected in Table 25.[5] As the com-

[4] T. E. Kihlgren, "Properties of Wrought Nickel Silvers," *Metals Handbook*, American Society for Metals, Cleveland, 1939, pp. 1443-1445.

[5] Based upon data in the sections on Properties of Copper and Its Alloys, in *Metals Handbook*, American Society for Metals, Cleveland, 1939, pp. 1380-1468.

TABLE 25. TYPICAL TENSILE PROPERTIES OF BRASS AND NICKEL SILVER

Alloy No.	Common name	Nominal composition, per cent						Condition	Tensile strength, lb. per sq. in.	Yield strength,* lb. per sq. in.	Elongation in 2 in., per cent
		Cu	Zn	Sn	Pb	Ni	Mn				
1	Muntz metal	60	40	....	....	....	....	Hot rolled sheet	55,000	......	45
								Cold rolled sheet	80,000	......	5
2	Manganese bronze	59	39	0.7	....	....	0.5	Hot rolled bars	60,000	25,000	25
								Cold rolled bars, half hard	70,000	35,000	20
								Cold rolled bars, hard	80,000	55,000	15
4	High brass	65	34	....	....	....	....	Annealed sheet	45,000	......	64
								Hard rolled sheet	76,000	......	7
								Spring temper sheet	92,000	......	3
5	Cartridge brass	70	30	....	....	....	....	Annealed sheet	53,000	......	54
								Spring temper sheet	92,000	......	3
8	Low brass	80	20	....	....	....	....	Annealed sheet	47,000	18,000†	47
								Spring temper sheet	91,000	70,000†	3
7	Nickel silver	65	17	....	....	18	....	Soft sheet, fine grain	64,000	37,000†	25
								Soft sheet, coarse grain	50,000	17,000†	40
								Hard sheet, fine grain	100,000	80,000†	3
								Hard sheet, coarse grain	93,000	68,000†	3
9	Commercial bronze	90	10	....	....	....	....	Soft sheet	38,000	......	45
								Spring temper sheet	73,000	......	3
11	Red brass	85	5	5	5	....	....	Cast	33,000	15,000	25

* For an elongation of 0.5 per cent under load.   † Apparent elastic limit.

mercial copper-zinc alloys do not respond to heat treatment, variations in properties are obtained by cold working and annealing which results, as in the case of some of the aluminum alloys, in various tempers, ranging from soft to half-hard, hard, and to spring temper. With the exception of manganese bronze and nickel silver, the tensile properties of all the annealed brasses are very similar to those of annealed or hot-rolled low-carbon steel. As the brasses cost five to ten times as much as low-carbon steel, the chief justification for their widespread use is, of course, their ease of working cold, their pleasing color, and their corrosion

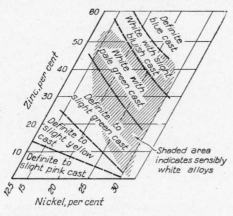

Fig. 110—Effect of composition on the color of nickel silver (Kihlgren).

resistance, especially to water and steam. In general, the low brasses are more corrosion resistant than the higher zinc alloys, especially in impure water and in salt water. The high brasses, in addition to being subject to season cracking (see p. 319), are also subject to "dezincification," or removal of the zinc, when the alloy is exposed to impure water or salt water. The action is apparently electrolytic and leaves a spongy mass of copper. Dezincification can cause failure in a relatively short time. Alloys containing 20 per cent or less zinc are not usually subject to this form of corrosion. Manganese bronze has high resistance to salt water but may be subject to season cracking and dezincification.

The endurance limits of the brasses are low, ranging between 10,000 and 20,000 lb. per sq. in. for 100 million cycles, which is equivalent to an endurance ratio of 0.20 to 0.35, or about half that of steel. Annealed brasses have a definite yield point (as evidenced by the drop of the beam) but cold-worked alloys do not. Values for yield strength reported in the literature are usually the stresses causing an extension of 0.5 per cent under load. These values are usually somewhat lower than the yield strength of steel which corresponds to a permanent elongation of 0.2 per cent of the gage length. The modulus of elasticity (secant modulus, see p. 124) varies from 15 million lb. per sq. in. for the copper-zinc alloys and for manganese bronze to about 19 million lb. per sq. in. for nickel silver. The mechanical properties of brass and of nickel silver are affected by grain size which, in the case of worked material, depends on annealing temperature. Material with large grains has lower strength and higher elongation that fine-grained material (except in very thin strip). This is shown for nickel silver in Table 25.

175. The Tin Bronzes—The most important industrial copper-tin alloys are the phosphor bronzes which contain from as little as 1 per cent to as much as 11 per cent tin. All wrought phosphor bronzes are alpha-phase alloys, deoxidized by adding enough phosphorus to remove all but a trace of oxygen. The two most commonly used of these alloys (alloys 13 and 14, Table 24) are the ones containing approximately 5 and 8 per cent tin; another popular alloy contains about 10 per cent tin. Owing to their high resiliency and endurance limit, these bronzes are used for springs and diaphragms.

Phosphor bronze is hot worked with difficulty, but cold working is easy and the alloys are available in six tempers. These, and the range of tensile strengths for each temper and each alloy, are given in Table 26.[6] The actual tensile strength depends on the thickness of the sheet. Elongation (in 2 in.) varies from 40 to 60 per cent for soft sheet to less than 10 per cent for the harder tempers. The endurance limit in the hard temper is approximately 25,000 lb. per sq. in., and the modulus of elasticity is 15 million lb. per sq. in., about the same as that of other copper-rich alloys.

Another important copper-tin alloy—which is used in the cast condition—is one containing a small amount of zinc. This alloy,

[6] H. C. Jennison and W. S. Girvin, "Properties of Wrought Phosphor Bronze," Metals Handbook, American Society for Metals, Cleveland, 1939, pp. 1457-1460.

known variously as government bronze, zinc bronze, or more commonly as gun metal (in the late Middle Ages it was used for casting cannons), contains 88 per cent copper, 10 per cent tin, and 2 per cent zinc—or 88 per cent copper, 8 per cent tin, and 4 per cent zinc. It is cast readily in the foundry, has a red color, and combines fine grain with considerable strength, toughness, and resistance to salt-water corrosion. Gun metal is used for joints and fittings, bolts, nuts, valve and pump parts, bushings and bearings for steam lines, and especially in naval construction.

TABLE 26.   TENSILE STRENGTH OF PHOSPHOR-BRONZE SHEET

Temper	Reduction by cold rolling, per cent	Tensile-strength range, lb. per sq. in., for bronze containing		
		5% tin	8% tin	10% tin
Soft	0	40,000 to 55,000	53,000 to 67,000	58,000 to 73,000
Half-hard	20.7	55,000 to 70,000	69,000 to 84,000	76,000 to 91,000
Hard	37.1	72,000 to 87,000	85,000 to 100,000	94,000 to 109,000
Extra hard	50.0	84,000 to 98,000	97,000 to 112,000	107,000 to 122,000
Spring	60.4	91,000 to 105,000	105,000 to 118,000	115,000 to 129,000
Extra spring	68.6	96,000 to 109,000	110,000 to 122,000	120,000 to 133,000

The tensile strength of cast and unmachined specimens varies from 30,000 to 45,000 lb. per sq. in., the yield strength from 13,000 to 15,000 lb. per sq. in., and the elongation (in 2 in.) from 15 to 40 per cent. Impact resistance is high. The modulus of elasticity is 15 million lb. per sq. in.

176. Aluminum Bronze—The copper-rich copper-aluminum alloys combine the strength of a medium-carbon steel with high resistance to corrosion by the atmosphere, by salt water, by a large number of neutral and acid salts of low concentration, and by sulphuric acid. They are more resistant than manganese bronze to salt water and have good strength and ductility. The single-phase commercial alloys contain 10 per cent or less aluminum. It was noted in section 151 that, if the aluminum is higher than this, the structure and properties can be changed by thermal treatment. This is also true of the complex alloys containing 5 to 10 per cent aluminum and several per cent of iron, nickel, or manganese. By controlling the composition and by heat treatment the tensile strength of the wrought alloys can be varied from

65,000 to 125,000 lb. per sq. in., with elongations varying inversely with the tensile strength from 5 to 70 per cent (Table 27). The composition and typical properties of alloys in common use (alloys 1 to 6) and of two special alloys (alloys 7 and 8) are given in Table 27.[7]

Aluminum bronze is hard to handle in the foundry. The alpha-phase alloys can be hot and cold worked readily, but they are hard to machine. Owing to its corrosion resistance, its strength and toughness, and its low coefficient of friction against steel, aluminum bronze is used for gears, valve stems, bolts and nuts for propellers, and for various small parts; as cast, it is used for gun mounts, gears, bearings, propellers, pump parts, and ornamental pieces, especially for service in salt air and salt water.

TABLE 27.   TYPICAL PROPERTIES OF ALUMINUM BRONZE

Alloy No.	Composition, per cent				Condition	Tensile strength, lb. per sq. in.	Yield strength, lb. per sq. in.	Elonga- tion in 2 in., per cent	Reduc- tion of area, per cent
	Cu	Al	Fe	Ni					
1	88	9	3	...	Cast	70,000	27,000	30	30
2	90	9	1	...	Cast	65,000	23,000	30	30
3	90	10	...	...	Cast	65,000	23,000	20	20
4	89	10	1	...	Cast and heat heated	85,000	55,000	8	10
5	88	9	3	...	Hot rolled	77,000	37,000	30	30
6	95	5	...	...	Hot rolled	57,000	....	25	25
7	87.5	5.5	...	7	Hot rolled	65,400	20,000	20	47
					Heat treated	110,000	103,000	73	69
8	92	7	1	...	Annealed	81,200	40,000*	45	62
					Cold rolled	126,100	93,000	7.5	35

* Proportional limit

177. Copper-silicon Alloys—The copper-silicon alloys, usually known as bronzes, of which some 20 to 25 are available under such brand names as Duronze, Olympic, Everdur, Herculoy, and others, contain 90 to 98 per cent copper, 1 to 4.5 per cent silicon, and small amounts of zinc, iron, or manganese, or—if easy machin-ability is desired—0.25 to 0.50 per cent lead. Strictly speaking, the copper-silicon alloys are copper strengthened by 1 to 5 per cent of other elements. The strength and ductility of these alloys

[7] Jerome Strauss and L. H. Fawcett: "Properties of Aluminum Bronze," *Metals Handbook*, American Society for Metals, Cleveland, 1939, pp. 1408 and 1425.

are approximately the same as those of low-carbon steel, and the corrosion resistance and ease of hot and cold working are about the same as those of copper. Strength as well as ductility increases as the silicon increases up to about 4 per cent. This is shown by the typical properties in Table 28. Thermal conductivity and electric conductivity are 8 to 10 per cent of the corresponding values for copper, and the modulus of elasticity is 15 million lb. per sq. in.

TABLE 28.   TYPICAL TENSILE PROPERTIES OF COPPER-SILICON ALLOYS

Composition, per cent			Condition	Tensile strength, lb. per sq. in.	Yield strength, lb. per sq. in.	Elongation in 2 in., per cent
Cu	Si	Others				
98.0	1.75	0.25 Mn or Sn	Soft	43,000	......	40
			Half-hard	55,000	23,000	15
			Hard	65,000	35,000	8
95.8	3.1	1.1 Mn	Soft	54,000	22,000	48
			Half-hard	75,000	40,000	25
			Hard	90,000	54,000	18

The principal advantage of the copper-silicon alloys is their corrosion resistance in both marine and industrial atmospheres, in sea water and in many industrial waters, in sulphuric and hydrochloric acids, sulphates and chlorides, and in most alkalis and alkali salts. They are also resistant to alcohol and to many organic acids but are readily attacked by nitric acid and other strong oxidizing agents. The alloys can be used for working stresses up to 10,000 lb. per sq. in. at temperatures of 250° F. (120° C.) or below, and they can be readily welded by oxyacetylene, metallic arc, and resistance methods.

The copper-silicon alloys are now used extensively for bolts, screws, rivets, boilers, tanks, equipment for laundries and sewage disposal, parts for fans, ducts, and other ventilating and air-conditioning equipment, chemical and electrical equipment, containers for gases and chemicals, and for many other purposes.

178. Copper-beryllium Alloys—Copper-beryllium alloys are a development of the past eight or ten years. Their strength and endurance limit, after age hardening, are high when compared with other copper-rich alloys. This, combined with a corrosion

resistance that is practically the same as of high-purity copper, and comparatively high electric conductivity, would be responsible for fairly extensive use if the cost were lower. Beryllium metal which cost $1000 a pound in 1927 had been reduced to less than $40 by 1937, and it is estimated that the price could be lowered further to $5 to $10 a pound if there would be more demand for the metal. Assuming, however, that the cost of beryllium is $15 a pound, an alloy of 97.5 per cent copper and 2.5 per cent beryllium would cost between 55 and 75 cents a pound in ingot form, which is still too high for extensive commercial use.

At present, copper-beryllium alloys contain 2 to 2.25 per cent beryllium. To some 0.35 per cent nickel or cobalt is added to refine the grain. The alloys can be hot and cold worked, but not easily, and are available as sheet, rods, wire, and tubes. As indicated, they respond to precipitation-hardening treatments. If hot worked or welded, they are given a solution treatment by heating to 1425 to 1475° F. (775 to 800° C.) for 30 min., followed by quenching in water. The alloys are usually cold worked after the solution treatment. They are aged at 480 to 615° F. (250 to 325° C.) for 1 to 4 hr. depending upon the properties desired. Typical properties are as follows: [8]

Condition	Tensile strength, lb. per sq. in.	Yield strength, lb. per sq. in.	Elongation in 2 in., per cent	Brinell hardness
Soft.....................	70,000	31,000	45	110
Average treatment...........	175,000	134,000	6.3	340
Maximum treatment.........	193,000	138,000	2.0	365

The endurance limit varies between 38,000 and 43,000 lb. per sq. in., and the modulus of elasticity is approximately 18 million lb. per sq. in. In these properties, the copper-beryllium alloys are superior to any other copper-rich alloy. The alloys also have relatively high wear resistance and are superior to phosphor bronze when run against steel. As stated, their cost has restricted their use. At present they are used to a limited extent for springs,

[8] Based on data in *Metals Handbook*, American Society for Metals, Cleveland, 1939, p. 1412.

gears, diaphragms, bearings, and for other small parts in the electrical and the aircraft industries.

179. The Copper-rich Copper-nickel Alloys—Copper and nickel dissolve in each other in all proportions in the solid state, and their alloys are free from phase changes. Some of the most widely used industrial alloys contain from 2 to 30 per cent nickel

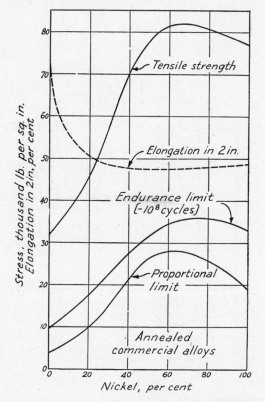

Fig. 111—Effect of nickel on the mechanical properties of copper-nickel alloys (Wise).

(the cupro-nickels) or 45 per cent nickel (Constantan). Of the important nickel-rich alloys, the best known is Monel, containing 68 per cent nickel. This group is discussed briefly in the next chapter.

Nickel increases the tensile strength, the yield strength, and the endurance limit of copper, as shown for annealed alloys in

Fig. 111.[9] Even the strongest alloys are ductile and have an elongation of 45 to 50 per cent in 2 in. As noted in the discussion of nickel silvers (section 173), the addition of increasing amounts of nickel to copper changes the red color to white. A 15 per cent nickel alloy has a faint pink tinge, and a 20 per cent nickel alloy is practically white. The five-cent coin of the United States, the "nickel," is an alloy of 75 per cent copper and 25 per cent nickel.

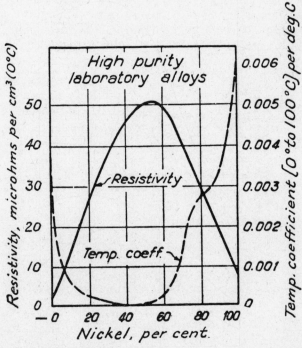

Fig. 112—Effect of nickel on the electrical properties of copper-nickel alloys (Wise).

The most common industrial alloys contain 15, 20, and 30 per cent nickel. The 15 and 20 per cent alloys are used for bullet jackets and for a large variety of parts in which the white color, high ductility, and corrosion resistance are of value. They were formerly used for condenser and other tubes for marine engines and oil refineries, but in these applications they have largely been

[9] Based on data summarized by E. M. Wise, *Metals Handbook*, American Society for Metals. Cleveland, 1939, p. 1413.

replaced by the 30 per cent alloy. This material can readily be hot and cold worked and can be soldered, brazed, and welded. It is one of the most resistant of the copper-base alloys to salt water and to many of the corrosive solutions of the chemical industry. The cupro-nickels are generally resistant to the atmosphere, to industrial waters, and to many acids and alkalis. The 30 per cent alloy, containing also 1 per cent manganese and 1 per cent iron, is cast into a large variety of couplings, ells, tees, and other fittings for valves, pumps, and other similar applications.

The cupro-nickels do not respond to heat treatment. As in the case of most solid-solution alloys, high strength can be attained only by cold working with concomitant loss of ductility. Cold working with a reduction of 60 per cent increases the tensile strength of a 30 per cent nickel alloy from 50,000 to 75,000 lb. per sq. in. and reduces the elongation from 45 to 4 per cent in 2 in.

Some of the copper-nickel alloys have important electric properties. As shown by Fig. 112,[10] the electric resistance is at a peak and the temperature coefficient of resistance is practically zero in the alloy containing 45 per cent nickel. This alloy, known as Constantan, has high and uniform thermoelectric force against copper and iron and is used extensively for thermocouples for the accurate measurement of temperatures below 1800° F. (985° C.).

It should be evident from the discussion in this chapter that the engineer has available a wide variety of copper-rich alloys for use in his structures and machines. There are so many of these alloys that an intelligent choice of a specific one is sometimes difficult, especially in view of the fact that a large number of them are proprietary alloys for which extravagant claims are occasionally made.

[10] E. M. Wise, loc. cit.

CHAPTER 19

MISCELLANEOUS HEAVY NON-FERROUS ALLOYS

OUR twentieth-century mechanized culture, and our twentieth-century mechanized depravity, known as war, are both built primarily upon six metals in addition to iron. These, in the order of their use by man, are copper, lead, zinc, aluminum, tin, and nickel. It will be noted that in the previous sentence the order given was "of their use by man" and not "of their usefulness to man." An author would need exceptional bravery to list these metals in the order of their importance in present-day civilization; and if this were done vocally in a company of engineers or metallurgists, the consequences would be disastrous. It is generally agreed that iron and steel are the most important—in peace and war—and could be spared the least. This has been emphasized repeatedly and, it is hoped, convincingly in' previous chapters. It is also generally agreed that, if there were no copper, there would be no electrical industry, and if aluminum had never become available for 18 cents a pound, modern airplanes would still be a designer's dream.

The metallurgist interested in tin or lead can make out an equally good case for his favorite metal. In the United States alone, more than 10 billion tin-coated cans are used annually for the preservation of foods or drinks. But this is not the most vital use for tin. Tin and lead are important metals for bearings, and how could man build or operate his locomotives, steamships or battleships, automobiles or tanks, and airplanes without bearing metals? Without these he could not travel far, nor could he construct or destroy much. The metallurgists of the zinc and nickel industries have a harder time establishing as good a case for their metals as the others, but they can do it with a little effort, citing copper-zinc brasses, galvanized iron and steel, nickel-chromium heating elements for electric furnaces, nickel steels, iron-nickel alloys in the communication industries, and other applications in which these metals are important.

An approximation of the amounts of the important metals used in the world and their prices in the United States in a fairly prosperous year are given in Table 29, with data on pig iron and on bituminous coal for comparison. Aluminum and copper as engineering materials have already been discussed. A brief survey of the other four—and of their principal alloys—and of a few other heavy metals and alloys follows in the present chapter.

180. Production of Lead, Zinc, Tin, and Nickel from Their Ores—The production of lead, zinc, tin, and nickel from their ores will be dismissed with a few words, not because the processes are simple—indeed they are rather complex—but because it is thought that these metals are not so important to most engineers as aluminum and copper and, thus, do not warrant detailed discussion.

TABLE 29. WORLD PRODUCTION OF THE COMMON METALS AND THEIR PRICES IN THE UNITED STATES (1937)*

Material	Price, cents per pound	Production, metric tons
Coal	0.1	1,500,000,000
Pig iron	1	100,000,000
Copper	13	2,100,000
Lead	6	1,700,000
Zinc	6	1,700,000
Aluminum	20	500,000
Tin	54	200,000
Nickel	35	115,000

* Data from *Mineral Industry*, McGraw-Hill Book Company, Inc., New York, 1937

The principal lead ore is galena, a lead sulphide, PbS, containing when pure 86.4 per cent lead. The ore is concentrated, and roasted to eliminate most of the sulphur, and the resulting oxide is reduced to lead bullion by coke in a blast furnace. This furnace is much smaller than the iron blast furnace: it is about 20 ft. high and smelts 150 to 300 tons in 24 hr. The lead bullion, which is contaminated by gold, silver, and other impurities, is refined by electrolysis or by melting and refining in a reverberatory furnace into the lead of commerce which has a purity of 99.95 to 99.99 per cent. About 25 per cent of the lead used in the United States is made into lead oxide for paints and chemicals.

Of the remainder, a large part is used for storage batteries, cable coverings, ammunition, pipe and sheet for building construction, and in solders, bearing metals, and alloys for type.

Most of the zinc metal produced is reduced from zinc blende (zinc sulphide) which is concentrated and roasted to the oxide, mixed with coal, and heated in a closed retort at a temperature of 1740 to 2460° F. (950 to 1350° C.). This zinc distills as a vapor and is condensed in a separate chamber. Several grades are produced, the most important of which are "spelter," which contains 98 to 99 per cent zinc and is used for galvanizing and to some extent for brass manufacture, and high-grade zinc, which contains 99.90 to 99.99 per cent zinc and is used for die castings and for high-grade brass. Approximately 40 per cent is used for galvanizing, 25 per cent for brass manufacture, and 25 per cent for zinc-base die castings.

The most important tin ore is cassiterite, a tin dioxide, SnO_2, which is found chiefly in the Dutch East Indies, Straits Settlement, and in Bolivia. The ore is calcined, concentrated, and smelted in a small blast or reverberatory furnace, and the resulting metal is refined if necessary by electrolysis or by melting under carefully controlled conditions to separate the tin from the impurities which have different melting points. The tin of commerce has a purity of 99 to 99.95 per cent. Of the tin produced 45 per cent is used for coating steel, 20 per cent for bearing metals and solder, and 15 per cent in bronze manufacture.

The greatest deposits of nickel ores in the world, found in Canada, contain between 1 and 4 per cent nickel as sulphide, usually associated with 0.5 to 3.5 per cent copper and with a large amount of iron, also as sulphides. The ore is crushed, concentrated, and then roasted and smelted in a reverberatory furnace to a matte containing 20 to 25 per cent nickel plus copper. This matte is Bessemerized to remove most of the iron, and the nickel and copper are separated by smelting with sodium sulphide in a blast furnace. The process is complex. The resulting nickel sulphide is roasted to the oxide, which in turn is reduced to nickel, which is refined electrolytically. The final product is 99 to 99.8 per cent pure. Approximately 65 per cent of the nickel produced is used as an alloying element in steel and cast iron, and about 20 per cent is used in nickel bronze and in nickel-base alloys.

181. Composition and Requirements of the Bearing Metals— Many requirements are to be met before an alloy can be used satisfactorily as a bearing. These may be divided into three principal classes. First in importance is proper structure, i.e., a soft matrix with sufficient plasticity to conform to slight irregularities in the machining and alignment of the shaft, to allow any abrasive particles in the lubricant to become embedded in the bearing metal (to prevent scoring of the steel journal), and to retain oil (to prevent metal-to-metal contact), combined with a number of uniformly distributed particles which resist wear. Some metallurgists, however, now claim that wear-resisting particles are not necessary for good bearings, and that the structure is of minor importance.

Second, the mechanical properties must be satisfactorily balanced. The bearing must resist the shock of impact loads, and it must have sufficient strength, ductility, and resistance to compression not to crack or to squeeze out under heavy loads, especially at the operating temperatures, which may be 200 to 300° F. (95 to 150° C.) or even higher.

The third requirement is easy melting and casting and, most important, good bonding properties. In other words, when cast in a strip as thin as 0.01 in., the metal must adhere firmly to the steel or bronze piece used as a backing and should not spall off or separate from the backing during operation. For some purposes, especially for large railroad bearings, it must be possible to remelt and recast the bearing metal without excessive loss by oxidation.

In addition, the bearing metal should have high thermal conductivity, resistance to corrosion by the lubricants used, and it should be cheap.

There are four classes of bearing metals. Typical compositions of some common alloys in these different classes, with the specification numbers adopted by the American Society for Testing Materials and the Society of Automotive Engineers, are given in Table 30.

182. The White Metals—The white metals include the tin-base (class *A*, Table 30) and the lead-base (class *B*) alloys. The 13 alloys in these two groups, and the numerous unimportant modifications which have been advocated from time to time, are old and well known. The tin-base alloys, commonly called babbitts, are widely used in automobile engines and in a large

TABLE 30. TYPICAL COMPOSITIONS OF SOME COMMON BEARING METALS

Class	Alloy No.	Specification		Composition, per cent						
		A.S.T.M.	S.A.E.	Sn	Sb	Pb	Cu	Zn	Cd	Others
A	1	B 23–26–1	10	91	4.5	......	4.5			
	2	B 23–26–2	110	89	7.5	......	3.5			
	3	B 23–26–3	......	83.4	8.3	......	8.3			
	4	B 23–26–4	......	75	12	10	3			
	5	B 23–26–5	......	65	15	18	2			
	6	....	11	87	6.8	......	5.7			
B	1	B 23–26–6	......	20	15	63.5	1.5			
	2	B 23–26–7	14	10	15	75				
	3	B 23–26–8	......	5	15	80				
	4	B 23–26–9	13	5	10	85				
	5	B 23–26–10	......	2	15	83				
	6	B 23–26–11	......		15	85				
	7	B 23–26–12	......		10	90				
C	1	B 22–38T–A	......	19	......	......	81			
	2	B 22–38T–B	......	16			84			
	3	B 22–38T–D	62	10			88	2		
	4	B 30–36–15	66	5		9	85	1		
	5	B 30–36–16	64	10		10	80	......		0.0 to 0.9 P
	6	B 30–36–17	......	10		10	79.3	0.7		
	7	B 30–36–18	......	8		15	75	1.5		
	8	B 30–36–19	......	4.5		17	71.5	4		
	9	B 30–36–20	......	6		20	70.5	1		
	10	....	660	7		7	83	3		
	11	B 66–38	......	5		25	70			
	12	....	48			28	71			
	13	....	481	3		25	71			
	14	....	480			40	60			
D	1	....	18				......		98.8	1.2 Ni
	2	....	180				0.5		98.8	0.7 Ag
	3	....				98+				*

* 0.5% Ca, 0.5% Na, 0.1% Li + Al

variety of machines where speeds are high and loads are light or at most only fairly heavy. Lead, added (alloys A 4 and A 5) primarily to reduce the cost, is objectionable if operating temperatures are high as it forms a fusible eutectic with tin and lowers the temperature at which incipient melting takes place. The following illustrates the effect of lead: the temperature at which alloy A 5 (18 per cent lead) is completely liquid is about 565° F. (295° C.); the corresponding temperatures for alloys A 1 and A 2 (no lead) are 680 and 670° F. (360 and 355° C.).

The properties of the tin-base alloys vary somewhat with composition but are usually within the following ranges:

Property	Range of values
Tensile strength, lb. per sq. in., at 70° F. (20° C.)	12,800 to 17,500
Tensile strength, lb. per sq. in., at 200° F. (95° C.)	6,700 to 10,000
Yield strength, lb. per sq. in., at 70° F. (20° C.)	4,500 to 6,500
Yield strength, lb. per sq. in., at 200° F. (95° C.)	2,100 to 3,200
Brinell hardness (500 kg.) at 70° F. (20° C.)	17 to 27
Brinell hardness (500 kg.), at 200° F. (95° C.)	8 to 14

In the case of these alloys, the "tensile strength" is the stress producing a deformation of about 25 per cent, and the "yield strength" is the stress producing an elongation of 0.125 per cent of the gage length.

The lead-base white metals (class *B*, Table 30) are cheaper than the tin-base alloys ·but are not so satisfactory for operation at high speeds and medium loads. They are used extensively by the railroads for freight- and passenger-car bearings, in electric

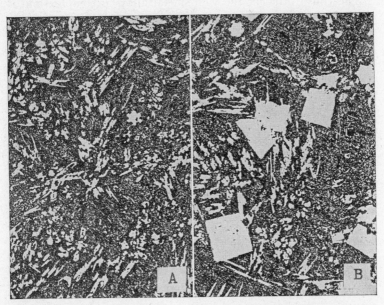

Fig. 113—Structure of tin-base bearing metals containing (*A*) 86 per cent tin, 6 per cent antimony, and 8 per cent copper and (*B*) 82 per cent tin, 10 per cent antimony, and 8 per cent copper; etched, 150× (Ellis).

motors, and in some machines. Alloys *B* 2 and *B* 4 are used in a number of bearings in automobiles. The properties of this group of alloys also vary with composition, usually within the following ranges:

Property	Range of values
Tensile strength, lb. per sq. in., at 70° F. (20° C.)	12,800 to 15,500
Tensile strength, lb. per sq. in., at 200° F. (95° C.)	5,000 to 8,000
Yield strength, lb. per sq. in., at 70° F. (20° C.)	2,800 to 3,800
Yield strength, lb. per sq. in., at 200° F. (95° C.)	1,200 to 2,000
Brinell hardness (500 kg.), at 70° F. (20° C.)	15 to 22
Brinell hardness (500 kg.), at 200° F. (95° C.)	6 to 11

It is evident from these values that the lead-base alloys are inferior in properties to the tin-base metals.

As the temperature increases above 200° F., the tensile and the yield strength of the white metals decrease still more; values of 2000 to 4500 lb. per sq. in. are common for tensile strength tested at 300° F. (150° C.). Elongation and reduction of area increase with temperature as, for example, from 15 to 30 per cent and from 18 to 40 per cent respectively.

The constitution of the white-metal alloys is complex and is imperfectly known. Essentially, the structure (Fig. 113 [1]) consists of a solid-solution matrix in which needles or cubes of a hard constituent, probably an intermetallic compound such as SbSn, are embedded.

Considerable work has been done recently to determine the effect of small amounts of cadmium on the tin-base alloys. Apparently, 1 per cent cadmium increases tensile strength and hardness 10 to 20 per cent at normal temperature and at 200 to 300° F. (100 to 150° C.).

183. The Copper-base Bearing Metals—The principal copper-base bearing metals are those in class C of Table 30. On a tonnage basis this group is more widely used than the others: according to Clamer,[2] about 10 million lb. of alloy C 5 (either deoxidized, or not, with less than 1 per cent phosphorus) are used annually in the United States. The leaded bronzes, alloys C 4 to C 9 (A.S.T.M. specification B 30-36), are employed by the railroads and the automotive industry: alloys C 4 and C 6 are suitable for small bushings and bearings; others are better fitted for general service bearings; alloy C 9 is suitable for high speeds and low bearing loads, and C 5 for moderate speeds and heavy loads.

The properties of the copper-tin-lead alloys vary with composition. At room temperature, the property ranges for alloys C 1 to C 10 inclusive are as follows:

Property	*Range of values*
Tensile strength, lb. per sq. in.	28,000 to 40,000
Yield strength, lb. per sq. in.	14,000 to 18,000
Elongation in 2 in., per cent	10 to 20
Compression, lb. per sq. in., for a deformation of 0.001 in.	10,000 to 13,000
Brinell hardness (500 kg.)	55 to 75

[1] Courtesy of O. W. Ellis.

[2] G. H. Clamer, *Metals Handbook,* American Society for Metals, Cleveland, 1939, p. 1428.

The hard bronzes (alloys C 1, C 2, and C 3) are used in castings for movable bridges and turntables which act as bearings subject to slowly or intermittently applied heavy loads. Most of the other alloys in the group C 1 to C 10 are used as large bearings ("brasses") in locomotives. The alloys favored for this purpose are C 3, C 5, and C 9. Alloys C 3, C 4, C 5, and C 10 are used extensively by the automotive industry.

The high-lead bearing alloys C 11 to C 14 are a fairly recent development and, as steel backed, are used in internal-combustion engines—C 11, C 12, and C 13 for aircraft, and C 14 for automotive engines. These alloys are inferior in tensile properties to the other copper-rich alloys: tensile strength varies from 12,000 to 22,000 lb. per sq. in., yield strength from 5000 to 10,000 lb. per sq. in., elongation from 5 to 12 per cent, and Brinell hardness (500 kg.) from 25 to 40. In general, however, they are superior to the white metals: their melting temperatures are much higher, and their properties are not so much affected by temperature. They are also resistant to repeated flexure which is important with present-day engine speeds. Most important, if lubrication fails momentarily, the heat generated by the friction sweats out a film of lead which acts as a lubricant and prevents seizure.

The railroads were the first to use the high-lead alloys on a general scale, adopting alloy C 11 (A.S.T.M. B 66-38) for a large number of bearings. In airplane and automobile engines, these alloys are now used for crankshaft, drive-shaft, and connecting-rod bearings. The most recent development is the addition of 1 to 2 per cent nickel, or up to 1.5 per cent silver, for controlling segregation and sweating of the lead, which is insoluble in copper both in the molten and the solid state.

184. Special Bearing Metals—There are a large number of recently developed special bearing metals, of which alloys D 1, D 2, and D 3 are the most important. The cadmium-base alloys now have S.A.E. specifications and are successfully replacing the white metals in internal-combustion engines operating at high speeds and high temperatures. Structurally the cadmium-base alloys consist of a soft, tough matrix of cadmium interspersed with hard particles which, for alloy D 1, are supposed to be $NiCd_7$. The alloys are characterized by a high solidification range—750 to 600° F. (395 to 320° C.)—and by the ease with which they are bonded directly to steel. Typical tensile properties of alloy D 1 are given in Table 31.[3]

TABLE 31. TYPICAL PROPERTIES OF A CADMIUM-NICKEL (98.8% CD, 1.2% NI) BEARING METAL

Property	70° F. (20° C.)	210° F. (100° C.)	390° F. (200° C.)
Tensile strength, lb. per sq. in..........	16,400	10,000	3,300
Yield strength, lb. per sq. in...........	11,000		
Elongation in 2 in., per cent...........	19	36	111
Reduction of area, per cent............	43	52	76
Brinell hardness (500 kg.).............	33	22	6

There are two trade-marked bearing metals containing more than 98 per cent lead (alloy D 3). One, developed in Germany, contains 98.5 per cent lead, 0.5 per cent calcium, 0.5 per cent sodium, and 0.05 per cent each of lithium and aluminum. It is now standard for German railways. The other, recently developed in this country, contains about 98 per cent lead, 1 per cent tin, and 0.5 per cent calcium. Both are precipitation-hardening alloys. They have poor corrosion resistance, are difficult to cast, and cannot be remelted without considerable change in composition. The tensile strength of the alloys at room temperature is about 12,000 lb. per sq. in. and the elongation is about 6 per cent; at 300° F. (150° C.), these values are 5000 lb. per sq. in. and 13 per cent. Hardness and compressive strength are relatively high, and the liquefication temperature is about 100° F. (55° C.) higher than that of the tin-base alloys.

An alloy recently developed [4] for aircraft-engine bearings contains 96.5 per cent silver and about 3.5 per cent lead. Results of preliminary tests indicate that the alloy is 50 per cent more resistant to seizure than a good-grade copper-lead bearing metal, and that it is strong enough to carry the high bearing loads in aircraft engines. It is difficult to bond this alloy to a steel backing; at present, electrodeposition seems to give the best results. The chief disadvantage of the silver-rich alloys, in all but the aircraft industry, is high cost.

One of the important results of the development of powder

[3] Based on data of C. E. Swartz, *Metals Handbook*, American Society for
[4] R. W. Dayton, *Metals and Alloys*, October 1939, p. 306.
Metals, Cleveland, 1939, p. 1332.

metallurgy (discussed later in this chapter) is the so-called "oil-less" bearing. In one variety, powdered copper and tin are mixed with graphite in the proper proportions, and the mixture is pressed and sintered. The result is an alloy of copper and tin containing uniformly distributed particles of graphite. In the other variety, powdered copper and tin are mixed with a volatile salt or a low-melting metal powder, and the mixture is pressed and sintered. During sintering, the salt or the low-melting metal volatilizes, leaving interlocking voids (equivalent to 5 to 25 per cent of the volume of the bearing) in which oil is absorbed. Oil-less bearings are used in increasing numbers by the automotive industry and by the railroads.

185. Lead and Tin as Engineering Materials—Lead and tin find important applications in other than bearing metals and certain heavy copper-base alloys. Lead is not only cheap—3 to 12 cents a pound has been the variation in price in the past 10 years —but it is the most corrosion resistant of all the common metals. It is resistant to sulphuric and hydrofluoric acids and to many chemicals, and its resistance to the atmosphere and to fresh or salt water is measured by decades and even by centuries. Lead has low tensile strength, which may be increased by alloying, but the resistance of lead and its alloys to slow deformation under load—or even under their own weight—is so low that they are seldom used because of their strength.

Owing to its corrosion resistance, lead is used as sheet and pipe for handling chemicals, in acid plants, for roofing, and in plumbing installations. Another well-known application is in solders, which are low-melting alloys of 40 to 60 per cent lead with tin. Still another field of usefulness for lead, where its low melting point is valuable, is in type metals, which contain 70 to 95 per cent lead, 3 to 10 per cent tin, and 3 to 20 per cent antimony.

Except as the oxide (in paints), the largest amount of lead (about 200,000 tons a year) is used in storage batteries, the plates of which are alloys of lead with 7 to 12 per cent antimony.[5] This amount of antimony suffices to triple the strength and hardness of lead. Lead-antimony alloys can be precipitation-hardened by quenching from 450° F. (230° C.) and aging at room temperature; the resulting tensile strengths are as high as 12,000 lb. per sq. in.

[5] This is essentially the same alloy as bearing metal B 7, Table 30, p. 334.

An extruded alloy of 99 per cent lead and 1 per cent antimony is used for sheathing for telephone cables. Even this small amount of antimony causes precipitation hardening, too much of which may be undesirable in the cable sheathing. A modification of the recently developed high-lead precipitation-hardening alloy containing calcium, described on p. 338 (alloy D 3, Table 30), is also used for cable sheaths. This contains as little as 0.05 per cent calcium, and its strength may be doubled or even tripled by quenching and aging at room temperature.

As indicated previously, the most important use for tin is as a coating. It is remarkable but true that relatively few laymen know that tin cans are low-carbon steel coated with 0.0001 to 0.0002 in. of pure tin. The object, of course, is corrosion resistance and, to a lesser degree, appearance. The tin coating is resistant to a large variety of foods, oil, paint, and many other products. In addition, the tin facilitates soldering and enables the preservation of enormous quantities of foods and other products by cheap mass-production methods.

186. Zinc and Zinc-base Alloys as Engineering Materials— One of the most valuable phenomena of metallurgy is the speed with which molten zinc combines with solid iron to form an intermetallic iron-zinc compound into which zinc diffuses with great rapidity. This is the basis of hot-dip galvanizing, in which an adherent corrosion-resistant coating of zinc plus the iron-zinc compound is obtained by immersion for a few seconds of scale-free low-carbon steel (sheet, tubes, or wire) in a bath of molten zinc. This coating is shown in Fig. 114.[6] Galvanizing greatly increases the resistance of steel to atmospheric corrosion (this is discussed in the next chapter) and is used so widely that in the United States, in the average year, about 2,500,000 tons of galvanized steel products are made, consuming 250,000 tons of zinc.

In addition to its use as a protective coating and as an alloying element in brass, the most important use of zinc is in die castings. From a small beginning 20 years ago, the art of casting metals in dies has developed steadily until now more than 100,000 tons of these castings are made annually in this country, about 75 or 80 per cent of which are zinc alloys. Die casting produces finished articles of high precision in size and shape, upon which little or

[6] Courtesy of Research Laboratory, Carnegie-Illinois Steel Corporation, Pittsburgh.

no machining is necessary.   Early zinc castings were subject to internal corrosion and to changes in dimensions during use and were, consequently, generally unsatisfactory.   About 15 years ago, it was found that the small amounts of lead and tin in the zinc were responsible for the difficulties.   In 1928, methods were developed for the production of high-purity (99.99 per cent) zinc at low cost, and from this time on, the zinc die-casting industry prospered.   Zinc die castings are used for a wide variety of parts, primarily in automobile manufacture, such as radiator grilles, carburetors, and hardware (which are nickel or chromium

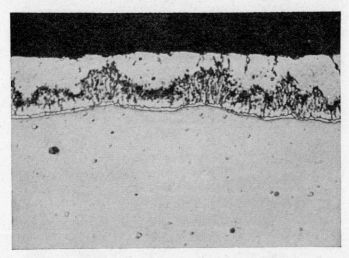

Fig. 114—Cross-section of galvanized low-carbon steel with zinc coating at top, 500× (Research Laboratory, Carnegie-Illinois Steel Corp.).

plated).   The location of zinc die castings in a modern automobile is shown in Fig. 115.[7]   They are also important in the construction of telephone apparatus, typewriters and other office equipment, radios, toys, and a large number of household appliances. Sizes range from zipper teeth, weighing a fraction of an ounce, to radiator grilles, weighing up to 30 lb.

The process consists essentially of forcing the molten metal into a closed steel die by a piston, under pressures (air or water) up to 2000 lb. per sq. in.   Owing to a fortunate combination of low cost, low melting point—about 715° F. (380° C.)—with

[7] Courtesy W. M. Peirce, New Jersey Zinc Co.

Fig. 115—Skeletonized automobile showing use of zinc die castings (Peirce).

accompanying long life of the steel dies, good properties, closely controlled and stable dimensions, and good surface, the use of zinc-alloy die castings, already extensive, will probably expand still further in the future. The low unit cost is largely dependent upon the quantity of the same article. The steel dies are expensive, and a large number of identical castings must be made to reduce this to a low figure.

187. **Properties of Zinc-base Die Castings**—Although experiments have been made with a number of alloys, the present tendency is to use only the three whose composition and properties are given in Table 32.[8] Alloy 23 is the most permanent of the three in dimensions. Its initial shrinkage in solidification and cooling is 0.004 in. in 6 in., or about $\frac{1}{16}$ in. in a bar 8 ft. long. Its strength is somewhat lower than that of the other two alloys, but its ductility is relatively constant over long periods of time. Alloy 21 becomes brittle upon aging and is used if high strength is more important than stability of dimensions and toughness. The dimensional changes shown in Table 32 are those occurring after an initial shrinkage of 0.0063 in. in 6 in. has taken place. Alloy 25 is slightly weaker than alloy 21 but is more stable in dimensions and is superior to alloy 21 in ductility.

188. **Nickel and Nickel-rich Alloys as Engineering Materials** —There are three important classes of high-nickel materials: (1) commercially pure nickel, (2) Monel and other nickel-rich nickel-copper alloys, and (3) nickel-chromium and other high-nickel corrosion- and heat-resisting alloys. The composition and principal characteristics of the most common of these are given in Table 33.

Commercially pure nickel (No. 1, Table 33) is resistant to corrosion by many dilute acids, providing an oxidizing agent is absent. It is also resistant to atmospheric corrosion, including attack by salt air, but not to industrial atmospheres containing sulphur compounds. It is resistant to sea water, provided the water is not stagnant enough to permit the growth of marine organisms which cause pitting. It is resistant to a large number of chemical reagents, especially organic compounds. Its most valuable property, however, is its resistance to strong alkalis. In many media, the corrosion resistance of nickel is increased by

[8] Based on W. W. Broughton, *Metal Progress*, April 1938, p. 381.

TABLE 32. TYPICAL PROPERTIES OF ZINC-BASE DIE CASTING ALLOYS

| Specification | | Composition, per cent* | | | Treatment | Tensile strength, lb. per sq. in. | Elongation in 2 in., per cent | Charpy impact, ft-lb. † | Modulus of rupture, lb. per sq. in. | Change in dimensions, in. in 6 in. |
A.S.T.M. B86-38T	S.A.E.	Al	Cu	Mg						
23	903	4.1	.....	0.06	Cast	40,300	4.7	20	95,000	0.0015
					Aged 10 days at 205° F. (95° C.)	34,400	9.0	23	....	0.0005
					Aged indoors 4 yr.	34,600	7.5	22	....	0.0011
					Aged indoors 7 yr.	32,900	8.1	17	....	
21	921	4.1	2.7	0.06	Cast	47,900	5.1	19	116,000	0.0144
					Aged 10 days at 205° F. (95° C.)	45,500	1.4	2	....	0.0044
					Aged indoors 4 yr.	49,200	4.1	5	....	0.0091
					Aged indoors 7 yr.	48,700	3.1	2	....	
25	925	4.1	1.0	0.06	Cast	45,400	4.9	18	105,000	0.0023
					Aged 10 days at 205° F. (95° C.)	37,400	6.6	16	....	0.0009
					Aged indoors 4 yr.	38,200	6.9	20	....	0.0007
					Aged indoors 7 yr.	37,400	5.6	18	....	

* Remainder zinc of high purity.   These three alloys are patented.   † Unnotched bar 0.25 × 0.25 in.

Table 33. Typical Compositions and Principal Characteristics of Nickel-rich Alloys

No.	Material	Composition, per cent					Principal characteristics
		Ni*	Cu	Cr	Fe	Mn	
1	Nickel	99.4	0.1	......	0.2	0.2	Tough and corrosion resistant
2	Ni-Cu (Monel)	67.0	30.0	......	1.4	1.0	Tough and corrosion resistant
3	Ni-Cu (Monel)	67.0	30.0	......	1.7	1.1†	Free-machining Monel
4	Ni-Cu (K-Monel)	66.0	29.0	2.75‡	0.9	0.4	Age-hardening alloy
5	Ni-Cr-Fe	79.0	0.2	13.5	6.7	0.3	High corrosion resistance
6	Ni-Fe-Cr	62.0	......	15.0	23.0	......	High electric and oxidation resistance
7	Ni-Cr	80.0	......	20.0	......	......	High electric and oxidation resistance

* Nickel plus a small amount of cobalt.   † Also contains 0.025 to 0.060 per cent sulphur.   ‡ Aluminum.

the addition of 25 to 30 per cent copper. Monel (alloys 2 and 3, Table 33) is a natural alloy made by refining ores containing both nickel and copper. Owing to the difficulty of machining the regular Monel, a free-machining grade containing 0.025 to 0.060 per cent sulphur (alloy 3) has been made available. Ease of machining, however, is attained with some sacrifice in mechanical properties. K-Monel (alloy 4) is Monel containing 2.75 per cent aluminum. By a suitable quenching and aging treatment a tensile strength of 170,000 to 200,000 lb. per sq. in. can be attained for wire and strip, as compared with 100,000 to 130,000 lb. per sq. in. for similar sections of regular Monel (alloy 2). The corrosion resistance in most media is about the same as that of Monel.

Alloy 5 is a stainless nickel, known under the trade name Inconel. The addition of chromium increases the resistance of nickel to oxidizing acids and does not lower appreciably its resistance to non-oxidizing media. Commercially pure nickel and alloys 2, 3, 4, and 5 (Table 33) are used widely in equipment for handling chemicals, food, and dairy products, and in marine construction.

Alloys 6 and 7, and their several modifications, are used primarily for heating elements in electric equipment—especially for such appliances as flat irons, toasters, heater pads, electric stoves, hot-water heaters, hair dryers, and permanent-waving equipment —and industrially for heating elements in heat-treating furnaces, for carburizing containers, and for other equipment subjected to temperatures of 1500 to 2000° F. (815 to 1100° C.). The high electric resistance of these two alloys (108 to 112 microhm-cm.) makes them of value for electric equipment as well as for heating elements.

All these alloys can be hot and cold worked into sheet, strip, tubes, wires, and many other shapes. In addition, they can be welded or soldered. Owing to their toughness, however, they are difficult to machine.

189. **Properties of Nickel and Nickel-rich Alloys**—Although nickel and the nickel-rich alloys are important engineering materials, owing to their cost their use is too restricted to warrant detailed discussion of their properties in this chapter, so only a brief survey is given here. In general, the properties of nickel

and nickel-rich alloys are superior to those of any other common non-ferrous material.[9] In addition to their high corrosion resistance, they have the advantage of strength and toughness. As the alloys consist essentially of solid solutions, none—except K-Monel—responds to heat treatment in the usual sense. The only method of changing the properties materially is by cold working.

The tensile strength of commercially pure nickel ranges from about 75,000 lb. per sq. in. for annealed sheet to 85,000 lb. per sq. in. for hot-rolled sections and to as much as 105,000 lb. per sq. in for cold-rolled material. The yield strength for annealed or hot-rolled material is usually less than half the tensile strength, elongation in 2 in. is 35 to 50 per cent, and reduction of area is 60 to 75 per cent. The impact resistance is high; the Izod value is about 100 ft-lb. Nickel is supplied in 8 tempers varying from dead soft through soft and skin hard to full hard. Alloys 2 and 5 have slightly better properties than nickel: tensile strengths of 75,000 to 90,000 lb. per sq. in. as hot worked and annealed, and of up to 120,000 or 130,000 lb. per sq. in. as hard rolled. Elongation, reduction of area and impact resistance are as high as for commercially pure nickel. Nickel, Monel, and Inconel are supplied in spring tempers for use in corrosive environments, with torsional elastic limits of 65,000, 70,000, and 100,000 lb. per sq. in. and torsional moduli of 11, 9, and 11 million lb. per sq. in. respectively. The moduli of elasticity are 30, 26, and 32 million lb. per sq. in. respectively, or close to those of steel. The properties of K-Monel depend on mechanical and thermal treatment. As rolled, its tensile strength is 90,000 to 110,000 lb. per sq. in.; as annealed and heat treated, it is 130,000 to 150,000 lb. per sq. in.; and as cold worked and heat treated, it varies from 125,000 to 200,000 lb. per sq. in., depending upon the temper and the treatment. Elongation may be as high as 45 per cent or as low as 2 per cent in 2 in., also depending upon the temper and treatment.

[9] The data in this section are based on G. F. Geiger, "Alloys of Nickel," in *Symposium on High-strength Constructional Materials*, American Society for Testing Materials, 1936, pp. 95-108, and on sections in *Metals Handbook*, American Society for Metals, Cleveland, 1939, pp. 1646-1669.

The endurance limits for nickel, Monel, and Inconel are:

Material	Endurance limit, lb. per sq. in.		
	Annealed	Hot-rolled	Cold-worked
Nickel........	30,000	33,000	50,000
Monel........	35,000	40,000	55,000
Inconel.......	32,500	36,500	40,000

These values give endurance ratios of 0.40 for nickel and of 0.46 and 0.37 for the two alloys, i.e., somewhat lower ratios than the average for steel (0.50) but considerably higher than for most non-ferrous alloys.

The oxidation-resistant alloys 6 and 7 (Table 33) are also strong and ductile. Their tensile strength, as annealed, is 100,000 to 110,000 lb. per sq. in., their elongation in 2 in. is 25 to 35 per cent, and their reduction in area is 45 to 55 per cent. Tensile-strength values as high as 175,000 lb. per sq. in. can be attained by cold working. In addition to high resistance to oxidation at red heat, the most important properties of alloys 6 and 7 are their strength at elevated temperatures and their high electric resistance. The latter makes it possible to use wires or strip of small cross-section; the former ensures that these will not sag or creep too much. In addition, the alloys are easily worked and are relatively moderate in cost. They are, therefore, superior to any other ferrous or non-ferrous material for heating elements to be used at temperatures below 1800 to 2000° F. (980 to 1100° C.).

190. Powder Metallurgy and Special Tool Materials—Powder metallurgy is an old and a new art. It was used at least 150 years ago for the production of platinum, which was infusible in the furnaces then available. When the oxyhydrogen flame came into use, powder metallurgy became a lost art and remained lost until a few years ago when it was found that useful articles of such refractory metals as tungsten, tantalum, and molybdenum could be produced by compressing and sintering powders of these metals. One of the most useful early developments of powder metallurgy was the method of making ductile tungsten for electric-light filaments.

Powder metallurgy also has other advantages. By compressing

and sintering powders, alloys of exact composition can be made without loss of a constituent by oxidation or without contamination by impurities during melting. In addition, intimate mixtures of metals that are immiscible in the liquid state or that have widely separated melting points can be readily obtained, as can intimate mixtures of metals and non-metals, such as the copper-tin-graphite bearings described briefly in section 184. Most of the preliminary work was done on tungsten and molybdenum; powder metallurgy as applied to other metals is still in its infancy.

The metal powders are prepared by mechanical disintegration (grinding or stamping), by reduction of an oxide by hydrogen or other gaseous reducing agent, by electrolytic deposition, or by precipitation from a solution. Powders of selected particle size are mixed in tumbling mills, packed in dies, and are then compressed, with the pressures applied varying from 5 to as much as 100 tons per sq. in. By regulating the particle size and the pressure, the density (and porosity) of the finished product can be varied. The compressed article is sintered, either by electric resistance in an atmosphere of reducing gas or in a furnace. The sintering temperature depends upon the metal or metals and the use to which the sintered product is to be put. Frequently it is just below the melting point. During the sintering of two or more powdered metals alloying and thorough diffusion usually take place.

The cemented or sintered hard carbides have received much attention in the past ten years owing to their superior and sometimes remarkable performance as tools and dies. To manufacture these carbides, powdered tungsten—or tantalum (plus, in some cases, titanium) or their oxides—is mixed with carbon in the form of lampblack and is heated in a carburizing atmosphere for several hours at 2730 to 4350° F. (1500 to 2400° C.). The carbides which are formed are intimately mixed with a definite amount of a binder, usually powdered cobalt, and are compressed in a mold with a pressure of 15 to 30 tons per sq. in. The mixture is sintered in an inert gas at 1470 to 1650° F. (800 to 900° C.), and finally at 2550 to 2910° F. (1400 to 1600° C.), which results in alloying and diffusion.

The strength of the sintered material depends upon the amount of cobalt: with 3 per cent, the modulus of rupture is 125,000 lb. per sq. in., and with 13 per cent, it is 300,000 lb. per sq. in. The hardness depends also upon the amount of cobalt and is very high, viz, between 87 and 93 Rockwell A (60-kg. load). These values cannot be converted to other hardness scales; probably they are equivalent to more than 1000 Brinell.

Sintered tungsten carbide tools are used for machining cast iron, aluminum, copper, and their alloys, hard rubber, bakelite, asbestos, porcelain, and other materials. Until recently they were not wholly satisfactory for machining steel owing to the tendency of the steel chip to weld to the point of the carbide tool, which causes particles of the tool to break off. This tendency is not so pronounced with tantalum carbide or with tungsten titanium carbide tools. Depending upon the composition of the tool, the composition and structure of the material cut, and the conditions under which the tool is used, the increase in production obtainable by the use of sintered carbide tools as compared with the best high-speed steel is 20 to 200 per cent, and the reduction in machining cost is 25 to 75 per cent. The hard carbides are also used as dies for wire drawing and for the extrusion of steel and of non-ferrous metals and alloys. Wide use of these materials was largely prevented by their high cost, but a drastic reduction in price, recently announced, doubtless will soon increase the number of applications in which they can be used effectively.

There is another important class of non-ferrous tool materials, used to machine metals at high speed; *viz.,* a series of alloys containing 50 to 60 per cent cobalt, approximately 30 per cent chromium, 4 to 16 per cent tungsten, and about 2.5 per cent carbon. This alloy group, known under the trade name *Stellite,* has high red hardness and wear resistance and in some machining operations greatly outlasts high-speed steel tools. Stellite is used also in welding rods to deposit a hard surface or edge on plowshares and steam valves, and on other articles subjected to abrasion or to some types of chemical corrosion. Because of high hardness at elevated temperatures, Stellite cannot readily be worked; it is, therefore, cast into the shape desired and is finished to exact size by grinding. Stellite castings are used as dies, rollers, shields for turbine blades, bushings, and in many other specialized applications.

CHAPTER 20

CORROSION AND CORROSION RESISTANCE

CORROSION is not a pleasant word. According to the dic tionary it means an eating away, a gradual decay. Roget, in his well-known *Thesaurus,* classifies it under deterioration in the same group as degeneracy, impairment, decline, and decay; metallurgists and engineers have been known to use considerably more picturesque, if not quite such polite, terms in describing it and its effect on metals and alloys, especially when dealing with that variety of corrosion which corresponds to internal rot in some fruits and vegetables, namely, the decay which starts inside and gives no clue on the surface that deterioration is under way. Corrosion, the thorn in the side of the man who wishes to build economically a metal structure that will last, is the joy of the paint manufacturer because a large percentage of his product is used to slow down the destruction wrought by corrosion. One metallurgist's idea of corrosion is pictured in Fig. 116.[1]

Corrosion is nature's method of indicating that man, as a builder of an efficient civilization, is not yet omnipotent. It is one of nature's subtle jokes that many of the metals that are most resistant to corrosion—palladium, platinum, rhodium, iridium, and gold—are scarce and costly and cannot, therefore, be used for industrial structures and machines.

Reference in earlier chapters to the corrosion resistance of various industrial metals and alloys was mostly confined to a brief statement of fact that a given metal or alloy is or is not resist- ant when exposed to certain corrosive media. The discussion in the present chapter deals generally with corrosion and corrosion resistance, what it is and how it is evaluated; and then gives a broad outline of the resistance of the more common metallic materials to specific media.

[1] Drawing by Robert Worthington. Frontispiece of *Corrosion Resistance of Metals and Alloys,* by R. J. McKay and Robert Worthington, Reinhold Publishing Company, New York, 1936.

191. Corrosion and Passivity—Most metals have a tendency to combine with other chemical elements to form the compounds in which they originally existed in the earth. This is known as chemical affinity and varies widely with the metal. If the tendency is weak, the metal is "noble." The metals as a whole show a decreasing degree of nobility from gold, palladium, and platinum—which have little chemical affinity for other elements—to sodium and potassium—which have very great affinity. Iron is about midway in this electrochemical series: it is nobler than

Fig. 116—Old Man Corrosion (Drawing by Robert Worthington).

aluminum, manganese, zinc, and chromium but is less noble than tin, copper, and lead.

Although the chemical affinity for oxygen, sulphur, and other elements is an important criterion of the metal's economic value, it is an inherent property, and man can do very little about it. He is, therefore, usually more interested in the rate with which the reaction goes on than in the fact that a reaction takes place. The elements which have the greatest effect on metals and which are, therefore, of first interest in corrosion are oxygen—especially in air, water, acids, and (combined with carbon) in gases—and sulphur, especially combined with oxygen in gases and acids.

When two metals are connected and are immersed in an electrolyte, the less noble one will usually go into solution preferentially and thus will protect the more noble metal from attack. This is a principle of great importance in corrosion. Thus, if iron or steel is coated with a more noble metal, for example tin, and the coating is porous, the iron where exposed will corrode more rapidly than if it were not coated. On the other hand, if iron or steel is coated with a less noble metal, for example zinc, the coating does not need to be wholly impervious to prevent corrosion of the metal, as the attack is confined to the coating.

Some metals, when combining with other elements, react rapidly at first, but the reaction slows down and, under certain conditions, stops. This is known as passivity. A good example is iron or steel immersed in concentrated nitric acid. The attack of the metal by the acid stops quickly and, so long as the temperature or the acid concentration does not change, there is no further attack. When the passive state is induced, the metal behaves as if it were nobler than would be expected from its position in the electrochemical series. There are various methods of inducing passivity and various degrees of passivity. It is usually supposed that passivity is due to the formation of a uniform, tightly adherent film which is insoluble in the passivating medium. This theory is given weight by the well-known fact that, when passivity for a certain corrosive medium has been induced, changing concentration, or temperature, or the corroding medium itself may result in a complete and rapid transfer from the passive to the active state.

192. Significance of the Corrosion of Iron or Steel—The rapid formation of rust or scale when iron or steel is in contact with air or water or hot oxygen-containing gas is one of the most important phenomena in a steel-using civilization. As the inherent tendency of iron to return to its oxide cannot be changed, man has given much thought and study to methods of slowing it down. So far, only two methods are available: one is to coat or cover the surface so that corrosive media will not come into contact with it; another is to add large amounts of alloying metals,

especially chromium, which, under some corrosive conditions, promote the formation of a tight adherent coating that slows further attack so much that it is almost imperceptible. Either method is costly, the second much more so than the first.

The annual economic loss by corrosion is great, and so is the amount of money spent in trying to slow it down by protecting steel structures with paint and various other coatings. Speller, an authority on corrosion, claims that in a year of economic depression more iron reverts to its oxide than is extracted from the ore and refined into steel, and that 120 million gallons of paint are used annually to protect ferrous products from the atmosphere.

Corrosion is important not only because it destroys useful materials and structures, but also because it and its near relation, oxidation at elevated temperatures, may go on so slowly or may be so well hidden by corrosion products or by occurring in inaccessible places that they are difficult to detect before they go too far. In many instances the first inkling of corrosion or elevated-temperature oxidation is sudden failure. This is true for non-ferrous alloys as well as for iron and steel.

Metallurgists know more about corrosion now than they did 20 years ago, but they have made relatively little progress in checking it. If cost is no object, the stainless steels can be used since they will resist certain corrosive conditions almost perfectly for long periods of time. Considerable advance has also been made in the development of alloys resistant to oxidation at elevated temperatures. These materials are costly, although for some applications the saving occasioned by their use more than offsets the high initial cost. In ordinary atmospheric and water corrosion of structures, however, about the only advance in controlling economically the destruction of steel has been improvement in coatings.

Leaving aside for a moment the oxidation or scaling of steel at elevated temperatures, the following facts are known about the corrosion of ferrous alloys: (1) moisture must be present in the air, and oxygen must be present in the water; (2) corrosion is more rapid in acids than in neutral solutions and is slowest in alkaline solutions; (3) corrosion usually increases with the concentration of salts, especially chlorides and other halides in the solution, and with the temperature; and (4) the condition of the surface is important in determining whether corrosion will be more or less uniform or localized.

The last point, whether corrosion is uniform over the surface or localized, is important. As it is impossible to prevent corrosion, it is much better if the material wastes away uniformly, since it is usually possible in such an event to watch the process and replace the section before too much damage has been done.

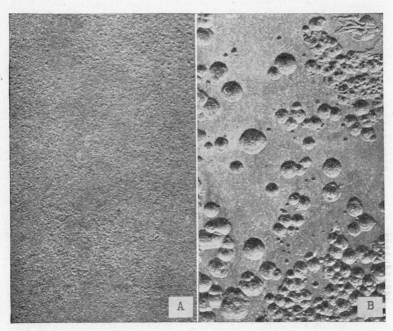

Fig. 117—Typical examples of (A) uniform surface corrosion and (B) pitting corrosion on carbon steel (Research Laboratory, Carnegie-Illinois Steel Corp.).

Moreover, if the surface is removed with some degree of uniformity, the only effect on the strength is that of reducing the cross-section. A localized attack may not be so readily detected and, thus, may be much more dangerous. In addition, it may cause irregularities where stresses become concentrated.

Both uniform surface corrosion and localized pitting (Fig. 117 [2]) are due primarily to the environment, although in the second

[2] Courtesy of Research Laboratory, Carnegie-Illinois Steel Corporation, Pittsburgh.

type differences in the material may play an important role. Local segregation of inclusions at the surface or a surface seam or, more commonly, the presence of oxide scale from the rolling or heat-treating process may accelerate or even start the attack at a definite spot. Environmental conditions, as irregularity of oxygen distribution in water, concentration of oxygen at the water line in materials partly submerged, and many others have a pronounced effect on localized corrosion. This type is common in pipe buried in soils.

193. Effect of the Environment on Corrosion of Ferrous Materials—During long exposure of a ferrous alloy to the atmosphere, so many things happen that it is impossible to duplicate them in a laboratory test. Rusting by the atmosphere involves the formation of hydrated ferrous oxide, which is normally adherent. If the weather is favorable, it may dry into a hard rust which for a considerable time will inhibit or at least slow down further corrosion. If there is rain, the hydrated oxide may be partly or wholly washed off before a hard rust layer is formed. The character of the rust and the rapidity with which it forms differ in a dry locality, a damp locality, or in one which is subject to frequent alternations of sunshine and rain, or sunshine and dew. Corrosion differs greatly in rural, in industrial, or in marine atmosphere. If other things are equal, a rural atmosphere is the least corrosive; corrosion in a marine atmosphere varies with climatic conditions which affect the amount of sodium chloride in the air; and in an industrial environment it varies with the climate and the amount of sulphur and other products of combustion which contaminate the atmosphere. Corrosion in water depends upon whether the material is totally immersed, partly immersed, alternately immersed and removed, whether the water contains much or little dissolved gas, whether it is stagnant or in motion, whether it contains large or small concentrations of sodium chloride or other salts, and upon many other factors.

As indicated, the initial surface condition and the character of the first corrosion products have an important effect in nearly all environments. If conditions are favorable, the initial oxide may form as a "tight coating" which, if environment is not strongly corrosive, may resist further corrosion for a long time. The classic example of this is the Delhi pillar of India. This mass of wrought iron, some 24 feet high and weighing about 6.5

tons, was made by hand welding small blooms. It was erected about A.D. 300. Owing to a "tight" oxide coating and a pure, dry atmosphere, it has resisted corrosion remarkably well for about 1600 years, but when Hadfield brought a piece of the pillar to England and moistened the surface, it rusted badly overnight.

The corrosion of metallic materials in acids, alkalis, and other chemicals is affected chiefly by the hydrogen-ion (pH) concentration of the solution and by the temperature. Broadly, solutions whose pH is below 4.3 cause rapid corrosion, and solutions whose pH values are above 10 cause slight corrosion; the corrosion by solutions with values between 4.3 and 10 pH depends on the oxygen content.

194. Evaluation of Corrosion Resistance—Regardless of whether the corroding medium is acid, water, or a chemical, there is only one method of evaluating corrosion resistance. This consists of exposing the material to the same environment to which it will be exposed in service, for sufficient time, examining it periodically to follow the progress of the attack, and finally measuring the loss in weight or the number of actual failures.

This is relatively simple in the case of many acids, alkalis, or other reagents. If it is planned to use a certain alloy as a container for acetic acid, a fair estimate of how it will stand up can be gained from observing the effect of immersing a specimen of the alloy in acid of the proper concentration, maintained at the proper temperature. This last item is very important as corrosion changes quickly with changes in temperature; on an average, the corrosion rate doubles for an increase of 20° F. (10° C.). It is also important that there be no great difference in the aeration of the acid used for the experiment and that which will be in the container in service.

Testing materials for atmospheric corrosion is tedious and costly. Atmospheres vary widely in corrosive action. Thus, a low-carbon open-hearth iron sheet showing an average life of 4000 days in rural atmosphere may last only 1000 days in an industrial atmosphere. Testing metals for corrosion in sea water involves even more difficulty in securing test conditions which approximate those in service, owing to differences in amount of oxygen, temperature of the water, the presence of marine organisms, and other factors.

Corrosion may be measured in a number of ways. The most common is to expose specimens of definite size for the required time, remove the corrosion products, and find the weight loss. This is expressed as milligrams per square decimeter per day (mg. per sq. dm. per day) which is frequently converted to inch penetration per year by the formula:

$$\text{mg. per sq. dm. per day} \times \frac{0.001437}{\text{density}} = \text{inch per year}$$

Zero mg. per sq. dm. per day indicates no measurable corrosion. Rates from 1 to 10 indicate slight attack, from 10 to 100 considerable corrosion, and rates of 100 or higher represent serious corrosion. A rate of 100 mg. per sq. dm. per day is equivalent, for ferrous materials, to a penetration of 0.017 to 0.020 inch per year.

Another method of measuring corrosion, especially for atmospheric attack, is to expose large specimens—frequently full-sized sheets—on racks in the desired location and determine by annual inspection over a 5- or 10-year period the number of failures. From this, the average life of a sheet of each grade of material can be calculated.

195. Oxidation of Ferrous Materials at Elevated Temperatures—Oxidation (or scaling) of metallic materials at elevated temperatures is a kind of corrosion. The process is often complicated by the presence of sulphur compounds originating from the combustion of fuel. High-temperature oxidation differs from the more general forms of corrosion mostly in that liquid water plays no part.

If a specimen of carbon or low-alloy steel with a machined or polished surface is heated in air, a thin oxide film forms which displays interference colors that change as the temperature increases. These "temper colors" were widely used before the day of the pyrometer to judge the temperature in tempering hardened steel. The principal temper colors are as follows:

Color	Temperature	
	° F.	° C.
Straw yellow................	445	230
Brown.....................	490	255
Purple.....................	530	275
Pale blue...................	565	295
Dark blue..................	600	315

These oxide films are very thin, varying in thickness from 4 to 15 × 10⁻⁷ cm. (0.00002 to 0.00006 mils). At temperatures where temper colors form, carbon and low-alloy steels oxidize very slowly; at higher temperatures, the formation of oxide is rapid and increases with the temperature; at temperatures corresponding to a red heat, oxidation is very rapid and the oxide, now known as scale, is so fragile that it drops off readily.

An approximation of the amount of oxidation of low-carbon steel at various temperatures is shown by the following data[3] obtained on ½-in. square blocks heated in air:

Temperature		Loss in weight in 1 week, per cent
° F.	° C.	
570	300	0.1
750	400	0.2
1020	550	0.5
1200	650	3.3
1380	750	15.0
1560	850	37.0
1830	1000	100.0

The oxide formed at elevated temperatures is a mixture of ferric and magnetic oxides ($Fe_2O_3 + Fe_3O_4$). At any elevated temperature, the amount of oxide formed depends on the time. The chief oxygen-containing media which react with ferrous alloys at these high temperatures are air, carbon dioxide, and steam. The potency of each of these depends upon its concentration in the gases and upon the temperature.

There is only one way to prevent elevated-temperature oxidation of carbon and low-alloy steels: heat them in a neutral or reducing gas. Such precautions, although expensive, are used in annealing low-carbon sheet and wire to prevent discoloration or the formation of an oxide coating of appreciable thickness. If it is necessary to prevent oxidation of medium- and high-carbon steels by heating in a neutral or reducing atmosphere—as is sometimes the case in heat treating tools—precautions must be taken to prevent decarburization of the surface layers. Removal of carbon

[3] C. E. MacQuigg, in *Symposium on Effect of Temperature on the Properties of Metals*, American Society of Mechanical Engineers and American Society for Testing Materials, 1931, pp. 589-609.

from the surface with the production of a soft outer layer is sometimes more of an evil than oxidation.

Because none of the carbon or low-alloy steels resists oxidation at elevated temperature, these materials are entirely unsuited in applications involving intermittent or continued heating to 900° F. (480° C.) or above. For such purposes it is necessary to use one of the recently developed high-alloy oxidation-resistant steels.

196. General Corrosion Resistance of Carbon Steel and Unalloyed Cast Iron—A 25,000-word exposition of the corrosion and the corrosion resistance of the metal iron by Cleaves and Thompson [4] is summarized by them with the succinct statement "iron rusts." High-purity and commercially pure iron and carbon steels all rust so rapidly in air and in most other corrosive media that it is hard to say which is the worst. There is frequently a difference in the behavior of very low carbon iron and the various unalloyed carbon steels when exposed to corrosive media, but this difference is valid only for the particular environment and usually for no other. Although extravagant claims have been made that ingot iron, wrought iron, carbon steel, or cast iron is more resistant than the others to the atmosphere, to water, or to some other media, these are not justified. Long tests of sheet, made under the supervision of a committee of the American Society for Testing Materials, have shown that under carefully controlled conditions no unalloyed ferrous material is much superior to another in its resistance to atmospheric, or to fresh- or salt-water corrosion.

A series of tests by the National Bureau of Standards on the corrosion of iron and steel pipe in soils has been under way for more than ten years. These have shown definitely that there are great differences in the corrosive action of the soil but no marked differences in the resistance of wrought iron, cast iron, or steel pipe. The most important means of controlling corrosion is to pack the soil uniformly which causes the occurring corrosion to be uniform over the surface of the pipe instead of being a localized attack of the pitting type.

Although the composition of ferrous materials has little influence compared with environment, it is generally true that in

[4] H. E. Cleaves and J. G. Thompson, *The Metal Iron*, McGraw-Hill Book Company, Inc., New York, 1935, Chapter 9.

a specific environment low-carbon steel resists corrosion better than high-carbon material. Heat treatment has little effect, nor have manganese and phosphorus in the amounts usually present. Cast iron frequently shows longer life than steel under certain corrosive conditions, which fact has been attributed to the tighter coating of rust which forms on cast iron.

Carbon steels—and cast iron and most low-alloy steels as well —are badly corroded by acids. In neutral solutions the corrosion varies between 1 and 30 mg. per sq. dm. per day, increasing as the amount of oxygen (aeration) increases. These materials are resistant to corrosion by alkaline solutions, weight losses of less than 1 mg. per sq. dm. per day being usual. This is due to the formation of an oxide film which is insoluble in the alkali and which protects the metal from further attack. Acids and alkalis usually corrode without pitting; neutral solutions on the contrary pit badly.

Corrosion of carbon steels and cast irons by the atmosphere is largely dependent upon the amount of moisture and upon the presence of sulphur compounds. If other things are equal, the most rapid attack by sulphur-free atmospheres occurs when the relative humidity is between 45 and 65 per cent. With this percentage of moisture weight losses range from 5 to 40 mg. per sq. dm. per day. With the exception of steels containing about 0.20 per cent copper, all carbon and low-alloy steels, and cast irons, have about the same resistance to atmospheric corrosion. There is very little exact information on the rates of corrosion of unalloyed steels and cast irons in sea water. The most that can be said is that composition of the material is of little or no importance. Corrosion rates are relatively high (sea water contains considerable oxygen) for the first few years but tend to slow down after that.

A corrosion problem which has been studied extensively is the deterioration of boilers. In general, this is corrosion by a neutral aqueous solution (boiler feed water is usually treated to reduce scale formation) containing considerable oxygen. The corrosive action of this water is reduced in some boiler installations by preheating the water to drive off the oxygen. Since boiler failure is generally caused by corrosion fatigue (discussed in section 80), it is necessary to keep the fiber stress in the boiler plate— which is usually an untreated 0.25 per cent carbon steel—as low as

10,000 lb. per sq. in. or preferably even lower. Boilers are also subject to corrosive attack at the riveted seam. This is apparently related to the amount of alkali in the water. If the sodium sulphate in the water is maintained at a definite ratio to the amount of sodium carbonate (the ratio varies with the boiler pressures), failures are largely prevented.

197. Corrosion Resistance of Low-alloy Steels—With the exception of carbon steel containing 0.15 to 0.30 per cent copper —this is actually a low-alloy steel but is not usually classified as such—and some of the low-alloy structural steels containing nickel and copper or copper and phosphorus as alloying elements, none of the low-alloy steels is much more corrosion resistant than the unalloyed carbon steels. It is true that some low-alloy steels containing copper and phosphorus or nickel and copper are more resistant than carbon steels to atmospheric and water corrosion, but, except for the new nickel-copper steels, the improvement due to these alloying elements is not usually enough to permit their economical use from the standpoint of corrosion resistance alone.

For resistance to rural and marine atmospheres the most effective economical method of improving carbon steel is to add copper. The effect of this element on the life of 22-gage (0.031 in. thick) low-carbon sheets is indicated by Fig. 118. In these tests, additions of 0.15 to 0.30 per cent copper doubled the life of the sheet. In industrial atmospheres, copper may or may not increase the useful life of steel depending largely upon the contamination of the atmosphere by sulphur and other corrosive agents, and to a lesser degree upon the composition of the steel. Copper steel cannot be considered corrosion resistant in industrial atmospheres.

Another element that retards atmospheric corrosion of carbon and low-alloy steels is phosphorus, especially when used together with copper. In tests by Lorig and Krause [5] in which sheet steels of various compositions were exposed to the atmosphere for three years it was found that the addition of 0.15 to 0.20 per cent phosphorus added 40 per cent to the average life of the low-carbon sheets and 25 to 30 per cent to the life of low-alloy steel sheets.

An important development in low-alloy steel for resistance to

[5] *The Iron Age*, v. 144, 1939, Oct. 26, pp. 28-31.

atmospheric corrosion was reported recently.[6] The steel is low in carbon and contains 2 to 4 per cent nickel, with or without the addition of up to 2 per cent copper. Tests (still going on) for

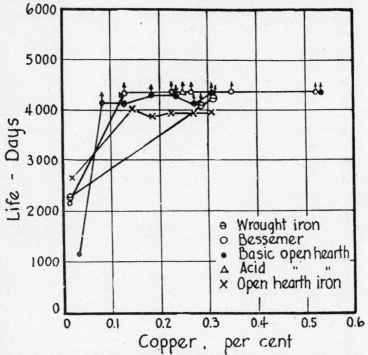

Fig. 118—Effect of copper on the atmospheric corrosion of low-carbon iron and low-carbon steel (McKay and Worthington; see footnote, p. 351).

seven years indicated that the probable life (defined as the time at which half of the sheets in a given class have failed) of sheets 0.015 in. thick is as follows:

Nickel, per cent	Copper, per cent	Probable life, months	Nickel, per cent	Copper, per cent	Probable life, months
0	0	24	2	0	37
0	1	32	2	1	62
0	2	32	4	0	>85
1	0	32	4	1	>85
1	0.5	37	4	2	>85

[6] N. B. Pilling and W. A. Wesley. Preprint 28, American Society for Testing Materials, June 1940.

It should be remembered that nickel, copper, and phosphorus do not prevent corrosion. Steels containing these elements as alloys start to rust as soon as do carbon steels. If the environment is such that the relatively adherent impervious film of oxide characteristic of these steels is formed, corrosion is, however, slowed down, but in unsuitable environments these steels corrode as rapidly and fail as soon as carbon steels. Since the surface on copper and copper-phosphorus steels becomes unsightly as rapidly as on unalloyed steels, they are not suitable for ornamental purposes. For roofing and in similar applications where exposure to rural and seacoast atmospheres is involved, these steels, especially if galvanized, usually have 2 to 5 times the life of unalloyed carbon-steel or ingot-iron sheets.

198. Protective Coatings for Carbon and Low-alloy Steels— For most purposes the best and the cheapest protective coating is paint, thoroughly and frequently applied. This method of protection is so well known that further attention is unnecessary here. The other method of protecting ferrous materials from corrosion (and in many instances also of increasing the ornamental value) is to coat with zinc, tin, lead, chromium, or nickel. In general a zinc coating (galvanizing) is the best protection, because electrochemically zinc is less noble than iron and will protect the steel even if the coating is broken. This is important as coated steel is rarely free from pinholes and scratches.

Zinc coatings are resistant to the atmosphere. Acids and alkalis attack the coating rapidly, but in fresh water (not distilled) and in salt water it is relatively resistant. Galvanized water pipes and tanks are widely used, but the coatings, both inside and outside, are heavy. Zinc-coated steel containers are not used for handling food products since many foods are sufficiently acid to attack zinc. Moreover, tin is considered to be less toxic. The toxicity of zinc, which is negligible in the amounts present in drinking water, might be serious if galvanized containers were used for food products. Thin galvanized sheet containing 1 to $1\frac{1}{4}$ oz. of zinc per sq. ft. of surface has an average life of 20 to 30 years in rural atmospheres, but the life is less than half this in industrial atmospheres. As the thickness of the coating decreases, the expected life of the steel decreases.

Tin-coated sheet steel, as noted in the previous chapter, is used chiefly for food containers. Tinplate has an attractive appearance, is ductile and easy to solder, and the tin is cheaply and easily applied to the steel by hot dipping. The coating is rarely free from pinholes, and as tin stands higher in the electrochemical series (i.e., it is nobler) than iron, it accelerates the corrosion of the underlying steel where there are discontinuities in the plate. Tinplate is resistant to corrosion by neutral or weakly acid liquids in the absence of air; in the sealed tin can corrosion will be negligible if, as is nearly always the case, the amount of oxidizing agent is insufficient to strip the tin from relatively large areas during the time the can is in use. For many purposes the possibility of appreciable corrosion is lessened by enameling or lacquering the interior of the can. Tin is resistant to most waters and to the atmosphere even in industrial districts, but its cost is too high for extensive use where atmospheric and water corrosion are important.

It is stated in Chapter 19 that lead is widely used because of its high resistance to corrosion by air, water, and many acids and other chemicals—mostly as the pure metal or as a lead-base alloy. A relatively small amount is used in lead-coated steel and in terne plate (75 to 85 per cent lead, remainder tin) used as roofing sheets. For atmospheric corrosion resistance steel is occasionally coated with cadmium. This element, like zinc, is less noble than iron. Cadmium-plated steel is not widely used because of its cost.

Chromium is deposited electrolytically on steel and on many non-ferrous alloys as a coating 0.00001 to 0.0001 in. thick. Heavier coatings do not have satisfactory properties. The corrosion resistance of chromium plate, like the corrosion resistance of high-chromium steel (see sections 130 and 133), depends upon the tendency of the material to become passive, in other words to form a thin tight coating which inhibits further attack. As an oxidizing agent is necessary for this passivity, it follows that chromium plate is resistant primarily to oxidizing agents (i.e., air, water, some salt solutions, and oxidizing acids). Because under such conditions the rates of corrosion are very low, chromium plate has been used extensively for automotive and marine hardware and plumbing fixtures where the ornamental value is an added asset. High cost has prevented wider application.

Nickel is plated on steel and copper alloys to increase the resistance of these materials to the atmosphere and to improve their appearance. The principal disadvantage of nickel plate, aside from its cost, is its porosity; with steel, galvanic cells are set up in the pores, and corrosion of the base metal is accelerated. In addition, the coating is usually so thin (0.001 in. or less) that the base metal is readily exposed by abrasion. Nickel plate lasts for years when used indoors; outdoors its life is much shorter; and it is not suitable for exposure to seacoast or industrial atmospheres. It is, furthermore, not resistant when immersed in fresh or salt water, acids, alkalis, or food products.

199. Corrosion Resistance of High-alloy Steels and Cast Irons—The effect of 10 to 35 per cent chromium, alone or together with nickel or other alloying elements, on the corrosion and oxidation resistance of carbon steel has been discussed in enough detail in Chapter 14 so that only a brief additional statement is warranted here. As noted previously, the outstanding characteristic of these alloys is their ability to become passive. Corrosion rates in this condition are from 1 or less to about 10 mg. per sq. dm. per day. Resistance to acids depends upon whether the oxidizing capacity or the acidity of the corrosive agent is the stronger. Nitric acids of nearly all concentrations cause passivity; hydrochloric acid on the other hand causes rapid corrosion. Some concentrations and some degrees of aeration of sulphuric acid produce passivity; others cause rapid attack. Mixtures of sulphuric and nitric acids produce passivity as does sulphuric acid containing copper or iron sulphate, and sulphurous acid. The high-chromium steels are passive to a large number of organic acids, to caustic alkalis, to ammonia, to salt solutions if enough air is present to maintain the protective film, to all fresh waters, and to food products. In rural and urban atmospheres, these materials approach the precious metals in resistance; in industrial atmospheres, corrosion increases with the amount of sulphur in the atmosphere.

High chromium, usually together with high nickel, is necessary for resistance to oxidation at elevated temperatures. These materials, which are discussed briefly in previous chapters (pp. 238 and 348) and which include low-carbon 18 per cent chromium, 8 per cent nickel steel, 25 to 35 per cent chromium steel, 35 per cent nickel, 15 per cent chromium steel, the 80 per cent nickel, 20 per cent chromium alloy, and the 62 per cent nickel, 15 per cent chromium, 23 per cent iron alloy, have long life at temperatures of 1300 to 1800° F. (700 to 980° C.) and are used in oil refineries, power plants, furnaces, and chemical plants.

There are two other high-alloy materials which are important because of their acid resistance. One of these is cast iron containing 13 to 15 per cent silicon. Castings of this alloy are so hard that they cannot be easily machined, yet, despite this handicap, this alloy is used extensively in chemical-plant equipment. Its corrosion rate is less than 1 mg. per sq. dm. per day in most concentrations of (cold) sulphuric, nitric, acetic, phosphoric, oxalic, and several other important organic acids. The high-silicon alloy is one of the few known materials that resist both oxidizing and non-oxidizing acids. The only acid which corrodes it fairly rapidly is hydrochloric. The resistance of this alloy is attributed to a thin adherent film of silica. The other high-alloy material is austenitic cast iron. It usually contains at least 20 per cent alloying metals of which nickel is about 15 per cent. One grade also contains 6 per cent copper and 2 per cent chromium, another contains more chromium and no copper. Castings of austenitic cast iron are used in applications where resistance to acids and other chemicals is important, especially in paper manufacturing and in oil refining.

200. Corrosion Resistance of Heavy Non-ferrous Alloys—As noted in the previous chapter (section 188), nickel and nickel-base alloys are resistant to non-oxidizing acids—sulphuric, hydrochloric, phosphoric, acetic—and to caustic alkalis, and are, therefore, used industrially where these corrosive agents are encountered. Their widest use, however, is for resistance to water, especially ground and sea water. Corrosion rates are usually less than 1 mg. per sq. dm. per day, and aeration is not an accelerating factor.

Nickel and nickel-copper alloys are also resistant to food and dairy products, and to the atmosphere. The corrosion rate of these materials when used for containers, conveyors, table tops, and other equipment in food-processing industries is low, and there is, moreover, practically no chance of toxic contamination. In sulphur-free atmospheres, nickel and nickel-copper alloys have corrosion rates of less than 2 mg. per sq. dm. per day.

Copper and copper-base alloys have, as noted in Chapter 18, excellent resistance to a wide variety of corrosive media. They are not resistant to oxidizing acids, aqueous ammonia, and a few strong corrodents such as chlorine but may be used for handling non-oxidizing acids, food products, salt water, and all kinds of fresh water. Copper is the most useful common metal for resisting sea water: upon submersion in quiet water, corrosion rates are less than 1 mg. per sq. dm. per day, and even under the worst conditions the rate is seldom more than 10 or 15 mg. Copper oxide is poison to marine life, which does not collect on submerged copper or high-copper alloys. The corrosion resistance of copper and its alloys in the atmosphere is less than 1 mg. per sq. dm. per day. Moreover, some of the corrosion products are so protective that a life of 100 years is usual for sheet 0.05 in. thick. Copper and copper alloys need no protective coating for atmospheric exposure.

201. Corrosion Resistance of Light Alloys—Magnesium is the least noble of the useful metals, and neither it nor its alloys should be used in contact with the other common metals in any corrosive environment, especially when moisture is present. Magnesium has great affinity for oxygen, but its oxide, if unbroken, is protective; and corrosion rapidly slows down. In rural and industrial atmospheres the film is protective, but it rapidly breaks down if salt is present. Magnesium and its alloys have satisfactory corrosion resistance in the atmosphere if the surface is roughened by chemical treatment and the proper paint is applied. Magnesium alloys are fairly resistant to fresh water, but in salt water the rates of corrosion vary from 50 to 10,000 or more mg. per sq. dm. per day; corrosion by pitting is frequently encountered. Magnesium is fairly resistant to hydrofluoric acid but is rapidly attacked by all the other acids.

Although aluminum is one of the least noble of the metals and is rapidly oxidized, it is one of the most generally corrosion resistant of all the metals owing to the thin, continuous, and tightly adherent film of oxide formed on the surface. This oxide film is readily soluble in alkalis and in some acids. Aluminum is, however, used industrially to handle concentrated nitric acid and all concentrations of acetic acid. Its corrosion resistance is high in water, the atmosphere, and salt solutions.

Pure aluminum is more corrosion resistant than its alloys. Of the latter, the wrought aluminum-manganese alloys (S.A.E. 29 and 20, Table 19) and the cast aluminum-silicon alloys (S.A.E. 35, 37, 322, 323, 305, and 307, Table 20) are more resistant than the others in sea water. Ornamental architectural sections of aluminum or any of its alloys last indefinitely in most rural and urban atmospheres.

Intercrystalline corrosion, briefly mentioned on p. 299, has been the subject of extensive study, and now can largely be prevented by proper heat treatment, i.e., by aging at room temperature and not at a higher temperature or—better yet—by the use of Alclad (see p. 300) properly heat treated. Intercrystalline corrosion is detected readily by the tensile test and is evidenced by a drop in tensile strength of about 50 per cent.

Pitting which may be frequent in aluminum alloys is caused by localized breaking of the oxide film and is most frequently encountered upon exposure to sea water and sea air. For rural and urban atmospheres aluminum and its alloys need no protection; for exposure to salt water and salt spray it is advisable to use Alclad, or to give the metal an anodic oxidation treatment—which increases the thickness of the oxide coating—followed by painting.

CHAPTER 21

THE EFFECT OF TEMPERATURE ON THE MECHANICAL PROPERTIES OF FERROUS AND NON-FERROUS ALLOYS

SINCE most high melting point metals and alloys are elastic when stressed at normal temperature, there is no appreciable plastic deformation (permanent set) so long as the applied load does not exceed the elastic limit. Furthermore, most metals and alloys when subjected at normal temperature to stresses above the elastic limit—as in cold working—strain harden; in other words, permanent deformation distorts the grains and increases strength and hardness. This is true of metallic materials stressed at elevated temperature as well as of those stressed at normal temperature, so long as the temperature is below that at which rapid recrystallization takes place. For many years certain metals and alloys, especially carbon steels, have been used successfully at temperatures considerably above normal in boilers, pipes, stills, valves, pumps, cylinders, pistons, and others; successfully, because the loads imposed were relatively low and because the temperatures were well below the recrystallization (softening) temperature.

When engineers, some 15 or 20 years ago, began to increase temperatures and pressures for the operation of power-generating, oil-refining, and similar equipment, they discovered that marked economies resulted. Thus, 25 years ago, with steam heated to 650° F. (345° C.) and pressures at 250 lb. per sq. in., it was necessary to burn 1.5 lb. of coal to produce 1 kw-hr. of electricity; by 1930, with steam pressures of 1250 lb. per sq. in. and temperatures of 750° F. (400° C.), only 1 lb. of coal was necessary. Modern power-generating plants use pressures of 2500 lb. per sq. in. with temperatures of 950° F. (510° C.) with further increase in efficiency and decrease in cost. Unfortunately, however, when engineers discovered the economy resulting from the use of higher temperatures and pressures, they uncovered a hornets' nest of trouble for themselves and several hornets' nests of trouble for the metallurgist. It happened that equipment operating at high temperatures and presumably designed conservatively with an ample factor of safety warped and even failed; the carbon and low-alloy steels being used, instead of deforming elastically as well-behaved steels should, deformed plastically under surprisingly low loads. In brief, the engineer discovered creep, and neither he nor the metallurgist knew what to do about it.

As is evident from this introduction, creep is a phenomenon involving small amounts of plastic deformation over long periods of time at elevated temperatures. Entering importantly into creep is strain hardening which is opposed by the softening that occurs during recrystallization. Recrystallization is a phenomenon which depends upon time, temperature, stress, and the previous structural condition of the material. For steel, the recrystallization temperature varies from about 700 to 850° F. (370 to 455° C.).

202. The Importance of Creep—It has been known for many years that some of the soft, ductile, low-melting metals—lead and tin are common examples—and their alloys are not elastic but deform plastically at room temperature when lightly stressed. Lead, in fact, will creep, or flow, under its own weight, and this phenomenon is taken into consideration in designing and using lead pipe and roofing sheets. It has also been known for a long time that steel and other high-melting metallic materials would deform plastically, or creep, if stressed at high temperatures, but little was known about the magnitude of this deformation, and little attention was paid to its industrial consequences until Dickinson[1] demonstrated in 1922 that steel deformed slowly at a red heat under stresses that were much lower than the values used in what was then considered good design. The connection between this slow creep at high temperature and the failure of certain power-generating equipment was established, and the importance of creep was quickly recognized. As a result, the American Society of Mechanical Engineers and the American Society for Testing Materials set up a joint committee in 1924 to study the phenomenon, to devise a method of determining creep, and to accumulate useful data on the creep of industrially impor-

[1] *J. Iron Steel Inst.*, v. 106, 1922, p. 103.

tant metallic materials. This committee, and similar organizations abroad, have done a notable job in all of these fields.

In addition to superheaters and other power-generating equipment such as turbine parts, bolts, tubes, valves, etc., there are many other fields in which the creep of metallic materials is important. In oil refining, for example, tubes in cracking stills are frequently operated with oil heated to 800 to 1200° F. (425 to 650° C.) inside and with outside temperatures as high as 1500 or 1600° F. (815 to 870° C.). In heat-treating furnaces and in the ceramic and chemical industries, vessels, conveyors, boxes, and other parts may be required to withstand loads of considerable magnitude at temperatures as high as 1900 to 2000° F. (1040 to 1095° C.).

203. The Engineering Significance of Creep—In the selection of a steel or other alloy for high-temperature use the mechanical properties of the material as determined at room temperature are of little importance. The requirements for metallic material which is to be used in various kinds of equipment operating at high temperatures vary widely, but in general the following are important: (1) the metal should be resistant to oxidation or other attack by the hot gases (including air) which are present; (2) it should have a stable structure which will remain relatively unchanged under the stress and temperature conditions imposed; (3) it should withstand the stress imposed with a negligible or at least with a harmless amount of distortion for the useful life of the equipment; and (4) it should withstand momentary overloads at the usual operating temperature, or short periods of fluctuating temperature at normal loads. There are few metallic materials which meet all these requirements. It is, therefore, not easy for the metallurgist to supply the engineer with materials suitable for equipment operating at high temperatures and fairly high loads. This difficulty is not lessened by the fact that engineers are usually uncertain about the exact loads and the exact temperatures in the equipment they design and use.

Engineering requirements for the stability of metallic materials at elevated temperatures vary widely in different industries. This was emphasized by Gillett [2] who noted as one extreme that turbine discs should not stretch more than 0.2 per cent in 25 years

[2] *Trans. Am. Inst. Min. Met. Eng.*, v. 135, 1939, pp. 15-58.

(approximately 200,000 hr.), which means that the permissible rate of creep is of the order of 1/100,000,000 in. per in. per hr. As the other extreme, in furnace parts, for tubes in oil-cracking stills, and for similar equipment, the total allowable deformation can frequently be 5 per cent in a useful life of approximately 5 years (approximately 45,000 hr.) or about 1 per cent in 10,000 hr. This is equivalent to 1/1,000,000 in. per in. per hr. The difficulty of determining accurately such small deformations is evident when it is recalled that thermal expansion in carbon steel is about 7/1,000,000 in. per in. for each 1° F.

204. The Determination of Creep—Despite the fact that a number of laboratories in the United States and abroad are working on creep, relatively few data are available on ferrous materials and practically none on non-ferrous metals and alloys. The cause for this is twofold. In the first place, the determination of creep is difficult, expensive, and time consuming; in the second place, much time was wasted early in the development of creep testing (1924 to 1930) in trying to find a rapid method of evaluating creep. It took a long time to discover that there is no short cut. As the result, a long-time method was finally worked out and was tentatively standardized by the American Society for Testing Materials [3] by which concordant results could be obtained by well-equipped laboratories working independently of each other.

The equipment necessary consists of an electric furnace capable of close temperature control and a suitable device for holding the specimen in exact alignment in the furnace. The load is applied by dead weights through a system of levers. A battery of modern creep-testing furnaces and their auxiliary equipment is shown in Fig. 119.[4] Test specimens are usually 0.505 in. in diameter (cross-section 0.2 sq. in.) and have a gage length of at least 2 in.

The most important variables in creep testing are temperature control and accurate measurement of elongation under load. Temperature variations for steel should not exceed ±3° F. for temperatures of 1200° F. (660° C.) or below, ±5° F. for temperatures between 1200 and 1600° F., and ±10° F. for temperatures of 1600° F. (870° C.) or above. The need for accurate temperature control is shown by the fact that with some loads increasing the temperature 10° F. may double the creep rate. The time for

[3] *A.S.T.M. Standards,* 1939, part I, Spec. E22-38T, p. 1261.
[4] Courtesy of Battelle Memorial Institute.

the test should never be less than 1 per cent, but preferably it should be 5 or 10 per cent, of the estimated life of the material in service. Gillett emphasized that in many instances it takes 500 hr. for a metal to make up its mind how it is going to creep. It is necessary, therefore, to run the test 1000 to 3000 hr. to evaluate the rate with any certainty. Thus at least 6 weeks, and frequently several months, are necessary for one test.

Fig. 119—Modern creep-testing equipment. The electric furnaces for heating the specimens are shown at the left (white); the lever system for loading the specimens is above the furnaces (Battelle Memorial Institute).

From the creep rates for the stresses used, as determined at a single temperature by a 1000- to 3000-hr. test, the stress producing the maximum creep permitted for the expected life, namely 10,000 to 500,000 hr., is arrived at by extrapolation (see Fig. 120). Creep is usually reported as the stress producing 1 per cent elongation in 10,000 or 100,000 hr. or preferably 0.1 or 0.01 per cent in 1000 hr. There is considerable question about the accuracy of such extrapolations. A number of methods of plotting have been proposed, and a number of mathematical formulas have been worked out in the hope of increasing the accuracy of extrapolation. This has been discussed in detail by Gillett,[5] and no further comment is necessary here other than the brief state-

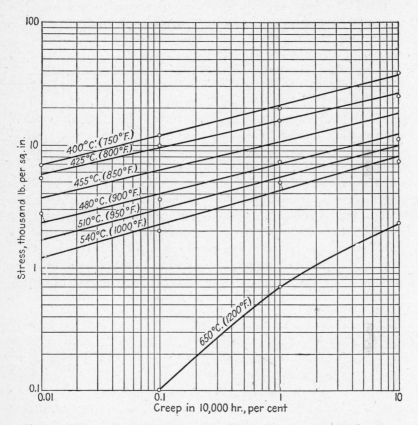

Fig. 120—Creep rate versus creep stress for a 0.30 per cent carbon steel (Kanter, American Society of Mechanical Engineers and American Society for Testing Materials, *Symposium on Effect of Temperature on the Properties of Metals,* 1931).

ment that, if the creep rate is determined carefully for various stresses and is plotted on a log-log scale of stress versus rate (Fig. 120), the values arrived at by extrapolation can be used in design provided a suitable factor of safety is applied.

[5] See footnote 2, this chapter.

205. The So-called Creep Limit and the Relation of Creep to Other Properties—Early in the history of creep testing much time and effort were wasted in trying to prove that metallic materials, especially steel, had a creep limit—in other words, that for each temperature there was a limiting stress below which creep would not take place, or below which the distortion was inconsequential —and that the "creep limit" or "limiting creep stress" could be determined and used in engineering design. It was finally found, however, that there can be no such thing as a creep limit or limiting creep stress. Much effort was also wasted in trying to correlate the stress causing a very small amount of creep with the short-time proportional limit, determined very accurately at the same temperature, or with some other short-time elevated-temperature property. This was also found to be impossible, as is evident from Figs. 121 [6] and 122 [7] for rolled and cast carbon steel, respectively. In Fig. 121, there is no correlation between the short-time tensile strength, yield strength, and proportional limit and the stresses producing 0.1 per cent, 1 per cent, and 10 per cent elongation in 10,000 hr. In Fig. 122, there is no correlation between the short-time properties and the stresses producing 1 per cent creep in 1 to 100,000 hr. except for the apparent connection between short-time proportional limit and the stress producing 1 per cent creep in 1000 hr., and this is purely coincidence. At temperatures at which strain hardening occurs, the creep stress (for 1 per cent elongation or less in 1000 hr.) is frequently higher than the short-time proportional limit; [8] at higher than recrystallization temperatures, it is usually lower, and no mathematical relation between the two has as yet been discovered.

In addition to these efforts, a serious attempt was made, especially in Germany, to determine creep by a short-time method, usually by guessing the amount of creep for 10,000 or 100,000 hr. from the amount that occurred between the fifth and the tenth, or between the fortieth and the sixtieth hour. It is impossible to determine creep until the test has been carried on long enough

[6] J. J. Kanter and L. W. Spring, *Proc. Am. Soc. Test. Mat.*, v. 28, II, 1928, pp. 80-116.

[7] J. J. Kanter, "The Creep of Metals and Alloys," in *Metals Handbook*, American Society for Metals, Cleveland, 1939, p. 504.

[8] Short-time proportional limits as determined by different laboratories seldom check each other.

to establish the character of the creep curve. Depending upon the load, the temperature, and the material being tested, this may take from a few days to a year or more. At present, tests carried on for less than 1000 hr. are not considered to have any significance in establishing the rate of creep.

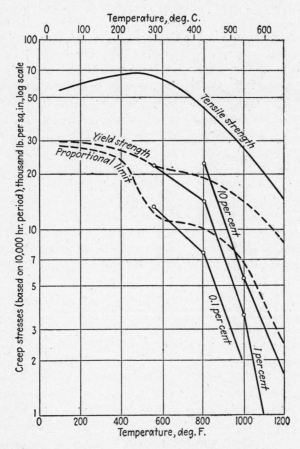

Fig. 121—Effect of temperature on short-time tensile properties and on creep stress of rolled and normalized 0.17 per cent carbon steel (Kanter and Spring).

206. **The Three Stages of Creep**—Three typical creep curves are shown in Fig. 123,[9] marked to show the three stages of creep. Depending upon the applied load, the temperature, and the mate-

[9] Babcock and Wilcox Tube Co., Tech. Bull. 6C, 1938.

rial, the curve may turn up as in *A;* the specimen stretches at an increasing rate until finally it necks down and breaks. It may

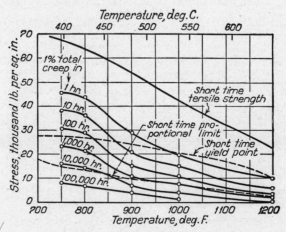

Fig. 122—Effect of temperature on short-time tensile properties and on creep stress of cast carbon steel (Kanter).

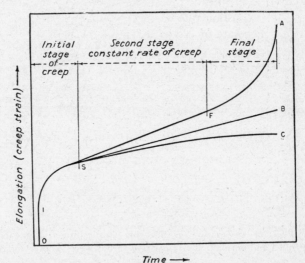

Fig. 123—Typical curves for three stages of creep (Babcock and Wilcox Tube Co.).

also turn down as in *C;* in other words, the amount of elongation may decrease with time. It may also continue without curvature, as in *B*, and give no indication, over many thousands of hours, whether the elongation will eventually increase as in *A* or decrease as in *C*.

The first stage of creep is called by Gillett the period of stress distribution. It is represented by a relatively large initial deformation, *OS*, as the favorably oriented crystals slip under stress, which then distributes itself and affects the crystals that are less favorably oriented. This continues until the total slip is uniform and is much smaller in magnitude than at the start. The length of time for stage 1 to be completed varies greatly; it is frequently as much as 500 hr.

During stage 2 (*SF*, Fig. 123), slip continues, but unless the temperature is so high that rapid recrystallization takes place, there is strain hardening which tends to slow down deformation. There is also recrystallization [10] which tends to speed up elongation under stress but which is a relatively slow process unless conditions are wholly favorable. Stage 2, therefore, represents an approximate balance between strain hardening and recrystallization and may continue for thousands of hours. During stage 2, creep is at a constant rate or an asymptotic approach to a constant rate. The rate of creep in stage 2, or the stress which at any given temperature produces a rate which can be extrapolated to 1 per cent in 10,000 or 100,000 hr., is the value used in engineering design.

If, after a period of time, the recrystallization (annealing) tendency is stronger than the strain-hardening tendency, creep increases. Finally the specimen necks down slightly, which increases the unit load. This increases the deformation as in curve *FA*, Fig. 123, and soon the specimen fails. If, on the contrary, the strain-hardening tendency is stronger than the annealing tendency, the rate of deformation decreases, and the curve turns down as in *C*, Fig. 123.

The shape of creep curves as dependent upon stress for two temperatures is shown by Fig. 124,[11] in which group *A* is for a

[10] Physicists call the restoration of perfect crystals from distorted ones of the same orientation "crystal repair," and the production of new crystals of random orientation from distorted ones "recrystallization." This is a distinction of minor importance here.

[11] H. J. Tapsell, *Creep of Metals*, Oxford University Press, London, 1931, pp. 127, 128.

temperature at which strain hardening is considerable and group
B for one at which strain hardening is small. It is evident from
this figure that to have reasonable assurance that no more than
the permissible creep (0.1 or 0.01 per cent in 1000 hr.) will occur
in a life of 200 days—as based upon a test of 1000 hr. (40 days)—
the rates of elongation should not be greater than is shown for
curves 6 and 7. Any upward inflection of a creep curve within
a testing period of 1000 hr. is an indication that in time the specimen will either break or elongate more than is desirable. When
the stresses producing no more than the permissible amount of

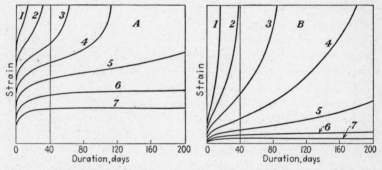

Fig. 124—Shape of creep curves at temperature (*A*) where strain hardening is
considerable and (*B*) where strain hardening is small (Tapsell).

creep—as evidenced by the curve for stage 2—have been determined for a number of temperatures, the whole series may then be
plotted. Fig. 121 shows for 0.17 per cent carbon steel the stresses
producing creep of 0.1 per cent, 1 per cent, and 10 per cent in
10,000 hr. in the temperature range 550 to 1200° F. (290 to
650° C.).

207. **Effect of Grain Size and Deoxidation on Creep**—In addition to temperature and applied stress, a number of other factors
influence creep. One of the most important is grain size. More
than 10 years ago it was noticed that coarse-grained steels generally resist creep better than fine-grained steels of similar composition. The conclusion which naturally followed was that the
actual grain size of the specimen tested had an effect on creep. As
noted by Gillett [12] this concept has changed. It is now held that

[12] See footnote 2, this chapter.

the important variable is the grain size of the austenite before it transforms to a constituent stable at room temperature, rather than the actual grain size of the specimen tested. It is, therefore, possible to change the creep characteristics of carbon and low-alloy steels materially by heat treating to produce coarse- or fine-grained austenite. Grain size is, however, not important in some of the austenitic steels, especially the 18 per cent chromium, 8 per cent nickel stainless grade, as little difference has been found in the creep behavior of specimens with widely varying grain size.

The effect of grain size on creep characteristics of non-ferrous alloys is erratic. Clark and White,[13] for example, found that coarse-grained brass was more creep resistant than fine-grained material if the testing temperature was high; at relatively low temperatures, the opposite was true. The same phenomenon was encountered in lead, tin, and alloys of these metals, but so many exceptions have been found that nothing definite can be stated.

Another important variable in the creep behavior of steel is the extent of deoxidation in melting and refining. Rimming steel—described briefly on p. 57—even if coarse-grained, has poor creep resistance compared with killed steel of similar composition.

It is now known that many of the discrepancies in early data, unexplained at the time, were due to unsuspected or undetermined differences in austenite grain size or in deoxidation. Because of this, most of the older creep values appearing in the literature, even if determined with satisfactory precision, should be used with caution.

In recent years many explanations have been offered for the effect of grain size and deoxidation on creep, but none is wholly convincing. It is evident that in this field alone much additional work is needed. The most that can be said at present is that rimming steels should not be used if creep is important, and that grain size has such a marked effect that the grain size as well as the composition of the steel used for high-temperature equipment involving creep should be the same as of the specimen upon which creep tests were made. As coarse-grained steels are not always of satisfactory ductility—especially in resistance to

[13] C. L. Clark and A. E. White, Univ. of Michigan, *Eng. Research Bull.* 27, 1936, 100 pp.

impact—engineers should be chary about specifying them for applications involving creep unless they are certain that low ductility is not a disadvantage.

208. Other Variables Affecting Creep—Carbon steels, owing to their instability of structure and their lack of resistance to oxidation at elevated temperature, are not used frequently where creep is a factor, except at temperatures below 1000° F. (540° C.). Little is known definitely about the effect of the elements present in all carbon steels. So far as can be determined from the data available,[14] creep is little affected by the amount of carbon, at least compared with the effect of grain size. The condition of the carbon, i.e., the structure of the steel, is much more important. Carbon steels containing lamellar pearlite, in which the cementite is present as relatively coarse plates, are more resistant to creep than steels in which the carbide is in the form of spheroids. Carbon and most low-alloy steels, if used in applications involving creep, should be deoxidized in melting and should be normalized to form lamellar pearlite. Quenching and tempering is of no value, as holding the steel for long periods at elevated temperatures promotes continued tempering and in most instances causes a breakdown of lamellar pearlite to spheroidized cementite. In addition it may cause such rapid recrystallization that the retarding effect of strain hardening, which normally occurs, is partially or wholly nullified.

The creep strength of carbon steels can be increased by adding a carbide stabilizer such as molybdenum. Permissible design values for rolled plates and forged flanges and for castings of carbon steel, low-nickel steel, and molybdenum steel containing 0.40 to 0.60 per cent molybdenum, as recommended tentatively by the American Society of Mechanical Engineers,[15] are given in Table 34. The effect of molybdenum is clearly shown. The values given in this table are not creep stresses; they are based upon the creep values with a factor of safety and have been used successfully in design.

In some alloys that are subject to precipitation hardening, changes occurring during long exposure to high temperature may

[14] Summarized by Gillett, *Trans. Am. Inst. Min. Met. Eng.,* v. 135, 1939, p. 36; and Sisco, *The Alloys of Iron and Carbon,* Vol. II, *Properties,* McGraw-Hill Book Company, Inc., New York, 1937, pp. 514-518.

[15] *Mechanical Engineering,* v. 60, 1938, p. 170.

TABLE 34. PERMISSIBLE DESIGN VALUES FOR PLATES AND FLANGES OF
CARBON STEEL, LOW-NICKEL STEEL, AND MOLYBDENUM STEEL

Temperature		Permissible working stress, lb. per sq. in.			
		Rolled sections		Castings	
° F.	° C.	Carbon or nickel steel	Molybdenum steel	Carbon or nickel steel	Molybdenum steel
650	345	14,000	14,000	10,000	10,000
700	375	13,300	14,000	9,500	10,000
750	400	11,900	14,000	8,500	10,000
800	425	10,000	14,000	7,200	10,000
850	455	7,850	12,000	5,800	8,800
900	495	5,600	10,000	4,400	7,800
950	510	3,800	8,000	3,200	6,700
1000	540	2,000	5,000	....	4,600

affect the creep rate in various ways. If the size of the precipitated
particles is small and if they act as keys to prevent slip, creep will
be retarded. If, on the other hand, the particles are large and if
they do not act as keys in the slip planes, the effect may be analogous to spheroidization in carbon steels, and creep may be accelerated. Precipitated particles may collect at the grain boundaries, as in 18-8, and may cause embrittlement, especially if the
precipitation is accompanied by accelerated corrosion. The relation of precipitation hardening to creep is complex, and no
generalities are permissible. All that can be said at present is
that it is important, and that, when precipitation-hardening alloys
are used, creep tests should be run to determine their behavior
at the important temperatures.

209. Creep Data on Carbon and Alloy Steels—Creep data for
carbon and a few alloy steels commonly used in high-temperature applications are given in Table 35.[16] Although they were
obtained in recent determinations by precise methods, they
should not be used in design without a liberal factor of safety.
They are valuable primarily in affording a comparison of steels

[16] The creep data in Table 35 were selected from a variety of sources, principally from the Alloys of Iron Research monograph series, from the comprehensive summary in Chapter 19 of Bullens and Battelle, *Steel and Its Heat
Treatment*, Vol. II, John Wiley & Sons, Inc., New York, ed. 4, 1939, and from
*Compilation of Available High-temperature Creep Characteristics of Metals
and Alloys*, American Society for Testing Materials and American Society of
Mechanical Engineers, 1938.

TABLE 35. CREEP STRENGTH OF COMMON FERROUS MATERIALS USED AT ELEVATED TEMPERATURES

Material	Creep stress, lb. per sq. in., at a temperature of						
	900° F. (480° C.)	1000° F. (540° C.)	1100° F. (595° C.)	1200° F. (650° C.)	1300° F. (705° C.)	1400° F. (760° C.)	1500° F. (815° C.)
Elongation 1% in 10,000 hr. (0.1% in 1000 hr.)							
Carbon steel, killed	8,000	4,000	1,500	800	.....	.....	.....
Molybdenum (0.5% Mo)	22,000	14,000	6,000	1,800	.....	.....	.....
5% Chromium, 0.5% molybdenum	20,000	10,000	5,000	1,800	.....	.....	.....
Low carbon, 15 to 18% chromium	13,000	8,000	3,500	1,800	.....	.....	.....
18% chromium, 8% nickel	.....	20,000	14,000	8,000	.....	2,500	.....
25% chromium, 20% nickel	.....	.....	.....	8,000	4,500	2,800	1,200
30% nickel, 20% chromium	.....	.....	13,000	8,000	4,000	2,500	.....
Elongation 1% in 100,000 hr. (0.01% in 1000 hr.)							
Carbon steel, killed	5,000	2,500	1,100	1,100	.....	.....	.....
Molybdenum (0.5% Mo)	16,000	7,500	2,500	1,000	.....	.....	.....
5% chromium, 0.5% molybdenum	15,000	6,500	2,000	1,000	.....	.....	.....
18% chromium, 8% nickel	.....	13,000	9,500	6,000	.....	1,800	.....
25% chromium, 20% nickel	.....	.....	.....	5,500	3,500	2,000	1,000

used in high-temperature equipment. As is evident from the table and from the discussion in the last section, the creep strength of carbon steel is low; moreover, the creep strength of low-alloy steels containing nickel, chromium, copper, manganese, silicon, and vanadium is of much the same order of magnitude as for carbon steels. Molybdenum, as noted previously, has a favorable effect. Plain molybdenum and chromium-molybdenum steels are used where a reasonably priced material with good creep strength is desired, as for tubes in oil-refining equipment.

Plain high-chromium steels, including the low-carbon (see Table 35) and the medium-carbon cutlery grades, while important because of their corrosion and oxidation resistance, are inferior in creep characteristics to the cheaper plain molybdenum steels. The austenitic steels including the 18-8 and the more highly alloyed chromium-nickel steels, are in a class by themselves, with creep strengths much higher than those of any other ferrous alloy. This high resistance to creep may be increased by the addition of 2 to 5 per cent molybdenum or tungsten.

210. Creep Data on Non-ferrous Alloys—With the exception of tests on lead at or near normal temperature, few data have been

TABLE 36. THE CREEP STRENGTH OF COPPER-RICH ALLOYS

Material	Nominal composition, per cent				Creep strength, lb. per sq. in., for a creep rate of			
					1% in 10,000 hr. (0.1% in 1000 hr.)		1% in 100,000 hr. (0.01% in 1000 hr.	
	Cu	Zn	Sn	Pb	400° F. (205° C.)	600° F. (315° C.)	400° F. (205° C.)	600° F (315° C.)
Brass	70	30	....	....	18,000	850	12,700	290
Brass	60	40	....	....	4,750	....	2,000	
Brass	85	15	....	....	12,000	2,600	8,800	1,000
Admiralty metal	70	29	1	....	19,000	1,950	13,000	1,000
Admiralty metal	77	22	1	....	13,000	2,500	10,500	1,200
Red brass	86	5	6	2	17,000	4,000		
Bronze	88	....	12	....	15,000	3,000		

reported on the creep behavior of non-ferrous metals and alloys. Most of the work on the creep of copper- and nickel-rich alloys has been done by Clark and White, from whose reports [17] many

[17] C. L. Clark and A. E. White, *Trans Am. Soc. Mech. Eng.*, v. 53, 1931, FSP 53-15; and Univ. of Michigan, *Eng. Research Bull.* 27, 1936.

of the data in this section have been taken. Some of them, plus values for red brass and bronze reported by Kanter,[18] are given in Table 36. The high-zinc copper-zinc alloys (yellow brass) have poor creep resistance, and are inferior to the copper-tin alloys. It is characteristic of the copper-rich alloys that the creep strength drops off very rapidly when the temperature of recrystallization—between 400 and 600° F. (205 and 315° C.)—is reached.

The creep resistance of nickel and nickel-rich alloys is much higher than that of the copper-rich alloys. Typical values reported by Clark and White for Monel (67.7 per cent nickel, 29.7 per cent copper, 1.77 per cent iron, and 1.28 per cent manganese) are as follows:

Temperature		Creep strength, lb. per sq. in., for an elongation of	
° F.	° C.	1% in 10,000 hr. (0.1% in 1000 hr.)	1% in 100,000 hr. (0.01% in 1000 hr.)
600	315	36,000	26,000
800	425	23,500	19,000
1000	540	4,300	1,650

At 800° F. (425° C.) the creep strength of Monel is usually somewhat higher than that of carbon steel, but it drops off more rapidly between 800 and 1000° F. (425 and 540° C.), and at the latter temperature it is usually somewhat lower than corresponding values for carbon steel.

Owing to the change in structure that takes place, the strong alloys of aluminum are not resistant to a steadily applied load at temperatures of 400° F. (210° C.) or higher.

211. Short-time Elevated-temperature Properties—The effect of temperature on the properties of ferrous and non-ferrous alloys as determined by the short-time tensile test has been investigated more thoroughly than creep. Although the accurate determination of these properties is not easy, it is much simpler and more rapid than the determination of creep. Standard tensile specimens are used, which are heated in an electric furnace attached to the testing machine. The chief difficulty is to ensure that the

[18] J. J. Kanter, in *Symposium on Effect of Temperature on the Properties of Metals,* American Society of Mechanical Engineers and American Society for Testing Materials, 1931, p. 364.

temperature of the specimen is uniform and that the temperature indicated by the pyrometer is the actual temperature of the specimen.

A typical chart of short-time tensile properties of low-carbon steel is shown in Fig. 121. As a rule, hardness and strength of all metallic materials vary inversely with temperature, while ductility varies directly. The magnitude of the changes is not the same for all metallic materials but varies with the material and its structural condition and, of course, with temperature. The changes are not necessarily uniform. In some materials, especially in carbon steels, tensile and yield strengths may increase at temperatures of 300 to 600° F. (150 to 315° C.) and then decrease at higher temperatures. Endurance limit usually follows tensile strength. Modulus of elasticity also decreases with temperature, but at 600° F. (315° C.) or above it is difficult to determine the modulus accurately.

Since short-time tensile and other properties of steel and non-ferrous alloys are not of great interest to engineers, no generalities will be attempted here except to state that for most ferrous materials, including the austenitic steels, the strength at 1200° F. (650° C.) is nearly always less than 50 per cent, and at 1400° F. (760° C.) less than 25 per cent, of the room-temperature value.

Some cast aluminum alloys retain their strength well at 400° F. (205° C.); others lose strength rapidly at 300° F. (150° C.) or above, as do most of the wrought alloys. At 600° F. (315° C.) or slightly above, the strength of aluminum alloys is 10 to 30 per cent of the room-temperature values. In general, the copper-rich alloys lose strength very rapidly at temperatures above 600° F. Alloys with a tensile strength of 60,000 to 70,000 lb. per sq. in. at room temperature and a strength of 50,000 to 60,000 lb. per sq. in. at 600° F. have a strength of less than 20,000 lb. per sq. in. at 800° F. (425° C.). Nickel-rich alloys lose strength at 800° F. or above: for example, Monel with a strength of 90,000 lb. per sq. in. at room temperature, and of about 75,000 at 800° F., has a strength of 40,000 lb. per sq. in. at 1200° F. (650° C.) and of about 20,000 at 1400° F. (760° C.).

Determination of short-time tensile properties is useful to the metallurgist as a rough preliminary estimate of elevated-temperature stability. To the engineer the short-time elevated-temperature properties are of limited value. They are perhaps a measure of the ability of a material to withstand occasional overload or occasional brief periods of increased temperature; and of the ability of a material to withstand without serious changes in structure and properties high temperatures where steady loading is not involved or where stresses are low—as in pistons and other parts of internal-combustion engines.

212. Effect of Low Temperatures on the Properties of Metallic Materials—In addition to knowing the properties of metallic materials at temperatures considerably above normal, the metallurgist and the engineer should know something of the behavior of metals and alloys at temperatures considerably below the normal range of 0 to 100° F. In northern latitudes the metals used for rails and railroad equipment, automobiles, and other machines are subjected occasionally to temperatures as low as 50 or 60° F. (45 or 50° C.) below zero. Aircraft operating at high altitudes also encounters low temperatures. In a number of fields, therefore, it is necessary to know the effect of these low temperatures on the properties of metals. The testing of metals at these temperatures is not easy, but the technique has been developed to such a degree of accuracy that reliable property values are readily secured. Refrigeration by ice and salt is used for moderately low temperatures, for −75 to −100° F. (−60 to −75° C.) solid carbon dioxide (dry ice) is available, and for lower temperatures liquid air, oxygen, or helium is used.

Some typical data reported by Russell [19] are given in Table 37. These show that tensile and yield strengths increase as the temperature decreases. Elongation and reduction of area depend upon the nature of the alloy. For some the ductility decreases, for others it increases. Most alloys, however, are embrittled to an appreciable extent by cooling to subzero temperatures.

The most marked effect is the decrease in the impact resistance of many steels at subnormal temperature, a phenomenon that is not common in non-ferrous alloys. This is shown by Fig. 125.[20] At temperatures between 0 and −40° F. (−18 and −40° C.) the impact value may drop to less than 5 ft-lb. In addition to de-

[19] H. W. Russell, in *Symposium on Effect of Temperature on the Properties of Metals,* American Society of Mechanical Engineers and American Society for Testing Materials, 1931, p. 658.

[20] Based on data in *Nickel Alloy Steels,* The International Nickel Company, Inc., New York, Section V, p. 2.

TABLE 37. LOW-TEMPERATURE TENSILE PROPERTIES OF SOME FERROUS AND NON-FERROUS ALLOYS

Alloy	Room temperature				Boiling liquid air −300° F. (−185° C.)			
	Tensile strength, lb. per sq. in.	Yield strength, lb. per sq. in.	Elongation in 2 in., per cent	Reduction of area, per cent	Tensile strength, lb. per sq. in.	Yield strength, lb. per sq. in.	Elongation in 2 in., per cent	Reduction of area, per cent
Annealed copper............	32,600	12,700	58	44	50,400	18,300	63	68
Cast tin bronze............	40,200	18,600	31	37	45,300	30,500	15	25
Rolled tin bronze..........	61,600	57,000	36	65	93,200	71,800	56	58
Rolled leaded brass........	35,600	24,400	17	22	42,800	32,100	13	19
Cast manganese bronze.....	68,500	31,600	39	33	82,700	40,800	26	26
Annealed nickel silver.....	64,900	29,500	47	62	83,000	38,200	57	70
Duralumin.................	57,800	35,400	27	27	71,800	42,700	28	29
Hot-rolled Monel..........	91,500	44,100	46	67	135,500	70,800	54	67
Annealed carbon steel (0.4%)..	79,400	45,800	31	49	139,400	114,100	7	7
Annealed nickel steel......	79,400	57,000	32	57	116,600	111,000	7	7
Low-carbon 16% Cr iron...	75,100	42,800	34	71	145,700	123,200	14	14
20% Ni, 8% Cr steel*.....	107,600	48,300	44	60	180,200	102,800	25	22
18% Cr, 8% Ni steel*.....	105,000	57,000	56	54	263,000	122,700	25	31

* The properties of austenitic steels at low temperature depend upon the amount of austenite that transforms to martensite.

veloping this brittleness, carbon and some alloy steels may be very erratic in their resistance to impact: material of essentially the same chemical composition may, at the same temperature, have considerable toughness or practically none at all. This is due primarily to a difference in grain size: fine-grained steels are

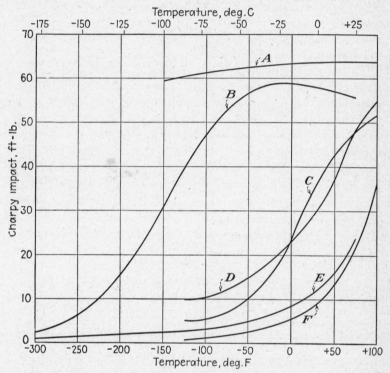

Fig. 125—Effect of low temperatures on the impact resistance of: (*A*) water-quenched low-carbon 18 per cent chromium, 8 per cent nickel steel; (*B*) annealed low-carbon 3.5 per cent nickel steel; (*C*) annealed low-carbon 13 per cent chromium steel; (*D*) normalized 0.35 per cent carbon, 1.5 per cent nickel, 0.6 per cent chromium steel; (*E*) annealed 0.35 per cent carbon steel; and (*F*) normalized 0.35 per cent carbon steel. Specimens for steels *B* and *E* had keyhole notch; others had V notch (The International Nickel Co.).

tougher and retain their toughness at lower temperatures than coarse-grained material.

In general, quenched and tempered low-alloy steels are reasonably resistant to impact at temperatures down to $-100°$ F. or even lower. Normalized steels, however, having properties otherwise satisfactory in pressure vessels for low-temperature distillation (as in dewaxing oil) are, with two notable exceptions, unsatisfactory because of rapid loss of toughness as the temperature falls below 0° F. These two exceptions are (1) low-carbon 3.5 per cent nickel steel and (2) low-carbon 0.75 per cent chromium, 0.50 per cent copper, 0.25 per cent silicon steel. Owing to the relatively high copper content of the second steel, it is frequently defective on the surface after rolling; this can be avoided by adding about 0.60 per cent nickel.

The low-temperature impact resistance of the nickel steel is shown in Fig. 125 (steel *B*), together with impact values of some other annealed or normalized steels for comparison. This steel and the low-carbon chromium-copper steel are used in welded pressure vessels under the Boiler Code Specifications of the American Society of Mechanical Engineers because one of the important characteristics of these two steels is that their satisfactory low-temperature impact resistance is not affected by welding. At temperatures below −150° F. neither is considered satisfactory, and non-ferrous alloys or the 18-8 austenitic steel (Fig. 125, steel *A*), which is tough even at −300° F., should be used.

QUESTIONS

CHAPTER 1

1. Describe the relation of metallurgy to chemistry, to physics, and to engineering.

2. Metallurgy is an art and a science. The art is old and the science is young. Why?

3. How do the concepts of physical metallurgy of today compare with those of 1900?

4. Why is a knowledge of metallurgy more necessary to the engineer now than it was 25 years ago?

5. What constitutes the value of a metal or an alloy to man?

6. When is the cost of a metal or an alloy important to the engineer?

7. Of the 40 or more important metals and the thousands of alloys, which metals and which classes of alloys are the most useful in modern engineering?

8. The trend line for the per capita use of metal products in the United States has flattened in recent years. Name six developments in metallurgy which have accompanied this change in the trend line.

9. What classes of metal products are commonly sold by brand name?

10. Give the advantages and disadvantages of purchasing metal products by their brand name.

CHAPTER 2

1. What are the principal properties of a metal? Give the reasons (a) why copper is classed as a metal, (b) why carbon is classed as a metalloid, and (c) why sulphur is classed as a non-metal.

2. Describe crystallization and orientation. What is the relation (a) between crystals and grains and (b) between orientation and strength?

3. What are the essentials of the crystalline state, and why are they important to the engineer?

4. Define space lattice and give the types important in physical metallurgy.

5. How is a crystal of a metal or an alloy related to the space lattice? How many atoms are there in the two common types of cubic lattice, and how are they spaced?

6. What is allotropy? What are the allotropic forms of iron, and in what temperature ranges are they stable? Why is the allotropy of iron important to the engineer?

7. What is an intermetallic compound, and why is it important in metallurgy?

8. What is an alloy? Name some of the factors which add to the complexity of the constitution of metallic alloys.

9. What is an equilibrium diagram? How is it constructed? What are its advantages and disadvantages to the metallurgist?

10. What happens to a crystal when a stress is applied? What is the importance of plastic flow, and how does plastic flow affect the properties of metallic materials?

Chapter 3

1. What is the composition of commercial carbon steel, and why is this material considered as an alloy of iron and carbon?

2. What is the composition of pig iron, and what is it used for? How is it made?

3. Give the two principal reducing reactions for the reduction of iron ore in the blast furnace and the approximate temperature levels at which they occur. What are the reducing agents, and where do they come from?

4. How is blast-furnace slag formed, and what is its function?

5. What is the essential difference between an acid and a basic steel-making process, and what are the advantages and disadvantages of each?

6. How does the chemistry of the basic open-hearth process differ from the chemistry of the acid Bessemer process? Why is more than 90 per cent of all steel produced made by the basic open-hearth process?

7. What approximate percentage of all the steel made in the United States is usually classed as high-quality steel, and by what processes are these materials made?

8. Why is acid open-hearth steel used for armor plate and ordnance?

9. What is the difference between the chemistry of the basic electric and the basic open-hearth process?

10. What are the objects of (a) hot working and (b) cold working? What is the procedure by which these objectives are attained?

Chapter 4

1. How much phosphorus is usually present in carbon and alloy steels? What is its effect?

2. How much sulphur and oxygen are usually present in carbon and alloy steels? What is the role of these two elements in forming solid non-metallic inclusions, and what is the effect of inclusions on the properties of carbon and alloy steels?

3. What is the source of the carbon monoxide gas present in steel refining? What is the relation between this gas and seams?

4. Define, and give the approximate carbon content of, rimming and killed steels. How are rimming and killed steels made, and what are they used for?

5. Is manganese a harmful, neutral, or beneficial element in steel? Why? What is the usual manganese content (a) of carbon steel, (b) of intermediate-manganese steels?

6. For what grades of steel is silicon used as a final deoxidizer? How much silicon is usually added as a purifier?

7. Name ten elements, in addition to carbon, manganese, silicon, sulphur, and phosphorus, which may be present in carbon steel, and indicate the source of these elements.

8. What is wrought iron and what is ingot iron, and how do these materials differ from carbon steel?

9. Give a practical definition of alloy steel. What is the difference between low- and high-alloy steels?

10. Name three classes of high-alloy steels and give the characteristic property of two of these classes. How is this property attained?

CHAPTER 5

1. Using the following two groups of metallurgical terms: (a) alpha iron, gamma iron, and carbon, (b) ferrite, cementite, and austenite, describe the microstructure of slowly cooled and slowly heated carbon steel at elevated and at room temperature.

2. What is the microstructure of ferrite and of austenite, and what are the properties of ferrite, cementite, and austenite?

3. What do the points and the lines on the iron-carbon phase diagram represent? Using Fig. 17, describe what happens if a 0.80 per cent carbon steel containing ferrite and cementite particles is heated slowly to 1350° F. (730° C.) and held at this temperature. What happens if the steel is then cooled slowly to 1300° F. (705° C.) and held at this temperature?

4. As the carbon content increases, what happens to the microstructure of slowly cooled carbon steel? What is an eutectoid carbon steel?

5. Using Fig. 17, describe the phase changes occurring in pure iron when it is slowly heated to 2900° F. (1595° C.) and cooled again. What change takes place when pure iron is heated and cooled through 1420° F. (770° C.)? How does this change compare with the one taking place at 1670° F. (910° C.)?

6. Using Fig. 17, describe the phase changes occurring in steel containing 0.50 per cent carbon when it is heated slowly to 2900° F. (1595° C.) and cooled again. Compare the phase changes in this steel with those in a steel containing 1.5 per cent carbon, similarly heated and cooled.

7. What is the effect of increasing the speed of cooling carbon steels upon (a) the transformation temperature and (b) the structure?

8. What is the shape and size of the grains of large ingots and castings? How does hot working affect these grains? Why should the finishing temperature of hot working be just above the transformation temperature?

9. What is the effect of cold working on structure and properties? What happens to the structure and properties when cold-worked steel is reheated to 800 to 1200° F. (425 to 650° C.)?

10. In slowly cooled steels what alloying elements can be used to increase the yield ratio? What elements form carbides, and what is the general effect of these carbides on the properties? What alloying elements are preferred if deep hardening is desired?

CHAPTER 6

1. What is the effect of temperature and time on grain growth of steel above the transformation range? What thermal treatment is used to refine the grain?

2. What is grain-growth tendency? How is it controlled?

3. What is critical cooling rate? What is its effect on the austenite-pearlite transformation and on the resulting structure of high-carbon steel?

4. What is martensite? What is its structure? Why is it hard?

5. Why is drastically quenched high-carbon steel unstable? What are the consequences of this instability, and how are they avoided?

6. What is tempering? What is its effect upon the structure of drastically quenched steel?

7. Why does tempering decrease the hardness and strength and increase the ductility of quenched medium- and high-carbon steel?

8. What effect do the alloying elements have on the transformation temperature at which austenite changes to pearlite? Why is this important?

9. What is hardenability? How is it related to grain size and to the various alloying elements?

10. In what class of steels is deep hardening important? Why?

CHAPTER 7

1. What are the objects of annealing? How is annealing carried on, and what is its effect on structure and properties? What is the difference between ordinary and process annealing?

2. What are the objects of normalizing and spheroidizing? How are these operations carried on, and what is their effect on the structure and properties? Why is homogenization of heavy forgings of medium-carbon steel advisable?

3. Describe the operations of quenching and tempering. What are the relative cooling speeds of water, oil, and air? Why is the size of the section important in quenching?

4. What causes internal stresses when high-carbon steel is quenched? How high may such stresses be, and what are the usual consequences? How may these consequences be avoided?

5. What is interrupted quenching? What are its advantages and disadvantages?

6. Describe patenting. What is it used for? Why?

7. What are the industrial processes included under the term surface hardening, and what is the object of such treatment?

8. Describe pack and gas carburizing and give the approximate carbon

content and the depth of case in commercial carburizing. Why is heat treatment necessary after carburizing? What is the effect of grain size on the carburized case?

9. What is nitriding? How is it done? Give four advantages and two disadvantages of nitriding. Why is nitriding not used more widely?

10. Describe flame and induction hardening. What are the advantages and disadvantages of each method?

Chapter 8

1. Name three classes of properties of metallic materials. Which class is most important to engineers interested in structures and machines?

2. Name the static tests that are standardized and the ones that are not standardized. How accurate is the tensile test, and upon what factors does the accuracy depend?

3. Define elastic limit and proportional limit, and give the relation between the two. Define modulus of elasticity. Can proportional limit and modulus of elasticity be determined on all metallic materials? Give the reason for your answer with examples.

4. What is the yield point? What is its importance to engineers? Compare yield point and yield strength. What are the advantages of the latter value? How does speed of testing affect the yield point?

5. What is the relation of elongation to gage length? What is the relation of reduction of area to size of the specimen? What is the relation of elongation and reduction of area to ductility?

6. What is hardness? What properties are components of hardness? What precautions are necessary in the accurate determination of hardness?

7. Describe the three most important methods of determining hardness, and give the advantages and disadvantages of each.

8. How accurate is the relation among hardness tests, and between hardness and tensile strength?

9. What is the value of shear tests? What properties can be determined by shear tests? What is the relation between torsional strength and tensile strength?

10. With what ferrous material is the compressive test most commonly used? Why? What is the value of the bend test (a) for ductile materials and (b) for brittle materials?

Chapter 9

1. What is notch sensitivity, and how is it manifested? What is technical cohesive strength?

2. What are the advantages and disadvantages of the notched-bar single-blow impact test? How is it used by the metallurgist, and in industry?

3. What is the mechanism of a fatigue failure? Explain the characteristic appearance of the fracture.

4. What is the endurance limit of a metallic material? How is it determined? How long is the test run (a) for steel and (b) for aluminum alloys?

5. What is the relation between (a) endurance limit and tensile strength and (b) endurance limit and Brinell hardness? What is the approximate endurance limit of a steel with (a) a tensile strength of 145,000 lb. per sq. in. and (b) a tensile strength of 275,000 lb. per sq. in.?

6. What is the effect of surface condition on the endurance limit? What is the relation between a notch and the endurance limit in (a) high-strength steels, (b) low-strength steels, and (c) gray cast iron?

7. What is corrosion-fatigue limit, and what is its relation to endurance limit? How can resistance to corrosion fatigue be increased?

8. If a steel that has an endurance limit of 50,000 lb. per sq. in. is stressed for a few million cycles at 40,000 lb. per sq. in., what is likely to happen? If it is stressed at 60,000 lb. per sq. in., what is likely to happen?

9. In selecting a steel for service where repeated stress over a long period of time is important, what factors should be considered?

10. What is damping capacity and what is damping ratio? What is the relation of damping to other properties? Why is damping capacity important to engineers?

CHAPTER 10

1. What is meant by machinability? What are the three metallurgical factors involved in easy machinability? Why are they important? What are the important mechanical factors?

2. How can machinability be evaluated? What is the relation between machinability of steel and its tensile strength or hardness?

3. What are the methods for improving the machinability of ferrous materials? What is the function of sulphur and lead in steel in relation to machinability?

4. Arrange the following in the order of their machinability: annealed copper, carbon steel, magnesium alloys, Monel, gray cast iron, free-machining steel, low-carbon high-chromium steel.

5. Why is wear resistance of metallic materials important to engineers? What are the principal types of wear?

6. What factors are involved in wear resistance? What kind of wear occurs in most machinery?

7. What is the relation between wear and other properties of metallic materials? What types of ferrous alloys are used for resistance to (a) metal-to-metal wear and (b) abrasive wear?

8. How is wear resistance evaluated? What are the chief limitations of wear tests?

9. Why is deep drawing an important industrial operation? What ferrous materials are most frequently used for deep drawing?

10. How is steel evaluated for deep drawing? What other properties give a clue to deep-drawing properties?

CHAPTER 11

1. What are steel castings used for? Why? How is the steel for castings usually melted? What are the average minimum tensile properties of untreated or annealed steel castings, and what is the effect of carbon on these properties? What is the advantage of heat treatment?

2. Name three classes of hot-rolled carbon steels and give the principal industrial uses of each. Which is the most important from the standpoint of tonnage?

3. What are the principal variables affecting the properties of hot-worked carbon steels? Compare the longitudinal tensile properties of a rolled steel containing 0.70 per cent carbon with those of one containing 0.30 per cent carbon. What is the effect of manganese and phosphorus on tensile properties?

4. What is the effect of carbon on notched-bar impact resistance, on endurance limit, and on modulus of elasticity?

5. Why are steels cold worked? What properties are usually determined on cold-worked bars, wire, sheet, and strip?

6. What is the general effect of cold working on tensile strength and on elongation? If a hot-rolled rod containing 0.25 per cent carbon has a tensile strength of 70,000 lb. per sq. in. and an elongation of 23 per cent in 10 in., what strength and elongation may be expected in drafting to wire with a reduction of (a) 40 per cent and (b) 65 per cent? What is the effect of carbon content on the increase in tensile strength and the decrease in elongation by drafting?

7. Give typical tensile properties of low-carbon steel strip cold rolled 50 per cent, of small music wire, and of suspension-bridge wire. For the same amount of reduction by drafting which is the strongest and the most ductile: low-carbon Bessemer steel or basic open-hearth steel?

8. What is the effect of cold working on endurance limit and on impact resistance? What is the usual endurance ratio of hard-drawn wire?

9. What classes of carbon steel are heat treated? Why? What is the general effect of annealing and normalizing on the properties? What is the general effect of tempering on the properties of quenched medium-carbon steels?

10. If a small specimen of hot-rolled carbon steel containing 0.45 per cent carbon has a tensile strength of 93,000 lb. per sq. in., a yield strength of 54,000 lb. per sq. in., an elongation of 20 per cent in 2 in., and a reduction of area of 35 per cent, what treatment can be used to increase these values to 103,000, 70,000, 25, and 60 respectively? With these latter tensile properties for a heat-treated small section, what would be the corresponding properties at the center of a 4-in. bar?

CHAPTER 12

1. In what form is the carbon in cast iron? What is the relation between the form of the carbon and (a) the appearance of the fracture and (b) the properties?

2. Name the properties which make gray cast iron suitable for some engineering applications and unsuitable for others.

3. How is gray cast iron melted? What raw materials are used? How much carbon, silicon, and phosphorus are usually present?

4. What are the primary metallographic constituents in gray cast iron? What is the role of carbon in the constitution of cast iron, and how is it influenced by silicon? What constituent is formed by phosphorus, and what is its effect?

5. What is the general relation among chemical composition, amount and distribution of the metallographic constituents, and the properties of gray cast iron? If a small specimen of cast iron poured into a sand mold contains 3.25 per cent total carbon, what will be the structure of the matrix if the silicon is (a) 1.25 per cent, (b) 2.00 per cent, and (c) 2.75 per cent? For similar specimens, what percentages of total carbon and silicon will result in an iron with a tensile strength of about 38,000 lb. per sq. in.?

6. What is the effect of cooling rate on the structure of gray cast iron? What is the effect of the size of the graphite flakes on the properties? What methods are used to produce high-strength cast iron? Why is gray cast iron heat treated?

7. What tests are used to evaluate gray cast iron for engineering applications? Which is the best of these tests, and how is it made? What is the approximate secant modulus of gray cast iron, and how is it determined?

8. What are the approximate minimum and maximum tensile-strength values of American gray cast iron? What are the approximate minimum and maximum values for (a) compressive strength, (b) modulus of rupture, (c) endurance limit and endurance ratio? As compared with carbon steel, what are the notched-bar impact resistance and the damping capacity?

9. What are the principal advantages in the use of alloying elements in gray cast iron, and how much is usually used? What are the general effects of (a) nickel, (b) chromium, and (c) molybdenum?

10. What is malleable cast iron, how is it made, and what is it used for? What are the approximate tensile strength and elongation of malleable cast iron, and what is the relation between the two? How do endurance ratio, impact resistance, and machinability compare with gray cast iron?

CHAPTER 13

1. What is balanced composition in low-alloy steels, and what are its advantages?

2. What are the general effects of the alloying elements in the low-alloy steels? Ignoring carbon, what elements are (a) the most potent and (b) the least potent in strengthening the ferrite?

3. Compare the effects of phosphorus, manganese, and silicon on (a) structure and (b) properties of carbon steel.

4. Compare the effects of nickel and chromium on (a) structure and (b) properties of carbon steel.

5. Using data given in Figs. 58 and 74, compare the approximate tensile

properties of a rolled steel containing 0.20 per cent carbon and (a) no alloying element, (b) 2.0 per cent nickel, and (c) 1.0 per cent chromium. What effect have the nickel and the chromium on tensile strength, yield strength, elongation, and reduction of area?

6. Compare the effects of molybdenum, vanadium, and copper on (a) structure and (b) properties of carbon steels.

7. What are the low-alloy structural steels? How do the properties and the cost of these steels compare with those of carbon steels? Why is the carbon usually low?

8. What is the significance of the S.A.E. classification of low-alloy steels? What is the carbon and the alloy range in (a) 3135, (b) 4615, (c) 2330, and (d) 6150. Why is a knowledge of the S.A.E. series numbers important to engineers?

9. What are the principal uses of the S.A.E. steels, and by what industries are they largely used? What is the advantage of these steels compared with carbon steels of the same tensile strength and hardness?

10. What factors should be considered in selecting one of the S.A.E. alloy steels for a specific engineering application?

CHAPTER 14

1. Name three classes of high-chromium steels. Give the approximate composition of six common high-chromium steels and the class to which they belong.

2. What is the effect of chromium on the phase changes of high-purity iron? What phase change occurs if a binary alloy of 10 per cent chromium and 90 per cent iron is heated slowly to 2550° F. (1400° C.) and cooled again? Give the corresponding changes in an alloy of 15 per cent chromium and 85 per cent iron.

3. What is the structure of a water- or oil-quenched steel containing (a) 0.06 per cent carbon and 18 per cent chromium, (b) 0.30 per cent carbon and 14 per cent chromium, and (c) 0.85 per cent carbon and 16 per cent chromium?

4. What is the relation between the tensile properties and the carbon content of heat-treated 14 to 18 per cent chromium steels? Give two peculiarities in tempering quenched cutlery steels and the effect of these on tensile strength and impact resistance?

5. What is the relation between the chromium content and the corrosion (and oxidation) resistance of chromium steels? What is the effect of carbides on corrosion resistance? To what corrosive media are the 12 to 18 per cent chromium steels especially resistant? Why?

6. What is the effect of nickel on phase changes in iron? What is the effect of adding chromium on the phase changes of iron containing 15 per cent or less nickel in solution? Why are the alloys containing 18 per cent chromium and 8 per cent nickel usually austenitic at room temperature?

7. Why does carbide precipitation occur in 18–8, and what effect does this have on corrosion resistance? How is carbide precipitation counteracted?

8. What are the characteristic tensile properties of 18–8? How do corrosion and oxidation resistance compare with those of high-chromium steels?

9. Give some important characteristics and uses of alloys of iron with (a) 35 to 60 per cent nickel, (b) 32 per cent nickel, 5 per cent chromium, and 2 per cent tungsten, (c) 78.5 per cent nickel, (d) 50 per cent nickel, and (e) 17 to 28 per cent nickel, 5 to 12 per cent cobalt, and 10 to 12 per cent aluminum.

10. What is the structure of a steel containing 1.3 per cent carbon and 13 per cent manganese (a) as slowly cooled and (b) as heated to 2000° F. (1095° C.) and quenched in water? What are its properties, and what is it used for?

CHAPTER 15

1. How are tool steels usually classified? How many types are there? Give eight essential characteristics which tool steel should have and indicate the three most important ones. How important is the cost of the steel from which a tool is made?

2. How are tool steels usually purchased? Why?

3. Give the chief characteristics of high-carbon tool steel. What is the carbon content of the steel that is generally used for files, hammers, brass-working tools, razors, battering tools, wire-drawing dies, rivet sets, taps, drills, and cutlery?

4. What is the relation between grain-growth tendency and deep hardening of high-carbon tool steels?

5. What are the composition and characteristics of the oil-hardening "non-deforming" tool steels? What are they used for?

6. What is the function of tungsten, molybdenum, and chromium in tool steel? What effect do these elements have on the hardness after tempering?

7. Give the characteristics and uses of the low-chromium, the low-tungsten, the high-chromium, and the high-tungsten tool and die steels. Describe the characteristic structure of the high-chromium die steels. Why are these materials valuable for dies?

8. What is the approximate composition of the four general types of high-tungsten high-speed steels? How is high-speed steel heat treated?

9. What is the most valuable property of high-speed steel, and what is the usual explanation for this property? What variables affect the cutting performance of high-speed steel?

10. Give the approximate composition of molybdenum high-speed steel. What are the advantages and disadvantages of this material?

CHAPTER 16

1. Define precipitation hardening. How common is it in non-ferrous alloy systems? Upon what two variables does precipitation hardening depend?

2. Give the salient features of the mechanism of precipitation hardening.

How does precipitation hardening differ from the hardening that occurs when high-carbon steel is quenched?

3. Describe the solution heat treatment and aging of aluminum-rich aluminum-copper alloys. What is the effect of this treatment on the properties of sand-cast material? What precautions are necessary in the heat treatment of duralumin-type alloys?

4. What common complex aluminum-rich aluminum-copper alloys are usually subjected to a solution heat treatment and aging? What are some of these alloys used for?

5. What is the hardening constituent in aluminum-rich aluminum-magnesium and aluminum-magnesium-silicon alloys? Give the principal characteristics of this class of light alloys and some of the important uses.

6. Name four classes of binary copper-rich alloys which cannot be heat treated. What is the chief characteristic of these alloys?

7. Name two classes of copper-rich alloys in which hardening by precipitation is possible. Describe the similarities in the copper-beryllium, the silver-rich end of the silver-copper, and the aluminum-rich end of the aluminum-copper diagram. How does the addition of small amounts of nickel affect the phase relationships in the copper-rich copper-tin alloys?

8. Name four industrial fields in which precipitation-hardened non-ferrous alloys are or may be effectively used.

9. In what binary iron-rich alloy is precipitation hardening possible? Distinguish between quench and strain aging in low-carbon steels. What is the effect of strain aging on the properties?

10. Name some other examples of ferrous alloys in which age hardening occurs or in which it may be induced.

CHAPTER 17

1. Describe the production of aluminum from its oxide. Why is it impracticable to reduce the oxide by carbon or to electrolyze an aqueous solution of an aluminum salt? How are aluminum alloys produced?

2. Name the tempers for the non-aging aluminum alloys. How do the tensile properties vary with the temper? By what methods are aluminum alloys worked? Name ten commercial wrought products.

3. How are the wrought alloys fabricated into finished structures? What precautions should be used in fabricating the heat-treated alloys? How does the machinability of aluminum alloys compare with that of steel?

4. What is the specific gravity of aluminum alloys? Give the usual range of tensile properties and endurance limits of the heat-treated wrought alloys. How do these compare with the properties of annealed alloys?

5. What is the general corrosion resistance of the wrought alloys? What is the effect of composition? What is Alclad, and what are its properties?

6. Compare the advantages and disadvantages of sand-cast and permanent-mold aluminum-alloy castings. Describe five classes of castings and give the general characteristics and uses of each class.

7. What is the range of tensile properties of aluminum alloys (a) as cast

in sand molds and (b) as cast in sand molds and heat treated? Compare the endurance limit and modulus of elasticity of cast aluminum alloys with the corresponding values for carbon steel.

8. What are aluminum-alloy permanent-mold and die castings used for? What are the usual tensile properties of these materials?

9. How is magnesium metal produced? Compare (a) weight, (b) tensile strength, (c) endurance limit, and (d) corrosion resistance of magnesium alloys with aluminum alloys, both as cast and as wrought.

10. Why is strength-weight ratio important? Rate the following on the basis of specific tensile strength, specific yield strength, and specific endurance limit: (a) cast carbon steel, cast and heat-treated aluminum-copper alloy, and cast and heat-treated magnesium-aluminum alloy; and (b) wrought duralumin, chromium-molybdenum steel heat treated to 190,000 lb. per sq. in. tensile strength, and extruded magnesium-aluminum alloy.

CHAPTER 18

1. What is blister copper? Why is it electrolyzed? What is tough-pitch copper, and how is it made? What is oxygen-free copper, and how is it made?

2. What properties of high-purity copper are most valuable to man? What methods are used to improve the strength?

3. Give some examples of confused nomenclature for copper-rich alloys. What is the structure of the common brasses? What is high brass, what are its characteristics, and what is it used for? What are the names of the alpha-beta brasses, and what are their characteristics?

4. What are the low brasses, what are their characteristics and their uses? What is nickel silver, what are its characteristics, and what is it used for?

5. How are variations in the properties of copper-zinc alloys usually obtained? As annealed brass is not usually superior to low-carbon steel in properties, and costs five to ten times as much, why is it so widely used? Compare the endurance ratio and modulus of elasticity of brass and low-carbon steel.

6. What are the composition, structure, and characteristics of the copper-tin bronzes? Why are these alloys used for springs, and what is their tensile strength in spring temper? What is gun metal, and what is it used for?

7. Give some typical compositions of aluminum bronze and of copper-silicon bronze. What are the principal characteristics of these alloys, and what are they used for?

8. What is the composition of the commercial copper-beryllium alloys? Give typical tensile properties and hardness before and after precipitation hardening? What are the copper-beryllium alloys used for, and what is their principal disadvantage? What is their endurance limit and modulus of elasticity?

9. What is the effect of nickel on the structure, tensile properties, and endurance limit of copper? What important electric properties do some of the copper-nickel alloys have?

10. Of the following alloys: nickel silver, tin bronze, cupro-nickel, high brass, copper-silicon bronze, admiralty metal, aluminum bronze, low brass, and manganese bronze, which would be selected for applications where salt-water corrosion is important?

CHAPTER 19

1. What are the major requirements for a good bearing metal?

2. What are the principal metals in the tin-base bearing alloys? Name some important characteristics and uses for this class of bearing metals. What is the effect of lead on these alloys?

3. What is the approximate composition of the lead-base bearing metals? Name some important characteristics and uses for this class. How do these alloys compare with the tin-base alloys in cost and properties?

4. What are the principal metals in the copper-base bearing alloys? Name some of their principal characteristics and uses. What are the high-lead copper-base alloys used for? How do these compare as bearings with the white metals?

5. What are the characteristics of the bearing metals containing 98 to 99 per cent lead or cadmium? Describe oil-less bearings.

6. Why are lead, tin, and zinc important engineering materials? What are the principal uses for these metals?

7. How are zinc-base die castings made? What are they used for? Why? What is the approximate composition of the principal zinc-base die-casting alloys, and what are the properties as cast and after long aging?

8. Give approximate compositions of commercially pure nickel, of three varieties of Monel, and of three important alloys containing nickel and chromium. Describe the characteristics and uses of these materials. What are their outstanding properties?

9. How are metal powders prepared? What are the advantages of powder metallurgy?

10. Name the principal sintered carbides used for tools. How are these made, and what are the properties of tools made from these materials? What are such tools used for?

CHAPTER 20

1. What is chemical affinity and how is it related to the electrochemical series of the elements? What is the significance of a metal's position in the electrochemical series? Define passivity. What is its relation to the electrochemical series?

2. What is the economic significance of the corrosion of iron? How is this corrosion slowed down? What variables affect the corrosion of iron? Define uniform and pitting corrosion. What causes the latter? Why is the environment so important in the corrosion of iron?

3. How is corrosion resistance evaluated in the case of (a) chemicals and (b) atmosphere? What is the effect of temperature on corrosion? How is corrosion measured?

4. Compare normal-temperature corrosion and high-temperature oxida-

tion. What is the mechanism of oxidation, and what is the result? How is it prevented?

5. What is the relative corrosion of high-purity or commercially pure iron, carbon steels, and unalloyed cast iron, in soils, acids, alkalis, and neutral solutions? What variables affect the corrosion of these materials in the atmosphere? Describe boiler corrosion.

6. What low-alloy steels have higher resistance to atmospheric corrosion than carbon steels? Why?

7. Of the five common metallic coatings used to protect steel against corrosion, which is most widely used? Why? What are the advantages and disadvantages of coating steel with tin, nickel, and chromium?

8. What high-alloy steels and cast irons are used for corrosion and oxidation resistance? Why?

9. What is the general corrosion resistance of (a) the nickel-base alloys and (b) the copper-base alloys?

10. What is the general corrosion resistance of the light metals and alloys?

CHAPTER 21

1. What is creep, and why is it important to engineers? What are the principal requirements for a metallic material to be used satisfactorily in equipment exposed to high temperatures?

2. How is creep determined? What are the most important variables in creep testing? How much time is necessary for a creep test?

3. How is the creep stress, which produces no more than the maximum distortion of the material over the expected life, determined? How accurate is such a procedure? What is the relation of creep to other mechanical properties?

4. Describe what happens during the three stages of creep. What is the effect of strain hardening and recrystallization on second-stage creep?

5. What is the effect on creep of (a) grain size, (b) deoxidation, (c) precipitation hardening, and (d) condition of the iron carbide?

6. What low-alloy steel has relatively high creep resistance?

7. What is the relative creep strength (at constant temperature) of carbon, plain molybdenum, chromium-molybdenum, plain high-chromium, and austenitic chromium-nickel steel?

8. Compare the suitability of carbon steel, brass, admiralty metal, bronze, and Monel for use at 600 to 800° F. (315 to 425° C.).

9. What is the general effect of elevated temperature on the tensile strength, yield strength, elongation, reduction of area, and endurance limit of metallic materials? If a steel has a tensile strength of 120,000 lb. per sq. in. at room temperature, what will be the approximate strength at 1200° F. (650° C.) and at 1400° F. (760° C.)?

10. Why is it important to know the effect of low temperatures on the properties of metallic materials? What is the usual effect of these temperatures on tensile and impact properties? What is primarily responsible for low-temperature brittleness in carbon steels, and what alloys reduce this brittleness?

SUGGESTED REFERENCES FOR FURTHER READING

In selecting the appended list of 100 references for the reader who wishes to pursue some phase of metallurgy further than it is done in this book, no effort was made to have the list exhaustive. On the contrary, the primary object was to furnish references, in the English language only, to books and to periodicals which are for the most part available in university libraries, and in the libraries of many of the larger cities as well. An effort was made also to give such a well balanced list that a thorough knowledge of the subject matter of these books and papers would constitute a complete metallurgical education.

References Applicable to Specific Chapters

Chapter 1. References 54, 60, 65

Chapter 2. References 33, 38, 39, 58, 59, 62, 64, 74, 81, 84, 86, 88, 98, 100

Chapter 3. References 27, 31, 33, 85, 94

Chapter 4. References 12, 27, 30, 31, 33, 34, 41, 57

Chapter 5. References 11, 12, 22, 30, 33, 36, 37, 38, 39, 41, 53, 59, 64, 74, 84, 86, 88, 98, 99

Chapter 6. References 9, 11, 12, 22, 30, 32, 33, 36, 37, 41, 53, 58, 64, 84, 86, 88, 98, 99

Chapter 7. References 12, 30, 33, 36, 37, 41, 58, 68, 86, 87, 88, 91

Chapter 8. References 12, 23, 26, 33, 43, 66, 70, 73, 82, 89

Chapter 9. References 12, 20, 23, 33, 43, 47, 66, 70, 80, 89

Chapter 10. References 8, 10, 12, 19, 33, 89

Chapter 11. References 12, 24, 30, 32, 33, 58, 68, 87, 89, 91

Chapter 12. References 3, 12, 14, 16, 25, 27, 33, 35, 48, 55, 58, 68, 71, 89, 90, 94

Chapter 13. References 5, 7, 11, 12, 17, 22, 24, 30, 32, 33, 35, 37, 48, 49, 50, 51, 58, 63, 68, 71, 90, 91

Chapter 14. References 7, 11, 12, 17, 22, 24, 30, 33, 35, 37, 48, 49, 58, 72, 75, 79, 91, 97

Chapter 15. References 12, 30, 33, 45, 49, 52, 58, 83

Chapter 16. References 1, 12, 13, 29, 33, 44, 58, 64, 77, 96

Chapter 17. References 1, 2, 4, 5, 7, 10, 12, 17, 29, 33, 40, 44, 56, 58, 69, 91, 96

Chapter 18. References 4, 5, 12, 17, 33, 58, 69, 91

Chapter 19. References 4, 5, 6, 12, 17, 28, 33, 58, 63, 67, 69, 75, 78

Chapter 20. References 7, 12, 18, 33, 34, 42, 50, 61, 76, 89, 92, 93

Chapter 21. References 12, 15, 21, 23, 33, 46, 89, 95

BIBLIOGRAPHY

1. Aluminum Company of America, *Alcoa Aluminum and Its Alloys*, The Company, Pittsburgh, 1935.
   Composition, heat treatment, and properties of cast and wrought alloys. Sizes and shapes of commercial sections with the usual tolerances.
2. Aluminum Company of America, *Structural Aluminum Handbook*, The Company, Pittsburgh, 1938.
   Manufacture, fabrication, and properties of aluminum alloys for structural use.
3. American Foundrymen's Association, *Alloy Cast Iron*, The Association, Chicago, 1939.
   Best single source of information on constitution, heat treatment, properties, and uses of alloy cast irons. Bibliography of 460 references.
4. American Institute of Mining and Metallurgical Engineers, *Modern Uses of Non-ferrous Metals*, Edited by C. H. Mathewson, The Institute, New York, 1935.
   Elementary discussion of all the non-ferrous metals and alloys, written by 21 experts.
5. American Institute of Mining and Metallurgical Engineers, "Symposium on the Role of Metals in New Transportation," *Metals Technology*, Oct. 1936.
   Authoritative papers on low-alloy structural steel, light and heavy non-ferrous metals and alloys, and on strength-weight ratios and their application to railroad and automotive construction and to ship-building.
6. American Institute of Mining and Metallurgical Engineers, "Symposium on Powder Metallurgy," *Transactions*, v. 128, 1938, pp. 37-103.
   Five papers on recent developments in powder metallurgy, including tungsten and tantalum carbides.
7. American Society of Civil Engineers, "Symposium on Structural Applications of Steel and Light-weight Alloys," *Transactions*, v. 102, 1937, pp. 1179-1483 (Paper 1979).
   Papers by metallurgists on low-alloy structural steels, high-alloy (especially stainless) steels, and light non-ferrous alloys suitable for engineering structures, and on the corrosion of these alloys, together with papers by engineers on their experience in using these materials.
8. American Society of Mechanical Engineers, *Manual on Cutting Metals*, The Society, New York, 1939.
   Tables of machining data for high-carbon steel, high-speed steel, and hard carbide tools, also the relative machinability of a large number of carbon and low-alloy steels. A valuable handbook.
9. American Society for Metals, "Symposium on Grain Size," *Transactions*, v. 22, 1934, pp. 861-1173.
   Twelve important papers on grain size and grain growth, their determination and their relation to properties.
10. American Society for Metals, *Machining of Metals*, The Society, Cleveland, 1938.

Lectures on the physics of metal cutting and on machining carbon and alloy steels, cast iron, and non-ferrous metals.

11. American Society for Metals, *Symposium on Hardenability,* The Society, Cleveland, 1938.

Collection of reports of research on hardenability of carbon and alloy steels with an excellent review and summary of theories of hardenability by R. F. Mehl.

12. American Society for Metals, *Metals Handbook,* The Society, Cleveland, 1939.

The most authoritative reference book on ferrous and non-ferrous metals and alloys, prepared by more than 2500 metallurgists. An 1800-page encyclopedia.

13. American Society for Metals, *Symposium on Precipitation Hardening (Age Hardening) of Metals,* The Society, Cleveland, 1939.

Eleven important papers on the precipitation hardening of ferrous and non-ferrous alloys, including theory and practice.

14. American Society for Testing Materials and American Foundrymen's Association, "Symposium on Malleable Iron," *Proceedings (A.S.T.M.),* v. 31, 1931, II, pp. 317-435.

Manufacture and properties.

15. American Society for Testing Materials and American Society of Mechanical Engineers, *Symposium on Effect of Temperature on the Properties of Metals,* The Societies, Philadelphia and New York, 1931.

Part I contains papers on engineering requirements for metals at high and low temperatures. Part II contains papers on the properties of available metals and alloys for high- and low-temperature service. The bibliography (615 references) is complete to 1931.

16. American Society for Testing Materials and American Foundrymen's Association, *Symposium on Cast Iron,* The Societies, Philadelphia and Chicago, 1933.

Structure and properties.

17. American Society for Testing Materials, *Symposium on High-strength Constructional Materials,* The Society, Philadelphia, 1936.

Papers on the properties of carbon, low-alloy, and corrosion-resisting steels, copper-base, nickel-base, and light alloys.

18. American Society for Testing Materials, *Symposium on Corrosion Testing Procedures,* The Society, Philadelphia, 1937.

Authoritative discussion of the present status of corrosion testing.

19. American Society for Testing Materials, *Symposium on the Wear of Metals,* The Society, Philadelphia, 1937.

Wear testing and its significance.

20. American Society for Testing Materials, "Symposium on Impact Testing," *Proceedings,* v. 38, 1938, II, pp. 21-156.

Nine papers on the theory and significance of impact testing.

21. American Society for Testing Materials and American Society of Mechanical Engineers, *Compilation of Available High-temperature Creep Characteristics of Metals and Alloys,* The Societies, Philadelphia and New York, 1938.

Reliable creep data on carbon and alloy steels.

22. Bain, E. C., *Functions of the Alloying Elements in Steel*, American Society for Metals, Cleveland, 1939.
Elementary physical metallurgy with a chapter on carbon steels and three chapters on the effect of the common alloying elements on structure, response to heat treatment, and properties.

23. Batson, R. G., and Hyde, J. H., *Mechanical Testing*, Vol. I—*Testing of Materials of Construction*, E. P. Dutton & Company, Inc., New York, 1931, 2nd ed.
Theory and practice of testing. Includes static and dynamic tests, and elevated-temperature tests.

24. Bethlehem Steel Company, *Bethlehem Alloy Steels*, The Company, Bethlehem, Pa. (*Catalog 107*), 1935.
Up-to-date handbook, containing property charts of carbon and alloy steels, grain-size charts, and 150 pages of useful tables.

25. Bolton, J. W., *Gray Cast Iron*, Penton Publishing Co., Cleveland, 1937.
Authoritative discussion of raw materials, manufacture, composition, constitution, structure, and properties of gray cast iron.

26. Boyd, J. E., *Strength of Materials*, McGraw-Hill Book Company, Inc., New York, 1935, 4th ed.
A standard work. Chapter 1 on stresses and Chapter 3 on stresses beyond the elastic limit are important.

27. Boylston, H. M., *An Introduction to the Metallurgy of Iron and Steel*, John Wiley & Sons, Inc., New York, 1936, 2nd ed.
Clearly written text on the manufacture of steel and cast iron.

28. Broughton, W. W., "Zinc-alloy Die Castings, An Industrial Achievement," *Metal Progress*, April 1938, pp. 381-386.
Production, properties, and uses of modern zinc-base die castings.

29. Budgen, N. F., *The Heat Treatment and Annealing of Aluminum and Its Alloys*, Sherwood Press, Cleveland, 1933.
Principles and practice of heat treatment of wrought and cast alloys written from the British viewpoint. Bibliography of 300 references.

30. Bullens, D. K., and Battelle Memorial Institute, *Steel and Its Heat Treatment*, Vol. 1—*Principles, Processes, and Control*, Vol. 2—*Engineering and Special-purpose Steels*, John Wiley & Sons, Inc., New York, 1938, 1939, 4th ed.
For the metallurgist and engineer interested in the heat treatment and properties of carbon and alloy steels this is the most important single work in existence. Bibliography follows each chapter

31. Camp, J. M., and Francis, C. B., *The Making, Shaping, and Treating of Steel*, Carnegie-Illinois Steel Corp., Pittsburgh, 1940, 5th ed.
Written for non-metallurgical employees of the United States Steel Corporation. Most comprehensive book available on manufacture and processing of iron and steel.

32. Carnegie-Illinois Steel Corporation, *U.S.S. Carilloy Steels*, The Company, Pittsburgh, 1938.
Up-to-date handbook on special carbon and low-alloy steels. It contains an elementary but adequate discussion of hardenability, grain size, and austenite decomposition and of their relation to the properties.

33. Carpenter, H. C. H., and Robertson, J. M., *Metals*, Oxford University Press, London and New York, 1939, 2 vol.

A 1500-page British encyclopedia of available knowledge on ferrous and non-ferrous metallurgy. Contains data on manufacture, treatment, constitution, and properties of high-purity metals and the most important alloys. Bibliography of 650 references.

34. Cleaves, H. E., and Thompson, J. G., *The Metal—Iron*, McGraw-Hill Book Company, Inc., New York, 1935.

Alloys of Iron Monograph. A summary of available data on manufacture and properties of high-purity iron. The chapter on corrosion is important to the engineer. Bibliography of 1100 references.

35. Climax Molybdenum Company, *Molybdenum in Steel* (13 sections), *Molybdenum in Cast Iron* (5 sections), The Company, New York, 1939. Loose-leaf handbooks on the properties, treatment, and uses of molybdenum-alloy steels and cast irons.

36. Davenport, E. S., and Bain, E. C., "Transformation of Austenite at Constant Subcritical Temperatures," *Trans. Am. Inst. Min. Met. Eng.*, v. 90, 1930, pp. 117-154.

The first paper to give quantitative data on interrupted quenching and on the rate of the decomposition of austenite.

37. Davenport, E. S., "Isothermal Transformations in Steel," *Trans. Am. Soc. Metals*, v. 27, 1939, pp. 837-886.

The effect of carbon and six alloying elements on the rate of decomposition of austenite. The bibliography contains all important references to this subject.

38. Desch, C. H., *Metallography*, Longmans Green & Co., London and New York, 1937.

Fourth edition of this standard British work for students of physical metallurgy.

39. Doan, G. E., *Principles of Physical Metallurgy*, McGraw-Hill Book Company, Inc., New York, 1935.

Fairly elementary treatise written from the approach of classical physics and chemistry.

40. Edwards, J. D., Frary, F. C., and Jeffries, Zay, *The Aluminum Industry*, McGraw-Hill Book Company, Inc., New York, 1930, 2 vol.

Ores and reduction processes; and the manufacture, fabrication, properties, and uses of aluminum and its alloys.

41. Epstein, S., *The Alloys of Iron and Carbon*, Vol. I—*Constitution*, McGraw-Hill Book Company, Inc., New York, 1936.

Alloys of Iron Monograph. Review and summary of available data on the constitution, structure, and heat treatment of unalloyed steels and cast irons. Bibliography of 675 references. See item 89.

42. Evans, U. R., *Metallic Corrosion, Passivity and Protection*, Arnold, London, 1938.

Revised and enlarged edition of this comprehensive work by one of the outstanding British authorities on corrosion.

43. Foster, P. F., *The Mechanical Testing of Metals and Alloys*, Pitman Publishing Corp., New York, 1936.

Theory and practice of tension, torsion, hardness, notched-bar impact, and endurance testing.

44. Fuss, V. (Translated by R. J. Anderson), *Metallography of Aluminum and Its Alloys*, Sherwood Press, Cleveland, 1936.

Constitution and structure of aluminum-rich alloys. Composition, properties, and trade names of modern alloys. Bibliography of 785 references.

45. Gill, J. P., *Tool Steels*, American Society for Metals, Cleveland, 1934.

Five lectures on manufacture, properties, and testing, by an authority.

46. Gillett, H. W., "Some Things We Don't Know about the Creep of Metals," and D. Hanson, "The Creep of Metals," *Trans. Am. Inst. Min. Met. Eng.*, v. 133 and 135, 1939, pp. 15-58.

Two important recent discussions of creep testing and of the factors that enter importantly into the creep of metals.

47. Gough, H. J., *The Fatigue of Metals*, Scott Greenwood, London, 1924.

Standard British work.

48. Gregg, J. L., *The Alloys of Iron and Molybdenum*, McGraw-Hill Book Company, Inc., New York, 1932.

Alloys of Iron Monograph. Summary of available data on molybdenum-alloy steels and cast irons. Bibliography of 515 references.

49. Gregg, J. L., *The Alloys of Iron and Tungsten*, McGraw-Hill Book Company, Inc., New York, 1934.

Alloys of Iron Monograph. Summary of available data on tungsten steels, including high-speed tool steel. Bibliography of 560 references.

50. Gregg, J. L., and Daniloff, B. N., *The Alloys of Iron and Copper*, McGraw-Hill Book Company, Inc., New York, 1934.

Alloys of Iron Monograph. Summary of available data on copper as an alloying element in steel, including the corrosion resistance of the low-copper steels. Bibliography of 400 references.

51. Greiner, E. S., Marsh, J. S., and Stoughton, B., *The Alloys of Iron and Silicon*, McGraw-Hill Book Company, Inc., New York, 1933.

Alloys of Iron Monograph. Summary of available data on steels containing silicon as an alloying element. Bibliography of 475 references.

52. Grossmann, M. A., and Bain, E. C., *High-speed Steel*, John Wiley & Sons, Inc., New York, 1931.

Manufacture, structure, heat treatment, and properties.

53. Grossmann, M. A., *Principles of Heat Treatment*, American Society for Metals, Cleveland, 1935.

Five educational lectures on heat treatment.

54. Hadfield, R. A., *Metallurgy and Its Influence on Modern Progress*, Chapman and Hall, London, 1925.

Lectures on the history of iron and of alloy steels and on metallurgical education and research.

55. Hatfield, W. H., *Cast Iron in the Light of Recent Research*, Griffin and Co., London, 1928, 3rd ed.

Constitution, composition, heat treatment, and properties, especially of British cast iron.

56. Haughton, J. L., and Prytherch, W. E., *Magnesium and Its Alloys*, His Majesty's Stationery Office, London, 1937.

British text on manufacture, constitution, and properties of magnesium and magnesium-base alloys.

57. Herty, C. H., Jr., "The Deoxidation of Steel," *Cooperative Bulletin 69*, Carnegie Institute of Technology and Metallurgical Advisory Board, Pittsburgh, 1934.

An important paper summarizing eight years of work by Herty and his associates on the physical chemistry of steel making, including deoxidation by manganese and silicon, the formation of inclusions, and their effect on quality.

58. Heyer, R. H., *Engineering Physical Metallurgy*, D. Van Nostrand Company, Inc., New York, 1939.

Written "to aid those making their first acquaintance with engineering metals and alloys." Comprehensive but not easy reading. Excellent bibliography.

59. Heyn, E. (Translated by M. A. Grossmann), *Physical Metallurgy*, John Wiley & Sons, Inc., New York, 1925.

Advanced text. Thorough and comprehensive, but somewhat out-of-date.

60. Hoyt, S. L., "The Scientific Method in Metallurgy," *Trans. Am. Soc. Metals*, v. 28, 1940, pp. 757-796.

The evolution, present status, and probable future of metallurgical science. A fine broad discussion.

61. Hudson, J. C., *The Corrosion of Iron and Steel*, D. Van Nostrand Company, Inc., New York, 1940.

An excellent summary, including all important research data, of the work of the Corrosion Committee of the (British) Iron and Steel Institute and published originally (1931 to 1938) as five special reports.

62. Hume-Rothery, W., *The Metallic State*, Clarendon Press, Oxford, 1931.

Advanced physical metallurgy based on modern physics. Metals, solid solutions, and intermetallic compounds from the standpoint of electron theory.

63. International Nickel Company, *Nickel Alloy Steels*, The Company, New York, 1934-1939.

Loose-leaf handbook of 7 sections, on manufacture, processing, properties, and uses of plain and complex nickel steels and high-nickel alloys.

64. Jeffries, Z., and Archer, R. S., *The Science of Metals*, McGraw-Hill Book Company, Inc., New York, 1924.

Elementary text on structure and properties of metals, metallic compounds, solid solutions, alloys, and aggregates.

65. Jeffries, Z., "Future Trends in Metals," *Metal Progress*, Jan. 1935, pp. 17-21.

All the industrially important metals.

66. Johnson, J. B., *Materials of Construction*, Rewritten by M. O. Withey and James Aston, John Wiley & Sons, Inc., New York, 1939, 8th ed.

A standard work, well known to all engineers, containing a discussion of theory and practice of testing and of the properties of ferrous and non-ferrous alloys. Of the 32 chapters, 19 are on metallic materials.

67. Jones, W. D., *Principles of Powder Metallurgy*, Longmans Green & Co., New York, 1937.

A review of the literature on principles, practice, properties, and industrial applications. The only book in English on powder metallurgy.

68. Judge, A. W., *Engineering Materials*, Vol. I—*Ferrous*, Sir Isaac Pitman & Sons, London, 1929, Rev. ed.

Manufacture, heat treatment, and properties of carbon steel, alloy steel, and cast iron, written from the British viewpoint especially for those in the automotive and aircraft industries.

69. Judge, A. W., *Engineering Materials*, Vol. II—*Non-ferrous and Organic Materials*, Sir Isaac Pitman & Sons, London, 1932.

Nine chapters on light and heavy non-ferrous alloys; see remarks for item 68.

70. Judge, A. W., *Engineering Materials*, Vol. III—*Theory and Testing*, Sir Isaac Pitman & Sons, London, 1930.

British text book on principles and practice of testing.

71. Kinzel, A. B., and Crafts, W., *The Alloys of Iron and Chromium*, Vol. I—*Low-chromium Alloys*, McGraw-Hill Book Company, Inc., New York, 1937.

Alloys of Iron Monograph. A summary of available data on steels and cast irons containing less than 10 per cent chromium. Bibliography of 475 references.

72. Kinzel, A. B., and Franks, R., *The Alloys of Iron and Chromium*, Vol. II—*High-chromium Alloys*, McGraw-Hill Book Company, Inc., New York, 1940.

Alloys of Iron Monograph. A summary of available data on steels containing more than 10 per cent chromium, including stainless steels. Bibliography of 525 references.

73. Lea, F. C., *The Hardness of Metals*, Griffin and Co., London, 1936.

British text on theory and practice of hardness testing.

74. Marsh, J. S., *Principles of Phase Diagrams*, McGraw-Hill Book Company, Inc., New York, 1935.

Alloys of Iron (special) Monograph. Based on thermodynamics and consequently not elementary. A small book "for the student, the chemist, the metallurgist, or any other confronted with a problem of heterogeneous equilibrium."

75. Marsh, J. S., *The Alloys of Iron and Nickel*, Vol. I—*Special-purpose Alloys*, McGraw-Hill Book Company, Inc., New York, 1938.

Alloys of Iron Monograph. A summary of available data on high-nickel steels and other ferrous alloys, including some of the corrosion and heat-resisting materials. Bibliography of 620 references. See item 90.

76. McKay, R. J., and Worthington, R., *Corrosion Resistance of Metals and Alloys*, Reinhold Publishing Corp., New York, 1936.

Summarizes in 500 pages all that is important to know about corrosion.

Part 1 is general and theoretical; part 2 is on the corrosion behavior of specific metal and alloy groups. Extensive bibliography.

77. Merica, P. D., "Precipitation Hardening: Its Scope and Possibilities," *Metal Progress,* Jan. 1935, pp. 31-35.

The present status of the theories of precipitation hardening, attractively presented.

78. Metals Disintegrating Company, *The Field of Powder Metallurgy,* The Company, Elizabeth, N. J., 1939.

Elementary booklet with a bibliography of 325 references.

79. Monypenny, J. H. G., *Stainless Irons and Steels,* John Wiley & Sons, Inc., New York, 1931, 2nd ed.

Standard British work.

80. Moore, H. F., and Kommers, J. B., *The Fatigue of Metals,* McGraw-Hill Book Company, Inc., New York, 1927.

Principles and practice of endurance testing. A standard work despite its age.

81. Mott, N. F., and Jones, H., *Theory of the Properties of Metals and Alloys,* Clarendon Press, Oxford, 1936.

For enthusiasts on quantum mechanics. A few engineers might be interested in the mental calisthenics.

82. O'Neill, H., *The Hardness of Metals and Its Measurement,* Chapman and Hall, London, 1934.

Theory and practice of hardness testing by a British authority.

83. Palmer, F. R., *Tool Steel Simplified,* Carpenter Steel Company, Reading, Pa., 1937.

Properties, selection, heat treatment, and testing of tool steel.

84. Rosenhain, W., *Introduction to Physical Metallurgy,* Revised and partly rewritten by J. L. Haughton, Constable, London, 1935.

Third edition of this well-known British text. Fairly elementary but in great detail.

85. Rosenholtz, J. L., and Oesterle, J. F., *Elements of Ferrous Metallurgy,* John Wiley & Sons, Inc., New York, 1938.

A good elementary discussion of steel manufacture.

86. Sauveur, A., *The Metallography and Heat Treatment of Steel and Cast Iron,* McGraw-Hill Book Company, Inc., New York, 1935, 4th ed.

At least 10,000 American metallurgists studied this book in college. The standard work on elementary physical metallurgy written by the Dean of American metallurgists.

87. Sherry, R. H., *Steel Treating Practice,* McGraw-Hill Book Company, Inc., New York, 1929.

Practical text by a practical man.

88. Sisco, F. T., *The Constitution of Steel and Cast Iron,* American Society for Metals, Cleveland, 1930.

A very elementary discussion of the constitution of steel and cast iron and the principles of heat treatment.

89. Sisco, F. T., *The Alloys of Iron and Carbon,* Vol. 2—*Properties,* McGraw-Hill Book Company, Inc., New York, 1937.

Alloys of Iron Monograph. Summary of available data on the properties of carbon steel and cast iron, including a discussion of the significance of the various tests. Bibliography of 820 references; see item 41.

90. Sisco, F. T., and Marsh, J. S., *The Alloys of Iron and Nickel,* Vol. **2**— *Steels and Cast Irons,* McGraw-Hill Book Company, Inc., New York, 1941 (in preparation).

Alloys of Iron Monograph. Summary of available data on the structure and properties of low-nickel steels and cast irons. Bibliography of about 1000 references; see item 75.

91. Society of Automotive Engineers, *S.A.E. Handbook,* The Society, New York, 1940.

Composition, recommended heat treatments, and expected properties of all the standard S.A.E. carbon and alloy steels and non-ferrous alloys. Pages 300 to 474 are devoted to metals.

92. Speller, F. N., "The Corrosion Problem with Respect to Iron and Steel," *Trans. Am. Inst. Min. Met. Eng.,* v. 113, 1934, pp. 13-33.

A broad discussion of the problem of corrosion.

93. Speller, F. N., *Corrosion—Causes and Prevention.* McGraw-Hill Book Company, Inc., New York, 1935, 2nd ed.

Part 1 is on general principles; part 2 is on preventive measures. There is an extensive selected bibliography.

94. Stoughton, B., *The Metallurgy of Iron and Steel,* McGraw-Hill Book Company, Inc., New York, 1934, 4th ed.

A standard work on iron and steel manufacture for students of metallurgy.

95. Tapsell, H. J., *Creep of Metals,* Oxford University Press, London, 1931.

The only book on creep and creep testing; now considerably out-of-date.

96. Teed, P. L., *Duralumin and Its Heat Treatment,* Griffin, London, 1937.

Small British text on history, constitution, heat treatment, and properties of duralumin-type alloys.

97. Thum, E. E. (editor), *The Book of Stainless Steels,* American Society for Metals, Cleveland, 1935, 2nd ed.

Cooperative and comprehensive work written by 85 experts. Discusses constitution, manufacture, properties, and uses of stainless irons and steels.

98. Van Wert, L. R., *An Introduction to Physical Metallurgy,* McGraw-Hill Book Company, Inc., New York, 1936.

Metallurgical theory for graduate engineers and undergraduate metallurgists. A difficult subject made as clear as possible. Especially recommended.

99. Williams, R. S., and Homerberg, V. O., *Principles of Metallography,* McGraw-Hill Book Company, Inc., New York, 1939, 4th ed.

This small book should be useful to engineers who want more knowledge of phase diagrams without too much thermodynamics.

100. Wilson, A. H., *The Theory of Metals,* Cambridge University Press, 1936.

Advanced text, based on modern electron theory. For engineers who may be curious to know to what lengths physics can go.

INDEX